Fundamentals of
Electronic Devices

**Merrill's International Series
in Electrical and Electronics Technology**

Samuel L. Oppenheimer, *Consulting Editor*

BOYLESTAD	Introductory Circuit Analysis
FABER	Introduction to Electronic Amplifiers
HARTKEMEIER	Fortran Programming of Electronic Computers
HERRICK	Introduction to Electronic Communications
HERRICK	Mathematics for Electronics
LENERT	Semiconductor Physics, Devices, and Circuits
OPPENHEIMER	Semiconductor Logic and Switching Circuits
PRISE	Electronic Circuit Packaging
TOCCI	Fundamentals of Electronic Devices
TURNER	Digital Computer Analysis

Fundamentals of
Electronic Devices

Ronald J. Tocci

Monroe County Community College

CHARLES E. MERRILL PUBLISHING COMPANY, COLUMBUS, OHIO

A Bell & Howell Company

To Cathy, Mike and Mark

for their undeserved tolerance of me
during the writing of this book

International Standard Book Number   0–675–09379–1

Library of Congress Catalog Card Number   79–102793

2 3 4 5 6 7 8 — 75 74 73 72 71

Printed in the United States of America

Preface

The process of educating highly qualified electronics personnel is becoming increasingly more complicated by the fact that both the traditional aspects and modern aspects of electronics have to be mastered in the same amount of time previously devoted to the traditional aspects alone. For this reason, it is essential that students in a two-year technology program should immediately start training in mathematics *and* in their technical specialty during the first semester.

Most technical schools, having realized this, have constructed their electronics technology programs so that the student is introduced to the basics of electricity in his first semester. More often than not, this is the only electrical course studied in the first semester. Although this has been sufficient in the past, the electronics faculty at the author's school believe that the combined effects of an expanding technology and the increasing requirements of modern industry dictate a change from this traditional approach if the limited time available is to be used to full effectiveness. At Monroe County Community College the electronics program is organized so that its students study both basic electricity (d-c circuits) and electronic devices in the first semester. The electronic devices course is concerned with how electronic devices work and the characteristics, parameters, limitations, and applications of these devices. This approach requires that the courses be closely coordinated to give maximum amount of subject coverage in a minimum amount of time. As soon as a mathematical tool is developed it is applied in the electrical courses. As soon as sufficient foundation is laid in the basic electricity course, this background is used to promote understanding of electronic devices. This process is continued through the second semester where a second term of basic electricity (a-c circuits) is studied along with a second term of electronics devices. The second course in devices is a continuation of the first in that it uses some devices studied in the first course in amplifier circuits as well as introducing new devices. We have seen many important advantages to this approach:

1. The student entered the program to study electronics. The fact that he immediately starts his training in this specialty provides motivation.

2. Introduction of electronics in the first semester makes it possible to achieve the depth of understanding of basics needed for advanced work later in the program.

3. The student sees immediate application for the principles he studies in the mathematics and basic electricity courses.

The material presented in this textbook makes up the semiconductor portion of the electronic device courses offered to the Monroe freshman. The instructor has the option to include coverage of vacuum tubes. The vacuum tube material most easily fits in between Chapters 3 and 4 and between Chapters 10 and 11, first covering the basics of tube operation and characteristics and then vacuum tube amplifiers. The text has been arranged so that amplifying devices are not introduced until the student has begun learning the concepts of a-c.

Some other features of the text should be pointed out. The mathematical level expected of the student is minimal—one year of algebra is sufficient. Calculus is not employed since it is not needed. To enhance understanding, the author has used the abbreviations Com. E, Com. B and Com. C instead of CE, CB and CC, to avoid confusion with abbreviations for collector-emitter (CE) and collector-base (CB).

The examples and problems are designed to review the important points of each chapter and to give the student practice in applying circuit analysis techniques along with device characteristics and specifications. An extensive glossary accompanies each chapter as a basis for review of new terminology.

The author wishes to acknowledge the untiring aid of his wife, Cathy, and the departmental secretary, Kathy Langworthy, in the typing and preparation of the manuscript. Special acknowledgment is also extended to the two classes of electronics students who not only served as valuable editors but were a constant source of encouragement.

R.J.T.

Contents

1 BASIC ATOMIC THEORY   1

1.1 Introduction   1
1.2 The Bohr Atom   1
1.3 Atomic Number and Atomic Weight   3
1.4 Electron Orbits and Energy   3
1.5 Valance Electrons   5
1.6 Excitation of the Atom   6
1.7 Combinations of Atoms   8
1.8 Electron Energies in Solids: Energy Bands   11
     Glossary   14
     Questions   15
     References   16

2 BASICS OF CURRENT FLOW   17

2.1 Introduction   17
2.2 Electric Current   17
2.3 Resistivity and Conductivity   19
2.4 Conditions Producing Current   20
     Glossary   23
     Questions   23
     References   24

3 GENERAL DEVICE ANALYSIS 25

3.1 Introduction 25
3.2 The General *n*-Terminal Device 25
3.3 Two-Terminal Device Characteristics 28
3.4 Three-Terminal Device Characteristics 29
3.5 Devices With Four or More Terminals 33
Glossary 34
Questions 35
References 37

4 SEMICONDUCTOR PRINCIPLES 39

4.1 Introduction 39
4.2 Conductors, Semiconductors and Insulators 40
4.3 Covalent Bonding in Semiconductors 41
4.4 Intrinsic Semiconductors 42
4.5 Extrinsic Semiconductors 48
4.6 Effects of Temperature on Extrinsic Semiconductors 54
Glossary 56
Questions 57
References 58

5 THE P-N JUNCTION 59

5.1 Introduction 59
5.2 The P-N Junction 59
5.3 Reverse Biasing a P-N Junction 65
5.4 Reverse Breakdown of a P-N Junction 67
5.5 Forward Biasing a P-N Junction 68
5.6 *I-V* Characteristic of a P-N Junction 70
5.7 P-N Diode Ratings 72
5.8 Effects of Temperature on Diode Characteristics 74
5.9 P-N Diode Circuit Analysis: Load Line Method 76
5.10 P-N Diode Circuit Analysis: Approximate Method 82
5.11 Applications of P-N Diodes 87
5.12 Power Dissipation in P-N Diodes 91
5.13 Comparison of Diode Materials 93
5.14 P-N Junction Capacitance 94
Glossary 95
Questions 96
References 102

6 ZENER DIODES   103

6.1 Introduction **103**
6.2 Zener Breakdown **103**
6.3 Zener Diodes **105**
6.4 Zener Diode Specifications and Ratings **106**
6.5 The Zener Diode as a Circuit Element **111**
6.6 The Zener Diode as a Voltage Regulator **113**
6.7 The Zener Diode as a Reference Element **118**
   Glossary **120**
   Questions **121**
   References **124**

7 TUNNEL DIODES   125

7.1 Introduction **125**
7.2 The Tunnel Diode **125**
7.3 Tunnel Diodè Specifications **128**
7.4 The Tunnel Diode as a Circuit Element **130**
7.5 Tunnel Diode Switching Circuits **133**
   Glossary **136**
   Questions **137**
   References **140**

8 PHOTOELECTRIC DEVICES   141

8.1 Introduction **141**
8.2 The Nature of Light **141**
8.3 Photoconductive Cells **142**
8.4 Photoconductive Cell Ratings and Specifications **146**
8.5 Applications of Photoconductive Cells **147**
8.6 Photovoltaic Cells **149**
8.7 Photovoltaic Cells as Circuit Elements **152**
8.8 Applications of Photovoltaic Cells **153**
   Glossary **154**
   Questions **155**
   References **158**

9 BASIC JUNCTION TRANSISTOR OPERATION   159

9.1 Introduction **159**
9.2 Junction Transistor Structure **159**

9.3 Junction Transistor Operation **161**
9.4 The Common Base Configuration **170**
9.5 Common Base Characteristic Curves **172**
9.6 Analyzing Common Base Circuits: Load Line Method **175**
9.7 Analyzing Common Base Circuits: Approximate Method **178**
9.8 The Common Emitter Configuration **183**
9.9 Common Emitter Characteristic Curves **187**
9.10 Analyzing Common Emitter Circuits: Load Line Method **190**
9.11 Analyzing Common Emitter Circuits: Approximate Method **193**
9.12 The Common Collector Configuration **195**
9.13 Analyzing Common Collector Circuits **196**
9.14 Some Important Transistor Maximum Ratings **197**
9.15 Temperature Effects **199**
     Glossary **201**
     Questions **202**
     References **211**

10 AMPLIFIER PRINCIPLES 213

10.1 Introduction **213**
10.2 Reproduction and Amplification **213**
10.3 Voltage Amplification **215**
10.4 Current Amplification **216**
10.5 Power Amplification **216**
10.6 The Impedance Concept **217**
10.7 Amplifier Relationships **218**
10.8 Impedance Matching in Amplifiers **223**
     Glossary **224**
     Questions **224**

11 TRANSISTOR AMPLIFIERS 227

11.1 Introduction **227**
11.2 How a Transistor Amplifies **227**
11.3 Common Base Amplifiers — Basic Circuit **234**
11.4 Common Base Amplifiers — Current Gain **235**
11.5 Common Base Amplifiers — Voltage Gain **237**

11.6   Common Base Amplifiers — Power Gain   **243**
11.7   Common Base Amplifiers — Input and Output
         Impedance   **244**
11.8   Common Base Amplifiers — General Representation   **246**
11.9   Common Base Amplifiers — Graphical Analysis of
         Amplifier Waveforms   **251**
11.10 Common Base Amplifiers — Summary   **256**
11.11 Common Emitter Amplifiers — Basic Circuit   **257**
11.12 Common Emitter Amplifiers — Current Gain   **257**
11.13 Common Emitter Amplifiers — Voltage Gain   **258**
11.14 Common Emitter Amplifiers — Power Gain   **262**
11.15 Common Emitter Amplifiers — Input and Output
         Impedance   **263**
11.16 Common Emitter Amplifiers — General Representa-
         tion   **265**
11.17 Common Emitter Amplifiers — Graphical Analysis of
         Amplifier Waveforms   **268**
11.18 Common Emitter Amplifiers — Q-point Stability   **272**
11.19 Common Emitter Amplifiers — Summary   **277**
11.20 Common Collector Amplifiers — Basic Circuit   **278**
11.21 Common Collector Amplifiers — Gain and Impedance
         Relationships   **279**
11.22 Common Collector Amplifiers — Summary   **287**
11.23 Transistor Equivalent Circuits — T-Equivalent   **287**
11.24 Transistor Equivalent Circuits — Hybrid Equivalent   **294**
11.25 Effects of Frequency on Amplifier Operation   **300**
11.26 Summary of Transistor Amplifier Configurations   **305**
         Glossary   **306**
         Questions   **307**
         References   **315**

12   THE TRANSISTOR AS A SWITCH   **317**

12.1   Introduction   **317**
12.2   Characteristics of a Switch   **317**
12.3   Steady State Operation   **319**
12.4   Transient Operation   **321**
12.5   Power Dissipation in Switching Transistors   **323**
12.6   Switching Circuit Applications   **325**
         Glossary   **330**
         Questions   **331**
         References   **333**

13   TRANSISTOR TECHNOLOGY   335

13.1   Introduction   335
13.2   Effects of Transistor Physical Characteristics on
       Electrical Characteristics   335
13.3   The Alloy Transistor   337
13.4   The Microalloy Transistor   338
13.5   The Microalloy Diffused Transistor   339
13.6   The Mesa Transistor   340
13.7   The Epitaxial Mesa Transistor   341
13.8   The Silicon Epitaxial Planar Transistor   342
13.9   Power Transistors   343
13.10 Transistor Data Sheets   344
       Glossary   347
       Questions   348
       References   349

14   PNPN DEVICES   351

14.1   Introduction   351
14.2   PNPNs — General Description   351
14.3   Structure and Basic Operation of PNPNs   352
14.4   PNPN Four Layer Diodes — Characteristics and
       Operation   356
14.5   Four Layer Diodes — Parameters and Ratings   360
14.6   The Rate Effect   360
14.7   Four Layer Diodes — Circuit Applications   361
14.8   The Silicon Controlled Rectifier — Basic Operation   368
14.9   SCR Ratings and Characteristics   371
14.10 SCR Gate Triggering   373
14.11 Gate Triggering Pulse Width   375
14.12 Gate Triggering Turn-on Gains   376
14.13 SCR Turn-off Considerations   376
14.14 The SCR Used as a d-c Switch   377
14.15 The SCR Used as an a-c Switch   380
14.16 Other PNPN Devices   386
       Glossary   387
       Questions   388
       References   391

15   THE UNIJUNCTION TRANSISTOR   393

15.1   Introduction   393
15.2   Basic Operation   393

15.3 UJT Parameters and Ratings **396**
15.4 UJT Circuit Operation **397**
15.5 The UJT as an SCR Trigger **403**
       Glossary **405**
       Questions **405**
       References **406**

16   FIELD-EFFECT TRANSISTORS   **407**

16.1 Introduction **407**
16.2 Junction Field-Effect Transistors (JFET) **408**
16.3 JFET Ratings and Parameters **413**
16.4 The Basic JFET Common-Source Amplifier **416**
16.5 JFETs — General Comments **418**
16.6 Insulated Gate Field-Effect Transistors (IGFET) **418**
16.7 Summary of FET Types **422**
16.8 IGFETs — General Comments **423**
       Glossary **424**
       Questions **424**
       References **426**

17   SPECIAL SEMICONDUCTOR DEVICES   **429**

17.1 Introduction **429**
17.2 Phototransistors **429**
17.3 Light Emitting Diodes — Junction Lasers **430**
17.4 Thermistors **431**
17.5 The Hall-Effect Generator **433**
17.6 Strain Gages **434**
17.7 Varactor Diodes **435**
       Glossary **435**
       Questions **435**
       References **436**

18   INTRODUCTION TO INTEGRATED CIRCUITS   **437**

18.1 Introduction **437**
18.2 Monolithic Integrated Circuits **438**
18.3 Formation of a Complete Monolithic IC **441**
18.4 Thin-Film Integrated Circuits **443**
18.5 Other IC Types **445**

18.6 MOSFETs in Integrated Form **446**
18.7 Advantages of Integrated Circuits **446**
      Glossary **447**
      Questions **448**
      References **449**

APPENDICES **450**

I   Periodic Table of the Elements **450**
II   Manufacturer's Data Sheets **454**
III   Transistor a-c Equivalent Circuit Formulas **473**
IV   Vacuum Tube Devices **475**
V   Device Symbols **489**

ANSWERS TO SELECTED PROBLEMS **492**

INDEX **493**

1

Basic Atomic Theory

1.1. Introduction

Any comprehensive study of semiconductor devices must begin with a study of atomic theory. The extent to which it helps explain semiconductor phenomena warrants at least a brief look at atomic structure, based on the simple Bohr model of the atom. Although modern science points out the limitations of the Bohr model, for a non-rigorous study like ours, we can stick with it as long as we are prepared to accept some rather strange additional rules governing atomic structure. The concept of energy bands shall be introduced to help classify matter electrically, and to explain certain electrical properties of matter.

1.2. The Bohr Atom

The most fundamental unit of all matter is the atom. We shall begin consideration of materials eventually leading to semi-conductors by studying the single, isolated atom. Investigation of the properties of solid materials containing many combined atoms shall then follow.

For purposes of this study, we can consider the atom to consist of three distinct types of particles: neutrons, protons and electrons. Neutrons and protons, the heaviest particles, make up the nucleus

1

or core of the atom. Neutrons have no electrical charge while the protons are charged positively. Electrons, which are negatively charged, have a weight of about 1/1800 that of a neutron or proton. An atom contains an equal number of electrons and protons.

The Bohr model of an isolated atom depicts the nucleus, containing the heavier protons and neutrons, as the center of a miniature solar system about which the atom's electrons revolve. Figure 1.1 shows a symbolic representation of the Bohr model for hydrogen, which consists of one proton making up the nucleus, and one electron orbiting about the nucleus.

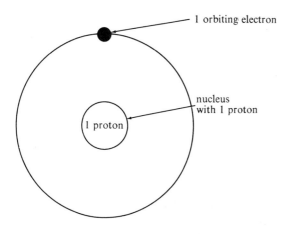

FIG. **1.1.**   BOHR MODEL FOR HYDROGEN ATOM

The analogy between the atom and the solar system is, in many instances, a good one. The forces and relationships between the nucleus and orbiting electrons are similar to those existing between the sun and its planets. There are, however, two major differences between atoms and our solar system. The more obvious is the extreme difference in physical size; whereas the solar system is billions of miles in diameter, a typical atomic diameter is 10^{-11} inches (10 trillionths of an inch). The other difference is in the nature of the attraction forces. Our solar system is acted upon by gravitational forces. The forces existing in the atomic system are electrostatic, pertaining to Coulomb's law which specifies that like charges repel and unlike charges attract. The positive charges in the nucleus exert an electrostatic force on the orbiting electrons. It should be noted that gravitational forces act only as attracting forces and never as repelling forces. Noting these differences, the basic model of the two systems can be considered the same.

1.3.   Atomic Number and Atomic Weight

The different types of atoms make up the many different elements. These elements differ in the numbers of each particle (electron, proton, neutron) which make up their atoms.

The *atomic number* of an atom or element is given by either the number of protons in its nucleus or the number of orbiting electrons. Copper, for example, has 29 protons in its nucleus (along with 34 neutrons) and 29 orbiting electrons. Thus, its atomic number is 29.

The *atomic weight* of an atom or element is given *approximately* by the number of protons and neutrons in its nucleus, in atomic mass units. Copper has an atomic weight of about 63. It should be noted that protons and neutrons have approximately the same weight, and electrons are much lighter (1/1800 of a proton or neutron).

1.4.   Electron Orbits and Energy

In accordance with the analogy to our solar system, the atom is made up of a heavy nucleus around which one or more electrons are revolving in orbits. For each isolated atom, however, there are only a certain number of orbits available. These available orbits represent energy levels for the electrons; that is, each orbit corresponds to a certain value of total electron energy, and, furthermore, no more than two electrons may exist in one level or orbit. This last rule is known in modern physics as *Pauli's Exclusion Principle*. It is very important to note that these energy levels, or orbits, exist at discrete levels for the atom.

At this point, it is advisable to introduce the energy unit which we will employ in all our work on atomic theory and semiconductors. The *electron-volt* is defined as that amount of energy gained or lost when an electron moves with or against a potential difference of one volt. In terms of *joules*, a common unit of energy, an *electron-volt* (abbreviated ev from now on) is equivalent to 1.6×10^{-19} joules. This is a very small amount of energy indeed, when one realizes that a 200-lb man climbing one stair exerts almost 300 joules of energy. In terms of an electron, however, it is a great deal since an electron has so small a mass.

Returning to the energy levels in an atom, it is necessary to understand the difference between having a continuum of energies and discrete values of energy available for electrons. To illustrate: if a continuum of energies were available, an electron could have *any* value of energy between, say, 1 ev and 2 ev. However, modern physics tells us that only discrete values of electron energies are possible. Thus, an electron could not have *any* value of energy between 1 ev and 2 ev, but only certain permissible values such as 1.00000000000000000001 ev or 1.5 ev, for example. No electron may exist at any energy level or orbit other than one of the permissible levels. At most, two electrons can have exactly the same energy level or occupy the same orbit at the same time.

For purposes of considering the chemical behavior of the atoms, a group of permissible levels or orbits are combined into electron "shells". The differences in energy levels within a shell are smaller than the difference in energy between shells. Thus, the shells can be regarded as appropriate groupings of the possible orbits. The number of electrons existing in the various shells determines the chemical properties of the atom.

The electron shells in an atom are usually denoted by the letters *K, L, M, N* . . . . . , the *K*-shell being the closest to the nucleus. Figure 1.2 shows the symbolic atomic structure of hydrogen, lithium and silicon atoms.

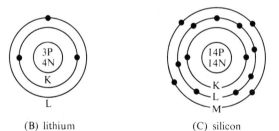

(A) hydrogen   (B) lithium   (C) silicon

FIG. 1.2.   EXAMPLES OF VARIOUS ATOMIC STRUCTURES

We say that a particular atom is more complex than another if it contains more orbiting electrons. In other words, the silicon atom, since it has three shells and 14 electrons, is more complex than a lithium atom which has only two shells and three electrons.

Electrons revolving in orbits far from the nucleus are influenced less by the electrostatic force of the protons in the nucleus than are

electrons in closer orbits.* Accordingly, these more distant electrons possess a greater total energy.† In general, we can state that
as the orbital radius (the distance of the orbit from the nucleus)
increases, the energy of electrons travelling these orbits increases.
In other words, as an electron moves further from the nucleus its
energy increases. An electron orbiting very close to the nucleus
in the *K*-shell is tightly bound to the nucleus by the electrostatic
force and possesses only a small amount of energy. It would be
difficult to knock this electron out of its orbit. On the other hand,
an electron orbiting further from the nucleus would have a greater
energy and could more easily be bumped out of its orbit. This
is analogous to trying to knock someone off the top of a concrete
wall. If the person is running along the wall, using lots of energy,
it is much easier to knock him down than if he were standing
rigidly still using no energy.

1.5. Valence Electrons

Many of the chemical properties of the different atoms are
determined by the behavior of the electrons existing in the shell
furthest from the nucleus. These electrons, being the most ener-
getic, are the ones involved in chemical bonding and chemical
reactions. The outer shell electrons are called *valence electrons*.
An atom with one electron in its outer shell, such as hydrogen, is
said to have a *valence* of 1. In general, an atom with *n* electrons
in its outer shell has a valence of *n*. Referring again to Figure 1.2,
we can see that hydrogen and lithium have a valence of one, while
silicon has a valence of four.

When the outermost shell of an atom is completely filled, that
atom is said to be inert and not capable of combining with other
atoms of another element to form a compound. Conversely, if the
outer shell is not completely filled, the atom is capable of forming
compounds with other atoms. In forming these compounds, two
atoms may share their electrons so that the combined electrons
will fill the outer shells of both. Or one atom may donate its
valence electrons to a second atom in order to fill the second
atom's outer shell. These two types of compounds will be discussed
in more detail when we talk about atomic bonding.

---

*Electrons in the inner orbits act as a shield from the nucleus; also, recall
that coulomb force varies indirectly as the square of distance.
†Total energy includes kinetic and potential energies.

1.6.   **Excitation of the Atom**

The energy of an orbiting electron consists of two parts. The electron has kinetic energy due to its motion, and potential energy due to the electrostatic attraction of the nucleus. When energy is added to an electron, both its kinetic and its potential energies are increased. It can easily be understood that, since an electron can only exist at discrete energy levels, the amount of energy it can receive must be discrete in value.

To re-emphasize the significant points concerning the orbits or energy levels of the electrons in an isolated atom: the atom contains many energy levels corresponding to orbits in which it is permissible for an electron to exist, and there are many more of these orbits or levels than there are electrons. Every atomic electron must exist in one of the permissible energy levels. Since there are many available orbits, it is possible for an electron to move from orbit to orbit as it gains or loses energy. If an electron gains energy it must move to a higher energy level in an orbit further from the nucleus (Section 1.4). An electron which loses some of its energy must drop to a lower energy level in an orbit closer to the nucleus (Section 1.4).

Since the electrons must exist in certain discrete energy levels, it is clear that when energy is absorbed or lost by an electron it is done so in discrete quantities. These discrete quantities, called *quantums of energy*, correspond to the difference in energy between the permissible levels for the electrons.

One of the most convenient mechanisms by which the energy of an atom may be increased is through the application of heat. If we can visualize a single atom isolated in space, the application of heat would result in some electrons in the atom being raised to higher energy levels (orbits further from the nucleus). Those electrons with the highest energy to start with will be the first to have their orbits changed. Thus it is the valence electrons in the outermost shell that will have their orbits raised first upon the application of external energy such as heat.

Another way to increase the electron energy of an atom is to direct light onto the atom. Light represents the visible portion of the entire electromagnetic spectrum and consists of the same radiation as radio waves, but the frequency is higher for the visible portion of the spectrum. If an atom absorbs electromagnetic radiation, the radiation will be converted into energy. Thus light represents a source of energy for raising the electron levels of an atom. Light may be considered as possessing little packets or quantums of energy. As the frequency of the light increases, the energy increases. In order for the radiation (light) to raise the level of an electron, its quantum of energy must be greater than that needed to raise the electron to the next highest energy level. It is for this reason that only a portion of the electromagnetic spectrum is capable of giving energy to the electrons of solids.

When an atom absorbs any form of energy, then, the energy levels of some of the electrons (usually the valence electrons) are raised and the atom is said to be *excited*. It must be understood that in an excited atom the permissible energy levels do not change; the electrons simply jump from one level to another.

To illustrate what has been said thus far about excitation of an atom, Figure 1.3 shows the process of excitation for the hydrogen atom. In 1.3A the one valence electron is depicted as existing in the first permissible orbit ($n = 1$) before external heat is applied.

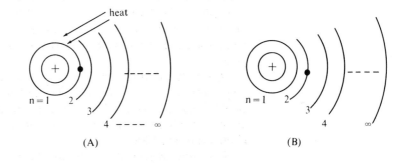

(A)   (B)

FIG. 1.3.   (A) HYDROGEN'S VALENCE ELECTRON IN ITS FIRST PERMISSIBLE ORBIT (ENERGY LEVEL) ABOUT THE NUCLEUS BEFORE APPLICATION OF HEAT (B) VALENCE ELECTRON IN SECOND PERMISSIBLE ORBIT AFTER APPLICATION OF HEAT

The application of heat is sufficient to raise this valence electron to its second permissible orbit ($n = 2$) in which it is further from the nucleus and at a higher energy. Further application of heat could raise the electron to the third orbit ($n = 3$). A sufficient amount of heat may be applied so that the valence electron can be completely removed from the influence of the atom ($n = \infty$). This process is called *ionization*, and it leaves the atom with an excess positive charge since it has lost an electron. The positively charged atom is now called a *positive ion*. If the valence electron in Figure 1.3 were to escape from the atom's influence, a positive hydrogen ion would result, denoted H^+. Negative ions are produced in a manner which is completely the reverse of this. An external electron attaching itself to a normal atom causes the atom to acquire a negative charge and become a negative ion.

When a positive ion is formed, such as H^+, the liberated electron is virtually free of any nuclear force of attraction and is unresistant to any externally applied force. It will become apparent in our study of semiconductor devices that it is these same liberated electrons and the valence electrons which play an important role in semiconductor operation.

1.7.   Combinations of Atoms

The discussion of the properties of isolated atoms leads us naturally to consideration of combinations of atoms as they occur in nature. We shall here be interested in combinations of atoms of the same element and of different elements. Our attention will be focused only on solid materials without considering liquids or gases.

When atoms link together or interconnect in some fashion, they form *molecules* of matter. The linkage or interconnection is called *bonding*. Atoms bond together to form molecules. This atomic bonding takes place through the interaction of the valence electrons of each atom.

It is now pertinent to discuss the forces which bind atoms together. These forces are electrostatic in nature and can be divided into three categories: (1) *ionic* binding forces, (2) *covalent* binding forces, and (3) *metallic* binding forces. Although our chief concern will be with the covalent type, each will be discussed briefly.

When atoms bond together to form molecules of matter, each atom attempts to have eight electrons in its outer shell. The outer shell of each atom is considered filled when it contains eight electrons. In ionic bonding, the binding forces occur when the valence electrons from one atom join together with those of another atom to fill the latter's outer shell. If an atom has four or more valence electrons, it has a tendency to acquire additional electrons when joining with other atoms in order to fill its outer shell. When this occurs, the outer shell contains eight electrons and the binding forces are termed ionic since the atom acquiring the electrons becomes a negative ion and the atom losing electrons becomes a positive ion. A common example of an ionically bound molecule is salt, or sodium chloride, shown symbolically in Figure

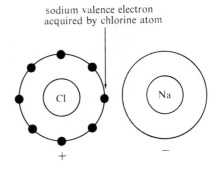

sodium valence electron
acquired by chlorine atom

FIG. 1.4.   SODIUM CHLORIDE IONIC BOND, NaCl

1.4. Only the valence electrons are shown. Sodium (Na), having one valence electron, donates it to the chlorine atom with seven valence electrons. The chlorine atom thus acquires a full outer shell of eight electrons. As a result of this electron transfer, the sodium atom becomes positively charged and the chlorine atom becomes negatively charged. Each atom has become an ion and the forces which bind them together are ionic forces.

Covalent bonding occurs when the valence electrons of neighboring atoms are shared among the atoms. An atom which contains four valence electrons may share one electron with each of four neighboring atoms. This concept of sharing electrons should be distinguished from the previous situation of gaining or losing valence electrons. The important difference is that no ions are formed in a covalent bond. The covalent forces are established

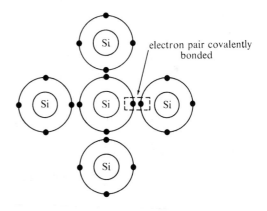

electron pair covalently
bonded

FIG. 1.5.   COVALENT BONDING OF SILICON ATOMS

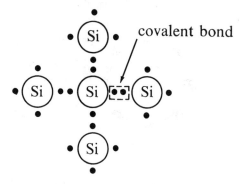

FIG. 1.6.   COVALENT BONDING OF SILICON ATOMS

when two electrons coordinate their motions so as to produce an electrostatic force between the electrons. An illustration of covalent bonding between silicon atoms is given in Figure 1.5. Again, only the valence electrons are shown. The center silicon atom shares one of its valence electrons with each of the four surrounding silicon atoms, each of which in turn shares one of its valence electrons with the center atom. This sharing of valence electrons produces pairs of electrons covalently bonded, giving each silicon atom an apparent eight valence electrons in its outer shell. Since in the following chapters we shall frequently be looking at covalently bonded structures, the abbreviated type of symbol as in Figure 1.6 will henceforth be used.

The metallic binding forces are neither ionic or covalent in nature but are rather thought of as occurring when positive ions

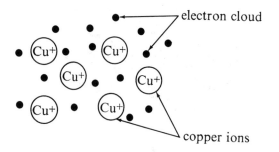

FIG. 1.7.   METALLIC BONDING IN COPPER

float in a "cloud" of electrons. There is an electrostatic force between the positive ions and the negative electrons which form a cloud about the ions. Since in a metal the electrons have such a great mobility, the electrons cannot be associated with any particular atom. The atoms are held together by the attraction of these electrons and the resulting positive ions. Figure 1.7 illustrates this for the metal copper, Cu.

1.8.   Electron Energies in Solids: Energy Bands

Referring to Section 1.4 concerning a single atom, it was stated that an atom possesses many permissible energy levels in which its electrons can exist. Recall, also, that no electron can exist at an energy level other than a permissible one. For a single atom, a diagram can be constructed showing the different energy levels available for its electrons. Figure 1.8 is the energy level diagram

FIG. 1.8.   ENERGY LEVELS OF A HYDROGEN ATOM

for the hydrogen atom. The permissible energy levels available to the single electron of the hydrogen atom are numbered $n = 1$, 2, ... in increasing order of energy. There is an infinite number of energies between the various levels shown. However, the hydrogen electron can only exist at one of the permissible levels. The higher the energy level, the further away from the nucleus is the electron's orbit.

When atoms bond together to form molecules of matter this simple diagram of electron energies is no longer applicable. In a solid the atoms are so close to each other that certain important changes occur in the state of the energy levels. When atoms are brought into close proximity as in a solid, the energy levels which existed for single isolated atoms split up to form *bands* of energy levels. Within each band there are still discrete permissible energy levels rather than a continuous band. Figure 1.9 shows the *energy band diagram* for an atom in a silicon crystal.

Figure 1.9 shows only the two upper (highest-energy) bands of energy levels. There are many bands below the level of the *valence band* shown in this figure; however, only the two upper bands are of interest in considering electrical properties. The uppermost energy band is the *conduction band.* Separating these two bands is a *forbidden energy band* which may not be occupied by any electron in the silicon crystal.

It must be stressed that the different energy bands contain many discrete energy levels which are much closer in energy than the levels in a single atom. Thus in a solid structure there are many more energy levels available for an electron and these levels are grouped in bands.

The valence band of electron energies contains all the energy levels available to the valence electrons in the structure. These valence electrons (Section 1.5) are more or less attached to the individual atoms and are not free to move about as are the electrons in the conduction band. Every valence electron has an energy in the valence band.

The conduction band is a band of energies in which the level of energy of the electrons is high enough so that electrons in these levels are not attached or bound to any atom but are rather mobile and capable of being influenced by an external force. Electrons

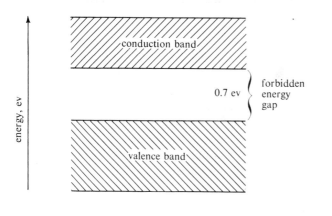

FIG. 1.9. ENERGY BAND DIAGRAM FOR SILICON

do not normally exist in the conduction band. The electrons that move to the conduction band are those electrons from the valence band that gain sufficient energy, through some form of excitation (Section 1.6), to be elevated to the conduction band. In order to do this, they must jump the forbidden energy band between the valence band and the conduction band. Referring to Figure 1.9 for silicon, an electron existing at an energy level near the top of the valence band needs to gain 0.7 ev of energy in order to jump the gap and reach the bottom of the conduction band. It is this energy difference across the forbidden energy band that determines whether a solid behaves as a *conductor, insulator* or *semiconductor*.

Electric current can be defined as the movement of charges. Since electrons are negatively charged particles, then it is logical to conclude that the ability of a material to conduct electricity depends upon the availability of free or conduction-band electrons within the material.

A conductor is a solid containing many electrons in the conduction band at room temperature. In fact, there is no forbidden region between the valence and conduction bands on a good conductor's energy band diagram. The two bands actually overlap as shown in Figure 1.10A. Since the valence band energies are the same as the conduction band energies for a conductor, it is very easy for a valence electron to become a conduction (free) electron. Thus, conductors have many conduction electrons available to conduct electric current without the need for applied energy such as heat or light.

An insulator material has an energy band diagram such as in Figure 1.10B with a very wide forbidden energy band. The forbidden energy band is so wide that practically no electrons can be given sufficient energy to jump the gap from the valence band to the conduction band. In the ideal insulator, all the levels of the valence band are occupied by electrons and the conduction band is empty. Thus, a perfect insulator has no conduction electrons and will not conduct an electric current. Practical insulators, of course, have a few conduction electrons and they conduct a very small current.

A semiconductor is a solid which has a forbidden energy band as shown in Figure 1.10C. Its forbidden energy band is much smaller than for an insulator but larger than for a conductor. Normally, since it has this forbidden energy band, it would be considered that a semiconductor has no electrons in its conduction band. However, the energy provided by the heat of room temperature is sufficient to overcome the atomic bonding forces on a few valence electrons so that some can jump the gap into the conduc-

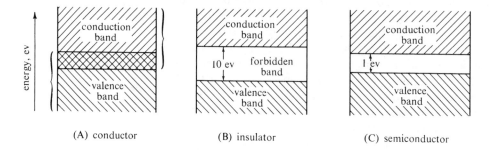

(A) conductor   (B) insulator   (C) semiconductor

FIG. 1.10.   ENERGY BAND DIAGRAMS FOR THREE
ELECTRICAL CLASSIFICATIONS OF MATTER

tion band. Therefore at room temperature semiconductors are capable of conducting some electric current. It is this class of materials in which we shall be interested.

GLOSSARY

Atomic number: equal to the number of protons or electrons of an atom

Atomic weight: equal approximately to the total number of protons and neutrons in an atom's nucleus

Electron-volt: unit of energy equivalent to 1.6×10^{-19} joules

Permissible energy levels: those values of energy available for the electrons of an atom

Electron shells: groupings of permissible energy levels

Valence electrons: the electrons existing in an atom's outermost shell

Atomic excitation: application of external energy of some form to an atom

Ionization: process of an atom either losing or gaining an electron so as to leave it with a non-neutral charge

Ion: a charged atom (either + or −)

Molecules: atoms bonded together

Bonding: linking or interconnecting of atoms

Ionic bonding: type of atomic bonding whereby one atom donates valence electrons to another

Covalent bonding: type of atomic bonding whereby the atoms share one another's valence electrons

Metallic bonding: type of electrostatic bonding between positive nuclei and negative electron clouds occurring in metals

Energy bands: groupings of energy levels which occur when atoms bond together in solid structures

Valence energy band: band of energies available for valence electrons

Conduction energy band: band of energies available for conduction of free electrons

Forbidden energy band: band of energies between valence and conduction bands containing non-permissible energy levels

Electric current: movement of charges

Conductor, semiconductor, insulator: electrical classification of matter in decreasing order of ability to conduct electric current

Questions

1.1 Describe the Bohr model of an isolated atom of silicon. (See Figure 1.2)

1.2 What is the atomic number and weight of lithium? (See Figure 1.2)

1.3 Explain the difference between discrete energy levels and a continuum of energy levels.

1.4 Will an electron in the *M*-shell of an atom have a higher or lower energy than one in the *L*-shell?

1.5 What is the valence of an atom with 3 electrons in its outer shell?

1.6 Why can't an orbiting electron have its energy increased to any value?

1.7 What happens to an electron's orbit if it loses energy?

1.8 Name 2 forms of energy which can excite an atom.

1.9   What happens to an atom when an electron receives enough energy to free itself from its atom?

1.10   Name the 3 types of atomic bonding.

1.11   When atoms share electrons what is their bonding called?

1.12   Explain the differences in conductors, semiconductors and insulators using the energy band diagram concept.

1.13   What will happen to the number of electrons in the conduction band of a semiconductor as temperature of the material is increased?

References

Anderson, D. L., *The Discovery of the Electron*. Princeton, N. J.: D. Van Nostrand Co., Inc., 1964.

Branson, L. K., *Introduction to Electronics*. Englewood Cliffs, N. J.: Prentice-Hall, Inc., 1967.

Foster, J. F., *Semiconductors, Diodes and Transistors*, Vol. 1. Beaverton, Oregon: Programmed Instruction Group, Tetronix, Inc., 1964.

Riddle, R. L. and M. P. Ristenbatt, *Transistor Physics and Circuits*. Englewood Cliffs, N. J.: Prentice-Hall, Inc., 1958.

Romanowitz, H. A. and R. E. Puckett, *Introduction to Electronics*. New York: John Wiley & Sons, Inc., 1968.

Basics of Current Flow[*]

2.1.   Introduction

The study of electronics is basically a study of the movement of
charges. This movement of charges constitutes current flow.
In this chapter we shall briefly discuss the concepts of current,
different materials' resistance to the flow of current and the conditions under which a current will flow. The terms "drift current"
and "diffusion current" will be introduced as necessary background
for the work in semiconductors to follow.

2.2.   Electric Current

If a potential difference or voltage is applied across a conductor
— for example, by connecting it across a battery — the free electrons in the conductor will move or drift toward the positive
terminal of the battery. This movement of electrons is an electrical
current. In a lightning stroke, mother nature's brilliant generation
of great electrical currents, both negative and positive charges
move — in opposite directions. In high-energy accelerators
(cyclotrons) charges are made to move about, and again this

---

[*]The popular term "current flow" is actually redundant since charge is what
flows and current is charge flow. However, we shall use this term throughout
the text.

17

movement or flow of charges constitutes an electrical current. The flow of electrons in conductors, semiconductors, and between the electrodes of vacuum tubes are examples of currents encountered in electronics.

Since current is a flow of charge, the unit of current is given in terms of a given amount of charge flowing past a certain point per second. The unit of charge used is a *coulomb* which is equivalent to the charge on 6.28×10^{18} electrons or protons. The unit of current is called the ampere. Thus

$$1 \text{ ampere} = 1 \text{ coulomb/second} \tag{2.1}$$

In terms of electron flow

$$1 \text{ ampere} = 6.28 \times 10^{18} \text{ electrons/second} \tag{2.2}$$

Figure 2.1 illustrates the ampere of electric current flowing in a conductor.

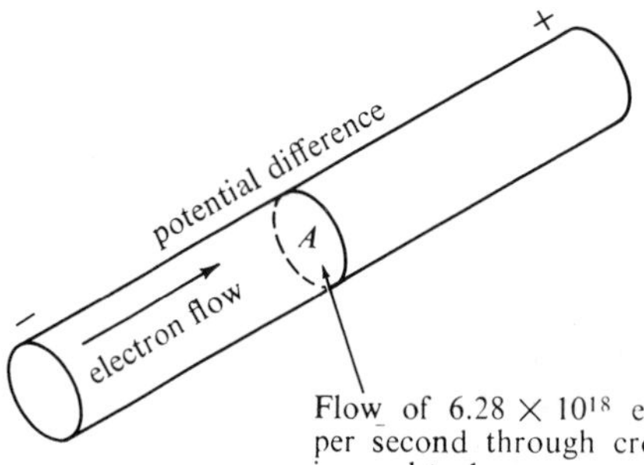

Flow of 6.28×10^{18} electrons (1 coulomb) per second through cross-sectional area, *A* is equal to 1 ampere.

FIG. 2.1.　　ELECTRIC CURRENT

In conductors or semiconductors the only charge which moves or flows is the charge carried by electrons. Even the movement of holes*, which are thought of as positive charges, in semiconductors is really caused by the jumping of valence electrons from hole to hole. In light of this, the direction of current flow will be defined as the direction of electron flow throughout this text. This conflicts with the traditional definition of current flow as being in the direction of positive charge flow. However, since in material bodies electrons are the particles which are free to move about, it will aid the understanding of semiconductor operation if current flow is synonymous with electron flow. Thus, in Figure

---

*"Holes" will be discussed in detail with semiconductor theory.

2.1 we shall consider the current in that case as flowing from left to right as the electrons flow.

Table 2.1 gives the fractional parts of an ampere which shall be used in this text and with which the student should become familiar.

TABLE 2.1

AMPERE UNITS

1 ampere = 1 ampere (amp)
10^{-3} ampere = 0.001 ampere = 1 milliampere (ma)
10^{-6} ampere = 0.000001 ampere
= 1 microampere (μa) (μ is the Greek letter mu)
10^{-9} ampere = 0.000000001 ampere
= 1 milli-microampere (nanoampere)
10^{-12} ampere = 0.001 nanoampere
= 1 micro-microampere (picoampere)

2.3.   Resistivity and Conductivity

In the previous chapter we defined conductors, insulators and semiconductors in terms of their energy-band structures. In this section we shall consider an equivalent definition of electrical properties of materials which will augment but not replace the previous definition.

Resistivity is a measure of the degree that a material opposes or resists the flow of electrical current. *Conductivity* is the degree that a material allows current to flow. A material which exhibits high opposition to current flow is said to have a high resistivity. The same material is said to have a low conductivity. The symbols ρ (the Greek letter rho) and σ (the Greek letter sigma) will be used for resistivity and conductivity respectively.

Different materials have different values of resistivity. The resistivity of rubber, which is an insulator, is far greater than that of copper, which is a conductor. The resistivity of silicon, which is a semiconductor, is between that of rubber and copper.

The resistivity of a material is determined by a number of factors including the atomic structure of the material, its temperature and the density of free charge carriers available to move under an external force such as an electric potential. Resistivity is a measurable quantity and is independent of the geometrical shape of the material. It is an intrinsic property in the same sense that mass or density is. Resistivity has the units of *ohm-centimeters* in the cgs (centimeter-gram-second) system. Ohms, of course, are the familiar units of electrical *resistance*. Electrical resistance, also a measure of a material's ability to resist current flow, depends on both the resistivity of a material and on its geometry (length and cross-sectional area). Thus, it is not a useful means of classifying materials electrically. Conductivity has the units of *mhos* per centimeter since it is the reciprocal of resistivity. That is

$$\sigma = 1/\rho \tag{2.3}$$

for a given material.

Table 2.2 lists several materials and their resistivities. Conductors are considered to have resistivities below 10^{-3} ohm-cm; semiconductors are in the range of 10^{-3} to 10^6 ohm-cm; and insulators are materials with resistivities greater than 10^6 ohm-cm. Thus, in Table 2.2 all the materials listed above and including porcelain are classified as insulators. Silicon, germanium and carbon are semiconductors and the metals platinum, aluminum, copper and silver are conductors. This classification of materials is exactly in agreement with the energy-band classification since materials with a very narrow forbidden band have the lowest resistivities and materials with a large forbidden band have the highest resistivities.

TABLE 2.2

RESISTIVITIES IN OHM-CM

Insulators	Fused quartz:	10^{19}
	Hard rubber:	10^{18}
	Nylon:	4×10^{14}
	Glass:	17×10^{12}
	Porcelain:	3×10^{11}
Semiconductors	Silicon (pure):	2×10^5
	Germanium (pure):	65
	Carbon:	4×10^{-3}
Conductors	Platinum:	10^{-5}
	Aluminum:	2.8×10^{-6}
	Copper:	1.7×10^{-6}
	Silver:	1.6×10^{-6}

2.4.   Conditions Producing Current

In the study of semiconductors two current-producing conditions or mechanisms are encountered. One is the already familiar electric potential or voltage. The other, less familiar, is called a *concentration gradient* and is very important in semiconductor work. Both of these mechanisms occur in many of the semiconductor devices which we shall study in this text.

Figure 2.2 illustrates the mechanism of current flow produced in a conductive material when a potential difference is applied across it. The free electrons in the material are accelerated by the potential difference toward the positive end of the material. These conduction electrons, however, move erratically through the material as they encounter collisions with atoms in the structure.

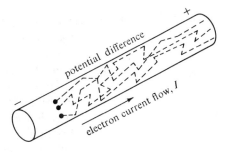

FIG. 2.2.   ELECTRON DRIFT CURRENT

We can ignore this erratic motion and consider that the electrons drift toward the positive end at a much slower speed than if they were moving in a vacuum with no atoms impeding their movement. This drifting of electrons caused by the potential difference constitutes an electric current in the direction shown. This type of current is often referred to as *drift current* and is the most common type. Whenever a voltage is applied to a conductor or resistor, the current which flows is actually a drift current.

It is possible for a current to flow in a material even in the absence of an applied voltage if a *concentration gradient* exists in the material. A concentration gradient occurs when the concentration of charges is greater in one part of the material than in some other part. Figure 2.3 depicts this situation in a bar of silicon. When a concentration gradient of charge carriers exists in a material, the charge carriers tend to move or diffuse from the region of high concentration to the region of lower concentration much as the molecules of a gas diffuse to fill a container. The current produced by this movement of charge is called *diffusion current* and is of major significance in semiconductor electronics. In the silicon bar above, the electrons will tend to move from left to right

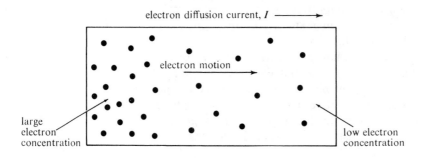

electron diffusion current, I ⟶

electron motion

large electron concentration

low electron concentration

FIG. 2.3.   DIFFUSION CURRENT RESULTING FROM A
CONCENTRATION GRADIENT OF ELECTRONS

from the region of high electron concentration to the region of lower electron concentration in an effort to reach an equilibrium situation of uniform concentration throughout the bar. The direction of the diffusion current is thus left to right as shown. The direction of the diffusion current is thus left to right as shown. The same action takes place for positive charge concentration gradients as shown in Figure 2.4. Here the positive charges are symbolized by little zeros or holes for reasons which will become clear later. Note that the diffusion current direction in this case is opposite to the flow of the positive charges since we have defined current flow to be in the direction of electron flow, that is, negative charge flow. Positive charges moving in one direction produce

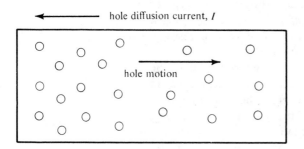

⟵ hole diffusion current, I

hole motion

FIG. 2.4.   DIFFUSION CURRENT RESULTING FROM A
CONCENTRATION   GRADIENT   OF   HOLES
(POSITIVE CHARGES)

the same current as negative charges moving in the opposite direction.

These two types of current flow, drift and diffusion, will occur simultaneously in much of the work to follow; they will also occur individually in many cases. Their presence in semiconductor materials is of paramount importance, and familiarity with the conditions which produce them is necessary to understand semi-conductor operation.

GLOSSARY

Electric current (I):   the movement of charges

Coulomb: the amount of charge on 6.28×10^{18} electrons or protons

Ampere: unit of electric current equivalent to one coulomb per second

Resistivity (ρ):   measure of the ability of a material to resist the flow of electric current

Conductivity (σ):   the opposite of resistivity

Drift current: current produced by movement of charges under influence of a potential difference

Concentration gradient: a difference in charge concentration within a material

Diffusion current: current produced by movement of charge due to a concentration gradient

Questions

2.1   Two copper wires, with cross-sectional areas of 1 cm² and 2 cm² respectively, both have charge flowing through them at the rate of 0.5 coulomb per second.   Which one has the larger current flowing through it?

2.2   Does a platinum wire necessarily have more electrical resistance than a copper wire when the same voltage is applied to each?

2.3   Explain the difference between resistivity and resistance.

2.4   What condition is necessary to produce a drift current?

2.5 What condition is necessary to produce a diffusion current?

2.6 Is the movement of positive ions such as H^+ considered to be a current flow?

References

Branson, L. K., *Introduction to Electronics.* Englewood Cliffs, N. J.: Prentice-Hall, Inc., 1967.

3

General Device Analysis

3.1.   Introduction

This chapter is intended to be a general introduction to device
analysis. In this discussion no attempt will be made to distinguish
between vacuum tube and semiconductor devices since the treatment is general enough to apply to either type of device. A device
will be treated as a "black box" with consideration given only to
its terminal characteristics and how these terminal characteristics
are used to analyze the device's operation. Two- and three-terminal
devices will be discussed in detail with the results then extended to
devices with more than three terminals.

3.2.   The General *n*-Terminal Device

Figure 3.1 depicts a general *n*-terminal device as a box with *n*
terminals or leads emanating from it (*n* can be any number greater
than one). The terminals are physically and electrically connected
by conductive material to points within the box. The box or
black box,* as it is commonly referred to, represents the actual

---

*The term "black box" usually refers to a physical device, circuit or system
whose internal makeup is not known but must be deduced from external measurements.

physical makeup of the device, which in general is not box-shaped. Each terminal of the device is available for electrical connection to external points such as the terminals of other devices, battery terminals, ground terminals or another of its own terminals.

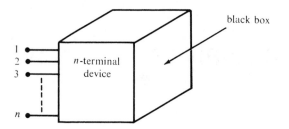

black box

FIG. 3.1.   SYMBOLIC REPRESENTATION OF A GENERAL
            n-TERMINAL DEVICE

The black box contains the internal physical and chemical properties of the device which determine its particular electrical characteristics. In this chapter we will not be concerned with what is happening inside the black boxes, but rather on what sort of information we can obtain and use simply by taking external measurements at the device terminals. After all, this is the information the circuit designer or analyst has to work with, and this is what he needs to know in order to determine how a device will operate in a circuit in conjunction with other devices and electrical components.

Figure 3.2 is an example of a familiar two-terminal device, the resistor. Its physical appearance is shown in part (A) and its standard electronic symbol is shown in part (B). In the resistor symbol the terminals are denoted a and b. The squiggly line with the letter R represents the physical resistance. Without examining or knowing the composition of the resistor we can find out all we

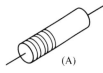

(A)

$a \circ\!\!-\!\!\bigwedge\!\!\bigwedge\!\!-\!\!\circ b$

(B)

FIG. 3.2.   THE RESISTOR, A 2-TERMINAL DEVICE
            (A) PHYSICAL APPEARANCE; (B) SYMBOL

need to know simply by measuring the resistance between its terminals or by determining the relationship between the current flow in the resistor and the voltage applied across its terminals.

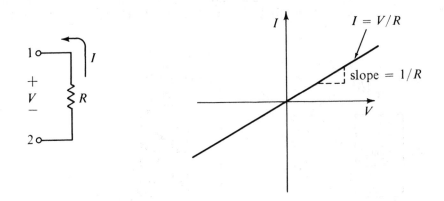

FIG. 3.3.   CURRENT-VOLTAGE RELATIONSHIP OF RE-SISTANCE, R, BETWEEN TERMINALS 1 AND 2

This is illustrated in Figure 3.3. For the resistor this relationship is a straight line relationship as indicated in the graph of resistor current, I, versus resistor voltage, V. This graph is called the static *I-V characteristic* of the resistor since it is obtained by applying a constant (static) voltage and measuring the resultant constant current or vice-versa. Throughout the text, consideration will be given to the static *I-V* characteristics of many devices. In doing so the word "static" will be dropped and *I-V* character-istics will be referred to with the understanding that they are static characteristics.

This procedure of obtaining the *I-V* characteristics between two terminals of a device will be followed for each device we study in this text, regardless of the number of terminals it has. However, the procedure is slightly more complicated for multi-terminal devices (with more than two terminals) than for two-terminal devices like the resistor above. The difference is that, for a multi-terminal device, the *I-V* characteristic between any two terminals depends on what is occurring at the other terminals. The next two sections describe the general procedure for determining the complete static electrical characteristics of two- and three-terminal devices. The procedure can then be easily extended to devices with four or more terminals.

3.3.   Two-Terminal Device Characteristics

A general two-terminal device is shown in Figure 3.4. Its terminals are denoted a and b. The voltage between terminals a and b is given by V_{ab}, which is defined as the voltage at a relative to the voltage at b. For instance, if we placed a 6-volt battery such

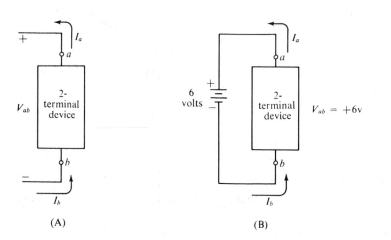

(A)   (B)

FIG. 3.4.   (A) GENERAL 2-TERMINAL DEVICE; (B) DEVICE WITH 6-VOLT BATTERY APPLIED BETWEEN ITS TERMINALS

that its positive terminal was at a, then V_{ab} would be $+6$ volts since terminal a is 6 volts positive with respect to terminal b. This is illustrated in part (B) of Figure 3.4. If we were to reverse this 6-volt battery, then V_{ab} would be -6 volts since terminal a would be 6 voltages negative with respect to terminal b. Thus, V_{ab} is positive if terminal a is more positive than terminal b, and negative if terminal a is more negative than terminal b.

The current flow, I_a, through terminal a is shown as coming out of terminal a. This direction is chosen since a positive value of V_{ab} will cause current to flow in this direction, electrons flowing toward the positive voltage. Similarly I_b flows into terminal b. In a two-terminal device, I_a and I_b are always equal.

For a two-terminal device the only I-V characteristic to determine is the relationship between I_a and V_{ab}. To re-emphasize a point, the information obtained from the I-V characteristic is needed in order to be able to determine the device's voltage and current as it operates in a circuit with other circuit elements. The *I-V* characteristic of a two-terminal device is obtained simply by applying various values of V_{ab} and measuring the corresponding values of I_a. Figure 3.5 shows typical *I-V* characteristics for two of the two-terminal devices which we will study in subsequent chapters. Note that these curves are nonlinear.

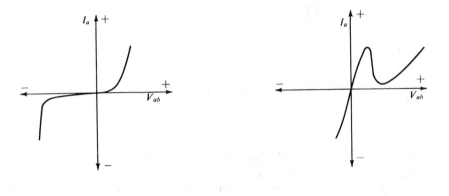

FIG. 3.5. EXAMPLES OF *I-V* CHARACTERISTICS FOR TWO-TERMINAL DEVICES

To summarize, it is a relatively simple matter to determine the characteristic curve (another name for the *I-V* characteristic) for a two-terminal device. We shall be looking at many two-terminal devices and their characteristic curves in the course of this text and utilizing these curves to determine the operating points (voltage and current) of these devices in some common circuits.

3.4. Three-Terminal Device Characteristics

We saw in the previous section that for two-terminal devices only *one* *I-V* characteristic is needed to describe its operation. For three-terminal devices *two* *I-V* characteristics are required, but the procedure is complicated somewhat by the effect of the third terminal on the *I-V* characteristics between the two terminals of interest. A general three-terminal device is shown in Figure 3.6 with its terminals denoted *a*, *b*, and *c*. Between terminals *a* and *c* the voltage is denoted as V_{ac}, the voltage at *a* relative to *c*. Similarly V_{bc} is the voltage at *b* relative to *c*. V_{ab}, which is the

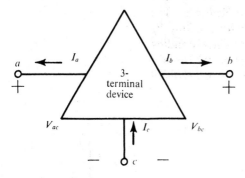

FIG. 3.6.   GENERAL THREE-TERMINAL DEVICE

voltage between *a* and *b*, is not shown since only two *I-V* characteristics are needed for a three-terminal device. A third *I-V* characteristic would give no new information. The assumed current directions indicated for each terminal are such that electrons flow from the negative voltage toward the positive voltage.

In Figure 3.6 terminal *c* is common to both voltages V_{ac} and V_{bc}. For this reason the two *I-V* characteristics obtained using these voltages, namely I_a *versus* V_{ac} and I_b *versus* V_{bc}, are called "common-*c* characteristic curves". We could choose *a* or *b* as the

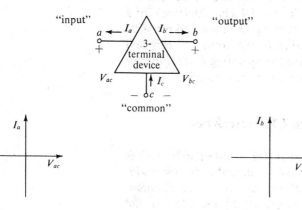

FIG. 3.7.   THREE-TERMINAL DEVICE: (A) LABELLED AXES FOR INPUT CHARACTERISTICS; (B) LABELLED AXES FOR OUTPUT CHARACTERISTICS

common terminal and obtain the common-*a* or common-*b* characteristic curves. However, since this is a general discussion we can concern ourselves with the common-*c* characteristics without loss of generality. In order to distinguish between the two common-*c* *I-V* characteristics we can arbitrarily refer to *a* as the *input* terminal and *b* as the *output* terminal. Thus the relationship of I_a to the voltage V_{ac} can be called the input common-*c* characteristic and the relationship of I_b to V_{bc} the output common-*c* characteristic. To help illustrate what has been said, Figure 3.7 summarizes the main points stated thus far.

We saw that for a two-terminal device the *I-V* characteristic consisted of one curve relating current to voltage. For a three-terminal device there are two *I-V* characteristics and in general each *I-V* characteristic will consist of more than one curve. This is so because for most three-terminal devices the relationship of current to voltage at a given pair of terminals, say *a* and *c*, depends on the current or voltage or both at terminal *b*. This dependence means that for each value of current or voltage at terminal *b*, there will be a certain *I-V* curve between *a* and *c*. This is illustrated hypothetically in Figure 3.8 where I_a is plotted against V_{ac} for four different values of I_b. The four distinct curves result from the fact that in general the relationship between I_a and V_{ac} will change if I_b changes. Another hypothetical possibility is shown in Figure 3.9. Here I_a versus V_{ac} is plotted for various values of V_{bc} with

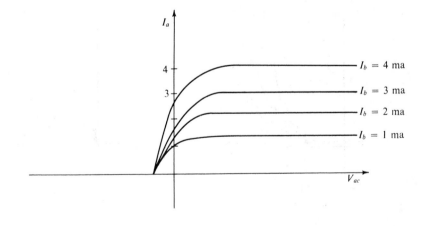

FIG. 3.8.   ILLUSTRATION OF INPUT CHARACTERISTICS FOR A HYPOTHETICAL THREE-TERMINAL DEVICE

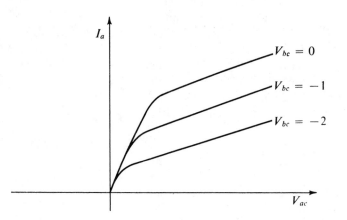

FIG. 3.9.   ANOTHER POSSIBLE SET OF INPUT CHAR-
ACTERISTICS

a different curve for each value of V_{bc}. Similar behavior occurs
when considering the output characteristics, I_b versus V_{bc}. In
this case there will be a different curve for each value of I_a or V_{ac}.

     The complete common-*c* characteristic curves for a three-
terminal device will consist of a set of input characteristics and a

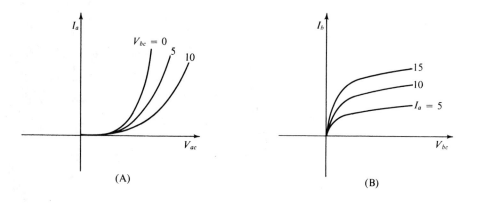

FIG. 3.10.   COMPLETE COMMON-*c* CHARACTERISTICS:
(A) INPUT CHARACTERISTICS; (B) OUTPUT
CHARACTERISTICS

set of output characteristics. Figure 3.10 shows the complete common-*c* characteristics for a particular three-terminal device. It must again be pointed out that the *I-V* relationship between any two terminals depends on the third. For example, in the device shown in Figure 3.10, the relationship between I_a and V_{ac} depends on the value of V_{bc}. In analyzing a circuit it is necessary to know the value of V_{bc} in order to determine which curve to use. Similarly, the value of I_a must be known in order to determine which output curve to use. This interdependency may present difficulty at this time. However, with most devices, approximations can be made which greatly simplify the circuit analysis.

In summary, the added complexity of three-terminal device characteristics over that of two-terminal devices is a result of the physical interaction among the three terminals. This causes the *I-V* characteristics between any two terminals to consist of a family of curves rather than one curve as for two-terminal devices.

3.5.   Devices with Four or More Terminals

The procedure for determining the complete characteristics of a device with greater than three terminals is the same as in the three-terminal case. A common terminal is chosen and the *I-V* characteristics between each terminal and the common terminal are found. Figure 3.11 illustrates one possible terminal designa-

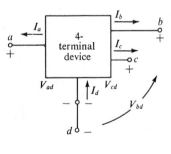

FIG. 3.11.   CONFIGURATION FOR DETERMINING "COMMON-*d*" CHARACTERISTICS FOR A FOUR-TERMINAL DEVICE

tion for a four-terminal device. Here d is the common terminal and the complete characteristics consist of the relationships I_a versus V_{ad}, I_b versus V_{bd} and I_c versus V_{cd}. Each of these relationships consist of a family of curves, a different curve for different conditions on the other two terminals. For example, Figure 3.12 shows an I_b versus V_{bd} family of curves for a particular device.

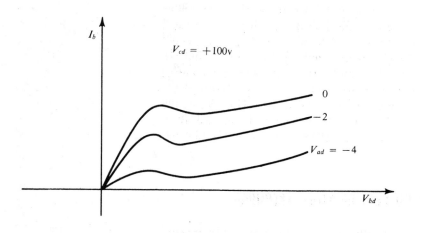

FIG. 3.12.   EXAMPLE OF CURVES RELATING I_b TO V_{bd}

In this particular example, a different curve relating I_b to V_{bd} is obtained for different sets of conditions on terminals a and c, namely V_{ad} and V_{cd} (I_a or I_c or both could also be used).

It is important to remember that, no matter how many terminals there are, the conditions on each terminal must be specified (current or voltage relative to common) and the *I-V* characteristics between each terminal and the common terminal constitute a complete set of characteristics. It is easily seen that using these characteristics can become extraordinarily complicated for more than two terminals unless some approximations can be made. We shall see that this is usually the case.

GLOSSARY

N-terminal device: an electronic device with n terminals or connections emanating from it

Black box: representation of the physical properties of a device used when one is interested only in its terminal characteristics

(Static) *I-V* characteristic: graph of current versus voltage between two terminals of a device (Sec. 3.2)

V_{ab}:   the voltage at *a* with respect to *b* (Sec. 3.3)

Common-*c* characteristics: the complete *I-V* characteristics of a device using the *c* terminal as the common terminal

Input (output) characteristic: the *I-V* characteristics between the designated input (output) terminal and the common terminal (Sec. 3.4)

Questions

3.1   In the circuit of Figure 3.13 what are the values of V_{ac}, V_{bc} and V_{ab}?

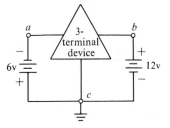

FIG.   3.13.

3.2   How many sets of *I-V* characteristics are needed for a two-terminal device? A four-terminal device?

3.3   In the circuit of Figure 3.14, is the three-terminal device in the common-*a*, common-*b* or common-*c* configuration? What is the direction of I_b?

3.4   For the circuit of Figure 3.14, choose one of the terminals as input and the other as output; then draw and label the axes needed to plot the input and output characteristics.

3.5   Figure 3.15 shows the output *I-V* characteristics between terminals *a* and *c* for a particular three-terminal device. What is the value of I_a when $V_{ac} = 20$ volts and $V_{bc} = 0$ volts? Repeat for $V_{bc} = -1$ volt; -2 volts.

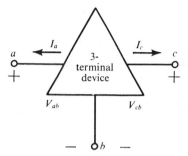

FIG. 3.14.

The value of V_{bc} determines which curve relating I_a to V_{ac} is to be used. A device whose output *I-V* characteristics are controlled by a voltage at another terminal is said to be a *voltage-controlled* device.

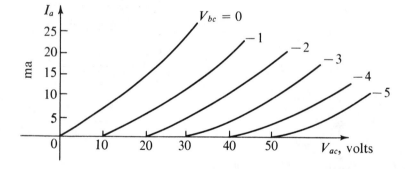

FIG. 3.15.

3.6   Figure 3.16 shows the output *I-V* characteristics between terminals *a* and *c* for a particular three-terminal device. What is the value of I_a when $V_{ac} = 10$ volts and $I_b = 1$ma? Repeat for $I_b = 2$ma; $I_b = 3$ma.

The value of I_b determines which curve relating I_a to V_{ac} is to be used. A device whose output *I-V* characteristics are controlled by a current at another terminal is said to be a *current-controlled* device.

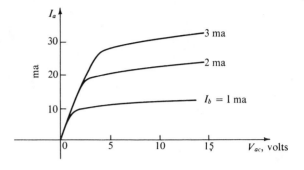

FIG. 3.16.

References

Gillie, A. C., *Principles of Electron Devices.* New York: McGraw-Hill
     Book Company, 1962.

4

Semiconductor Principles

4.1. Introduction

Although the use of semiconductor materials in electronics is not new, semiconductors played only a minor role in electronics for many years and only a token effort was directed toward developing an understanding of their unique characteristics. In recent years a remarkable concentration of effort has been given to the field of semiconductors. This emphasis on semiconductors was brought about principally by the development of the transistor by Schockley, Bardeen and Brattain in 1948. From its initial applications in hearing aids and pocket radios, the transistor has spearheaded a complete revolution in most areas of electronics, particularly in the design of computers and space vehicles. A whole new family of related semiconductor devices has been developed since the appearance of transistors—diodes, zener diodes, controlled rectifiers, unijunction transistors, photo devices, field effect devices, etc.—culminating in the recent development of integrated circuits which consist of complete functional circuits produced on a single minute chip of semiconductor material.

The brief description of electronic processes in solids presented in the previous chapters is sufficient for comprehending the basic electronic properties of solid materials. However, considerable elaboration is necessary to bring about a full appreciation of material behavior. For the purposes of understanding semiconductor devices the following discussion will emphasize semiconductor principles and properties almost to the exclusion of conductors and insulators. In particular we will study the types of atomic bonding peculiar to semiconductors, the two types of current carriers in semiconductors, and how they are produced. The effects of heat on the electronic behavior of semiconductor material will also be studied. Throughout this discussion energy band diagrams will be utilized in an effort to relate the new material in this chapter to what has already been presented.

4.2.   Conductors, Semiconductors and Insulators

In Chapter 1, solid materials were classified according to their energy band structures as conductors, semiconductors or insulators. Just what determines whether a material has the electrical characteristics of a good, fair or poor conductor? Obviously, the number of free charge carriers available within a material is a major factor. This is determined by the complexity of the atom, the number of valence electrons and the type of bonding between atoms.

Recall that an atom is considered more complex than another if it contains more orbiting electrons. More complex atoms have their valence electrons further from the nucleus than simpler atoms. Electrons in the valence band of more complex atoms possess more energy than those in the valence band of simple atoms. The farther the electron is in its orbit from the nucleus, the more loosely bound it is to the nucleus, since it possesses more energy (Sec. 1.4). Atoms with few valence electrons tend to give them up more readily than atoms with many valence electrons. Atoms possessing few valence electrons have them more loosely bound to the nucleus than the atoms with many valence electrons. An atom with two valence electrons will more easily give up a valence electron than an atom with a valence of five. A complex atom with a valence of one will lose its valence electron more readily than a simple atom with a valence of one. This follows from the fact that a complex atom's valence electrons are less tightly bound to the nucleus. This all means that complex, low valence atoms have narrow forbidden energy bands between the valence and conduction bands and thus are good conductors. On the other hand simple, high valence atoms have wide forbidden energy bands making them poor conductors.

If we look at the periodic table of elements in Appendix I, we can confirm some of these ideas. Silver and copper are both excellent conductors. Each is a fairly complex atom; silver has 47 electrons, copper has 29 electrons, and each has a valence of one. Since silver is more complex than copper, it is a better conductor. Indicated in the valence IV column are the two most important semiconductor materials, silicon and germanium. Germanium has an atomic number (the number of electrons) of 32 and silicon has an atomic number of 14. Thus, both have the same number of valence electrons. However, since germanium is more complex we can expect it to be a better conductor than silicon. It is, although both are not good conductors but rather semiconductors with germanium possessing a forbidden band gap of 0.7 ev and silicon possessing a forbidden energy gap of 1.1 ev. Aluminum is considered a conductor even though it lies in the valence III column, indicating that the number of valence electrons is not the only determining factor.

The type of atomic bonding in a material also governs the electrical characteristics.

4.3.   Covalent Bonding in Semiconductors

We saw in Chapter 1 that in solid materials there are several bonding processes; however, in semiconductor work our prime interest is in covalent bonding (Sec. 1.7). In semiconductor materials the bonding between atoms is covalent bonding. Recall that covalent bonding refers to the type of interconnection or bonding between atoms in which the atoms share their valence electrons so that each atom essentially possesses eight valence electrons.

Taking germanium as an example, the covalent bonding process is illustrated in Figure 4.1. Germanium has a valence of four and shares its four valence electrons with four adjacent atoms of germanium. Each germanium atom thus appears to have a valence of eight. A covalent bond is made up of one electron from each of two atoms strongly bonded together. This type of bonding is also prevalent in silicon, a semiconductor. Silicon and germanium are elements which are semiconductors. There are semiconductor materials made up of compounds such as gallium arsenide. Gallium, which has a valence of three, bonds together with arsenic, which has a valence of five, covalently to form the semiconductor compound gallium arsenide. Generally speaking, materials made up of three, four or five valence atoms in a covalent bond are semiconductors.

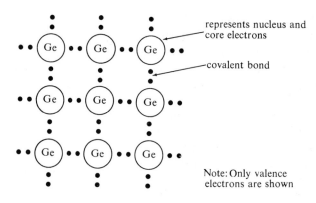

represents nucleus and
core electrons

covalent bond

Note: Only valence
electrons are shown

FIG. 4.1.   COVALENT BONDING IN GERMANIUM STRUC-
TURE

Structures formed by atoms bonded together covalently are called *crystal* structures. Atoms in crystals arrange themselves to share each other's valence electrons in a uniform three dimensional pattern depicted in Figure 4.1 in only two dimensions. Throughout the text we will continually refer to germanium and silicon crystals. In the next section we will look closely at intrinsic (pure) semiconductor crystals and their electrical characteristics.

4.4.   Intrinsic Semiconductors

Very pure semiconductor material is called *intrinsic* material. Even minute amounts of certain impurities can drastically affect the electrical properties of semiconductors. Consequently, a semiconductor would not be called truly intrinsic unless its impurity content were very small; for germanium, this is about one impurity per 10^8 germanium atoms. Silicon is called intrinsic with one impurity atom per 10^{13} silicon atoms. In practice, impurity concentrations somewhat higher than this are sometimes referred to as intrinsic.

A perfectly intrinsic germanium crystal would have a structure exactly as shown in Figure 4.1 since it consists solely of germanium atoms covalently bonded, with no impurity atoms present. The structure in Figure 4.1 shows that *all* of the valence electrons are tightly bound to the parent atoms and to other atoms by covalent bonds. These electrons are not free to move through the crystal and, therefore, cannot conduct an electrical current. This is precisely the picture at a crystal temperature of absolute zero

(−273°C or −460°F). Thus, at *absolute zero* an intrinsic semi-conductor behaves like an insulator since it has no electrons available to conduct a current. The energy band diagram of an intrinsic semiconductor crystal at absolute zero, Figure 4.2, indicates that the valence band of energies is completely filled by covalently bonded valence electrons and the conduction band is completely empty since there are no free electrons in the crystal. With no electrons in the conduction band, the semiconductor crystal cannot conduct a current and behaves essentially as an insulator.

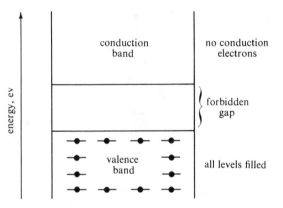

FIG. 4.2.   ENERGY BAND DIAGRAM OF AN INTRINSIC SEMICONDUCTOR AT ABSOLUTE ZERO TEMPERATURE

   Let us now consider what happens as the temperature of the crystal is increased above absolute zero. External energy, such as heat, applied to an intrinsic semiconductor increases the energy of each atom in the crystal. This increase in energy may be imparted to some of the valence electrons in the structure. Through this process, a valence electron, particularly one at an energy level near the top of the valence band, may acquire sufficient additional energy to break away from its atom and become a free electron. In doing so it must break its covalent bond and acquire enough energy to jump the forbidden energy gap. Then it will exist at an energy level in the conduction band as a free conduction electron. To illustrate this process Figure 4.3 shows the intrinsic germanium crystal of Figure 4.1 after heat energy has been applied. In this illustration a covalent bond has been broken by one of the valence electrons as a result of heat energy. The liberation of this valence

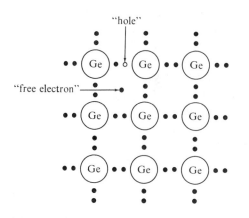

FIG. 4.3.   INTRINSIC GERMANIUM STRUCTURE AFTER
APPLICATION OF HEAT SHOWING A BROKEN
COVALENT BOND, A FREE ELECTRON AND
A HOLE

electron has left a vacancy in the covalent structure. This vacancy is called a *hole*. The loss of a valence electron has left the parent germanium atom with a net positive charge. The broken covalent bond, or hole, is considered then to be positively charged with the same charge as an electron. However, a hole is not the positively charged counterpart of an electron since it has no mass. It is simply a vacancy or absence of an electron, thus giving it a positive charge. A hole, by virtue of its positive charge, has a great attraction for an electron, if one should wander by.

The excitation of a valence electron into the conduction band is always accompanied by the appearance of a hole. The freed electron and the hole it left behind are called an *electron-hole pair*. When heat is the form of energy the generated electron-hole pairs are said to be thermally generated. The number of electron-hole pairs thermally generated depends on the temperature of the crystal. As temperature increases, more heat energy is available and more valence electrons will acquire the necessary energy to jump the forbidden gap into the conduction band. The energy band picture of this process is shown in Figure 4.4. Notice that only the higher-level valence electrons can attain the necessary energy at room temperature (21°C or 70°F) to jump the gap.

The effect of temperature on the electrical properties of a semiconductor should now be apparent. The thermally generated electrons are free from atomic forces and are capable of producing a current if a potential difference (voltage) is applied to the semi-

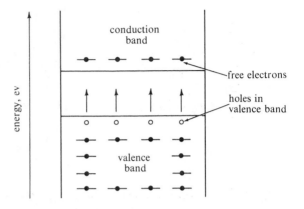

FIG. 4.4.   ENERGY BAND DESCRIPTION OF THERMAL
GENERATION OF ELECTRON-HOLE PAIRS
IN AN INTRINSIC SEMICONDUCTOR AT ROOM
TEMPERATURE

conductor. Thus, as one would expect, the resistivity of the semiconductor decreases with temperature since more electrons become
available current carriers. Meanwhile, what has happened to all
the thermally generated holes? The answer to this is that they too
have become current carriers, though not in the same way as
electrons. When a hole is created by an electron breaking a
covalent bond, a valence electron from a neighboring atom can
easily fill the hole by breaking its own covalent bond and jumping
over to the first atom, leaving behind a hole in the neighboring
atom. As this occurs, it appears that the hole has moved from
one atom to another. This sequence of events is illustrated in
Figure 4.5. Figure 4.5 (A) shows a hole existing in the silicon atom
in the lower left hand corner of the figure. No other holes are
present. In Figure 4.5 (B) we see that a valence electron from the
silicon atom in the lower right hand corner of the figure has broken
its bond and jumped over to fill the original hole, leaving behind
a hole in its atom. Thus, the hole has seemingly jumped from one
silicon atom to another. This movement of holes, which are
positively charged, constitutes a current flow. Current flow in a
semiconductor, then, is composed of electron movement and hole
movement.

If a voltage is applied to a semiconductor containing free electrons and holes, as shown in Figure 4.6, the free electrons will
move from the negative terminal toward the positive terminal, and
holes will move from positive to negative. From the discussion of

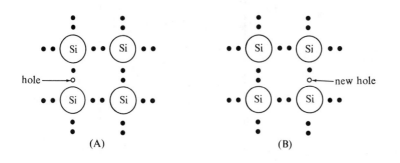

FIG. 4.5.   ILLUSTRATION OF HOLE MOVEMENT CAUSED
               BY VALENCE ELECTRONS JUMPING FROM
               HOLE TO HOLE

hole movement above, it is clear that a hole moving to the right is
a valence electron moving to the left. The flow of holes, then, from
positive to negative is essentially the same as the flow of electrons
from negative to positive. Remember that holes do not actually
move but have apparent motion. Electrons are the only charges
which actually move. Thus, the current in a semiconductor can be
thought of as consisting of two parts: free electrons moving in one
direction and holes moving in the opposite direction. The total
current is actually the sum of the two parts.

It may not be apparent just what happens to the holes as they
reach the edge of the semiconductor material in Figure 4.6. What
actually takes place is called the process of *recombination* in which

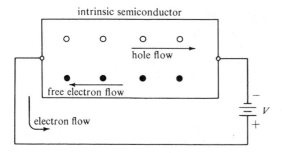

FIG. 4.6.   FLOW OF CHARGES IN A SEMICONDUCTOR
               UNDER AN APPLIED VOLTAGE

some of the electrons flow from the negative terminal of the battery and fill the holes as they enter the semiconductor. This recombination, or filling of holes, causes both the hole and electron to disappear. In reality, the process of recombination is taking place continuously throughout the semiconductor material. Free electrons wandering through the crystal may encounter holes and recombine with them, thus annihilating a hole-electron pair. What, then, keeps all the hole-electron pairs from disappearing? The answer to this is that hole-electron pairs are continuously being thermally generated. These thermally-generated electron-hole pairs compensate for the recombination losses so that at a given temperature the number of electron-hole pairs in a semiconductor crystal is essentially constant.

One of the most important points to be derived from the above discussion is that although hole current is actually due to the movement of electrons, it is *not* the same type of free electron motion that makes up electron current. The electrons which cause hole current are *valence* electrons which jump from hole to hole and do not have enough energy to become free electrons. On the other hand free electrons move freely through the crystal without being bound to any atom. Thus, free electrons are able to move much more quickly through the crystal than holes, which have to move in a succession of jumps. We can say that free electrons have a higher *mobility* than holes. This aspect will be encountered in later discussions.

We have seen that due to thermal energy an intrinsic semiconductor, which is essentially an insulator at absolute zero temperature, will contain free electrons and holes which can conduct current. At room temperature, intrinsic semiconductors such as silicon and germanium contain enough current carriers to make them fair electrical conductors, being much poorer conductors than copper or silver, but much better than an insulator such as rubber.

In summary, the resistivity and resistance of an intrinsic semiconductor decrease as its temperature increases because more valence electrons are able to break away from their covalent bonds and become free electrons. Thus, more current carriers, free electrons and holes are available, increasing the semiconductor's ability to conduct current. In an intrinsic semiconductor the total number of free electrons *equals* the total number of holes. We will see in the next section how addition of certain types of impurities will cause either free electrons or holes to be the majority current carrier.

4.5.   Extrinsic Semiconductors

Pure silicon (or germanium) is of little use as a semiconductor, except maybe as a heat- or light-sensitive resistance. Most of our modern semiconductor devices contain semiconductor materials to which certain impurities have been added to give it a predominance of either free electrons or holes. Semiconductor materials containing different types of impurities are combined to produce the many useful devices presently on the scene. The process of adding impurities to the semiconductor, called *doping*, is performed after the semiconductor material has been refined to a high degree of purity. The concentration of the added impurity, called *dopant*, is typically very minute, on the order of one part of impurity per ten million parts of pure semiconductor. The doped semiconductor is referred to as *extrinsic* semiconductor.

As was mentioned above, the effect of the impurities is to produce a predominance of either free electrons or holes. Doping impurities which add free electrons to the semiconductor material are called N-type impurities, since they add *n*egative carriers. Hole-producing impurities are called P-type impurities since they add *p*ositive carriers to the semiconductor crystal.

Let us first consider N-type impurities. The element *arsenic* is an example of this type of impurity. Referring to the periodic table of elements in Appendix I, arsenic has an atomic number of 33 and falls in the valence V column. If a small amount of arsenic is introduced into an intrinsic semiconductor crystal such as silicon, the arsenic atoms will enter into the crystalline structure and form covalent bonds with the silicon atoms. The arsenic impurities occupy positions in the crystal structure which are otherwise occupied by silicon atoms. The arsenic atoms, since they have *five* valence electrons, do not fit in exactly with the silicon crystal structure. Only *four* of their valence electrons are required in the crystal structure. The fifth valence electron does not enter a covalent bond and is thus only loosely bound to its parent arsenic atom. Only a very small amount of energy is needed to remove this electron from its atom, making it a free conduction electron. Figure 4.7 illustrates the effect of an arsenic atom in the silicon structure.

For each arsenic atom present in the crystal, one virtually free electron is *donated* to the semiconductor material. For this reason arsenic and all impurities with a valence *greater* than four are called *donor* impurities.

At absolute zero temperature the fifth valence electron of each arsenic atom is bound to its parent atom even though it is not part

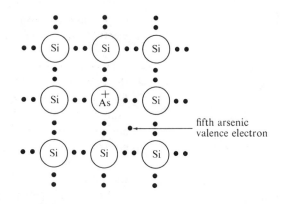

FIG. 4.7.   ADDITION OF AN N-TYPE IMPURITY, AR-
SENIC, PRODUCES A FREE ELECTRON

of a covalent bond. However, at room temperature all these
electrons have absorbed the small amount of energy needed to
become conduction electrons. This point may be made clearer
if we employ the energy band concept. Figure 4.8 contains the
energy band diagrams of a silicon crystal doped with arsenic, one
at absolute zero, the other at room temperature. With the addition
of a donor impurity a new energy level is introduced, the *donor*
level. As shown in Figure 4.8, it exists in the forbidden gap very
close to the conduction band. At absolute zero, Figure 4.8 (A)

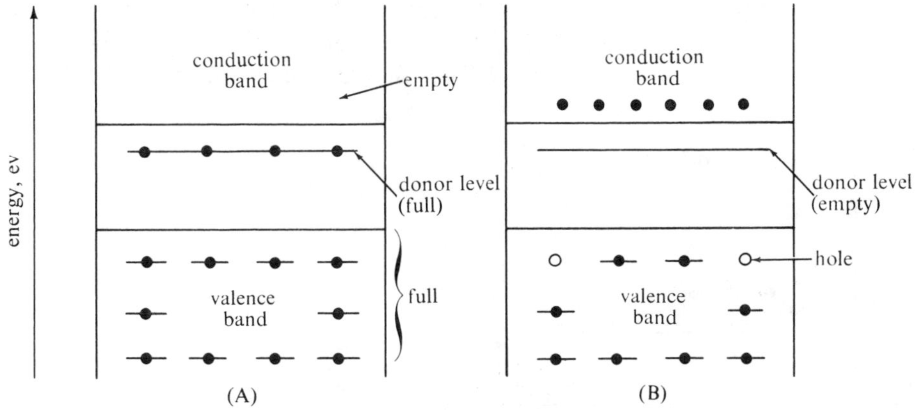

FIG. 4.8.   ENERGY BAND DIAGRAM OF SILICON DOPED
WITH N-TYPE IMPURITY (A) AT ABSOLUTE
ZERO (B) AT ROOM TEMPERATURE

indicates that the valence band is filled, the conduction band is empty, and the donor level is filled, being occupied by the donated electrons from each arsenic atom which are not yet free. At room temperature this picture changes somewhat. As we know, some valence electrons will receive enough energy to jump the gap into the conduction band, leaving holes behind. This is the electron-hole pair generation we previously discussed. In addition, the donor electrons existing at the donor level easily absorb enough energy to jump into the conduction band. However, these free electrons leave no holes behind since they have broken no covalent bonds. Thus there are more free electrons in the conduction band than there are holes in the valence band. For this reason, in an N-type semiconductor, one doped with N-type donor impurities, *electrons* are the *majority* current carriers and *holes* are the *minority* carriers.

Typically, the number of donated electrons is much greater than the number of thermally generated electron-hole pairs at room temperature—about one million times greater. Therefore, for an N-type semiconductor at room temperature the number of free electrons is around one million times the number of holes. This large increase in current carriers, mainly electrons, causes the resistivity to drop well below its value for the intrinsic undoped semiconductor. Recall that in intrinsic semiconductors the number of holes and free electrons are equal, both producing current. In N-type semiconductors the majority of carriers are electrons, so current in these materials is primarily carried by electrons. This is illustrated in Figure 4.9.

A donor impurity must be an atom with a valence greater than four. The most common are phosphorous, antimony and arsenic, each with a valence of five. These atoms donate *one* free electron

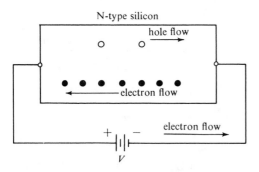

FIG. 4.9.   CURRENT FLOW IN N-TYPE SEMICONDUCTOR

each. Impurity atoms with *six* valence electrons would donate *two* free electrons, and so on. It is important to note that a donor atom becomes a *positive ion* when it donates its electron. The positive ions, however, are locked into the crystal structure and cannot move.

Let us now turn our attention to P-type impure atoms. The element *indium* is a common P-type impurity. Referring to the periodic table of elements in Appendix I, indium has an atomic number of 49 and a valence of *three*. If a small amount of indium is introduced into an intrinsic semiconductor crystal such as silicon, the indium atoms will enter into the crystalline structure and form covalent bonds with the silicon atoms. The indium impurities occupy positions in the crystal structure which are otherwise occupied by silicon atoms. The indium atoms, since they have only *three* valence electrons, do not fit in exactly with the silicon crystal structure. Because each indium atom has three valence electrons, it can bond covalently with only three silicon atoms. Thus, one covalent bond will not be formed. This is illustrated in Figure 4.10. Figure 4.10 (A) shows the indium atom bonding with *three* neighboring silicon atoms. The fourth bond is empty since indium has only *three* valence electrons to share. This makes it very easy for an electron in a bond between two neighboring semiconductor atoms to jump in and fill this vacant

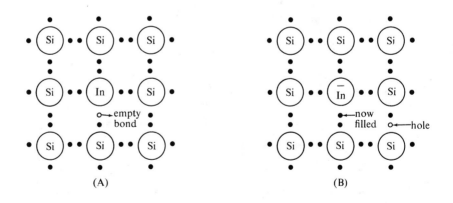

(A) (B)

FIG. **4.10.** P-TYPE IMPURITY, INDIUM, ADDED TO SILICON (A) PRODUCES AN UNFILLED COVALENT BOND; (B) A VALENCE ELECTRON FROM NEIGHBORING SILICON ATOM JUMPS TO FILL THIS EMPTY BOND LEAVING A HOLE BEHIND

bond, leaving a hole behind. Only a small amount of energy is required for this to occur. At room temperature virtually every indium atom has *accepted* a valence electron from a neighboring bond to fill its empty bond, thus producing a hole in the structure. For this reason indium and all impurities with a valence *less* than four are called *acceptor* impurities.

At absolute zero temperature the fourth covalent bond of each indium atom is empty. However, at room temperature each of these bonds is filled by a neighboring valence electron which has absorbed the small amount of energy needed to break its own bond. This produces a hole in the semiconductor crystal. This process may become clearer if we look at the energy band diagram of the silicon crystal when it is doped with a P-type impurity such as indium. Figure 4.11 shows this diagram at absolute zero and at room temperature. With the addition of a P-type acceptor impurity a new energy level is introduced, the *acceptor* level, which exists in the forbidden gap very close to the valence band. At absolute zero, Figure 4.11 (A) indicates that the valence band is filled and the conduction band is empty. Also, the acceptor level which is the energy level of the unfilled covalent bonds, is empty at absolute zero. At room temperature this picture changes somewhat. Thermal generation of hole-electron pairs produces some free electrons in the conduction band and holes in the valence band. In addition, electrons from the valence band have jumped

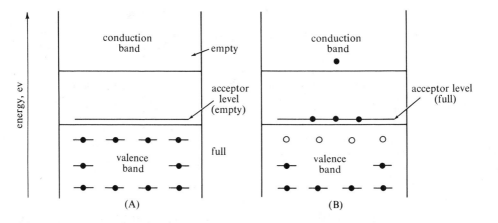

FIG. 4.11.   ENERGY BAND DIAGRAMS OF SILICON DOPED WITH A P-TYPE IMPURITY (A) AT ABSOLUTE ZERO (B) AT ROOM TEMPERATURE

up to fill the vacancies at the acceptor level. The energy required for this is much less than that required for a valence electron to jump the forbidden gap into the conduction band. Thus, virtually all the vacancies at the acceptor level are filled, leaving holes in the valence band without a corresponding conduction electron. For this reason a semiconductor doped with a P-type impurity such as indium will have, at room temperature, more holes in the valence band than electrons in the conduction band. For a P-type semiconductor, then, *holes* are the *majority* current carrier and *electrons* are the *minority* current carrier.

Typically, the number of holes produced by the P-type impurity atoms is about one million times greater than the number of thermally-generated electron-hole pairs at room temperature. A P-type semiconductor, then, has about one million times more holes than free electrons available to act as current carriers at room temperature. Figure 4.12 illustrates current flow in a P-type semiconductor which has a much lower resistivity than the intrinsic semiconductor at room temperature.

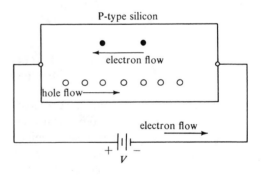

FIG. 4.12. CURRENT FLOW IN A P-TYPE SEMICON-
DUCTOR

An acceptor (P-type) impurity must be an atom with a valence less than four. The most common are indium, boron, aluminum and gallium, which all have a valence of three. These atoms produce one hole each. Impurity atoms with two valence electrons produce two holes each and so on. It is important to note that an acceptor atom becomes a *negative ion* when its empty covalent bond is filled by a neighboring valence electron. These negative ions, however, are locked into the crystal structure and cannot move.

The fundamentals of the two types of doping impurities have been discussed up to this point. Table 4.1 summarizes the principal characteristics of N- and P-type semiconductors.

TABLE 4.1

SUMMARY OF N-TYPE AND P-TYPE MATERIAL

	N-type	P-type
Number of valence electrons of impurity atom	greater than 4	less than 4
Name of impurity	donor	acceptor
Typical impurities	arsenic, phosphorus, antimony, bismuth	indium, boron, gallium, aluminum
Majority carrier	electron	hole
Minority carrier	hole	electron
Energy band in which majority carriers move	conduction band	valence band

4.6.   Effects of Temperature on Extrinsic Semiconductors

We have seen that a small quantity of impurities, N-type or P-type, can produce a large quantity of current carriers in an extrinsic semiconductor, depending on the number of donor or acceptor impurities added. This has the effect of reducing the semiconductor's resistance to current flow. For example, if we were to place an ohmmeter across a piece of N-type germanium, we might measure a resistance of about 100 ohms, whereas the same piece of intrinsic germanium would have a resistance of about 7000 ohms.

It is apparent that the case with which current flows in an extrinsic semiconductor depends upon how many current carriers are available, and for a given amount of material this is a function of the number of impurity atoms introduced into the material. There is another important factor which contributes to the number of current carriers and thus to resistance; this important factor is the temperature of the material.

At absolute zero temperature no current carriers are available in the semiconductor material and it behaves essentially as an insulator with very high resistivity. As temperature is increased, two separate mechanisms produce current carriers in an N-type semiconductor: thermal generation of hole-electron pairs and impurity-produced free electrons (majority carriers). At room temperature all the donor atoms can be presumed to have contributed to the liberation of free electrons and these are in much greater abundance than the thermally-generated carriers. Further increases in temperature only serve to increase the thermally-generated carriers since the donor atoms have already donated their free electrons. Eventually a temperature is reached, 85°C for germanium and 200°C for silicon, where the number of covalent bonds that are broken is very large and the resistivity of the material is now determined by the number of temperature-produced hole-electron pairs rather than by the effects of doping. This means that at elevated temperatures the desirable effects of doping completely vanish and the material fails to perform as an extrinsic semiconductor. At these temperatures it has approximately the same number of holes as electrons and is essentially intrinsic.

The same general effect is present in P-type material. At absolute zero, no carriers are available. At room temperature all of the acceptor atoms have provided a hole (majority carrier) to the semiconductor material. These holes greatly outnumber the thermally-generated electron-hole pairs. As the temperature is increased to the critical temperature the thermally-generated

TABLE 4.2

TEMPERATURE EFFECTS ON N-TYPE AND P-TYPE MATERIAL

	N-type	P-type
Absolute zero	No carriers, very high resistance	Same
Room temperature	Many donor-provided free electrons—few thermally-generated carriers—low resistance—electrons in majority	Many acceptor-provided holes—few thermally-generated carriers—low resistance—holes in majority
Critical temperature (85°C for germanium and 200°C for silicon) and above	Many thermally-generated carriers—loss of extrinsic properties—holes and electrons about equal—very low resistance	Same

carriers are far greater in number than the acceptor-produced holes and the semiconductor loses its extrinsic properties.

The effects of temperature on both N-type and P-type semiconductors are summarized in Table 4.2.

This concludes our study of semiconductor fundamentals and, up to this point, no useful semiconductor device has been mentioned. Beginning with the next chapter we will study most of the important semiconductor devices on the market today. Practically all of these contain extrinsic semiconductor materials of both types in one crystal. The simplest combination, called a P-N junction, is the next subject to be covered.

GLOSSARY

Crystal: a structure formed by atoms covalently bonded together

Intrinsic semiconductor: a semiconductor with no impurities present in its crystal structure

Absolute zero: coldest possible temperature; — 273°C or 460°F

Thermal excitation: the absorption of sufficient heat energy by a valence electron such that it can break its covalent bond and become a free electron

Hole: the vacancy caused by a valence electron breaking its covalent bond and becoming a conduction electron. It is charged positively.

Electron-hole pair: the free electron and hole produced by the thermal excitation of a valence electron

Recombination: the process whereby a free electron fills a hole. This action eliminates both the electron and the hole.

Mobility: the ease with which current carriers can move through the crystal

Doping: addition of impurities to an intrinsic semiconductor

Extrinsic semiconductor: a doped semiconductor

N-type impurities
(donor impurities): impurities with a valence of greater than four which donate free electrons to the semiconductor crystal

P-type impurities
(acceptor impurities): impurities with a valence of less than four which provide holes to the semiconductor crystal

Majority carriers: the carrier (electron or hole) of greatest number in a semiconductor material

Minority carriers: the carrier of least number in a semiconductor material

Questions

4.1 Which should be a better conductor: sodium or lithium?

4.2 What three factors determine the number of current carriers within a material?

4.3 Are metals such as copper considered crystals?

4.4 Sketch the symbolic crystal structure of intrinsic silicon at absolute zero. Sketch its energy band diagram.

4.5 Sketch the same crystal structure at room temperature. Sketch its energy band diagram.

4.6 Why is a valence electron at the top of the valence band more apt to be thermally excited than one at a lower level?

4.7 Why isn't a hole the exact positively charged counterpart of an electron?

4.8 What causes the decrease in resistivity of an intrinsic semiconductor at high temperatures?

4.9 If holes cannot really move, then what causes "hole current"?

4.10 What process is the opposite of thermal generation of electron-hole pairs?

4.11 Which current carrier has more mobility: a hole or an electron?

4.12 Which of the following atoms could be used as N-type impurities? Which as P-type impurities?
(a) zinc
(b) gallium
(c) carbon
(d) sulfur
(e) beryllium

4.13 In an N-type semiconductor, does it take more energy to thermally excite a valence electron or to liberate a donor electron? Explain.

4.14 At absolute zero, which current carriers in a semiconductor are available?

4.15 In a P-type semiconductor, does it take more energy to thermally excite a valence electron to the conduction band or to the acceptor level?

4.16 What are the majority current carriers in an N-type semiconductor? A P-type semiconductor? An intrinsic semiconductor?

4.17 Of what polarity are the impurity ions in N-type and P-type semiconductors?

4.18 Compare the relative number of electrons and holes in an N-type semiconductor at
(a) absolute zero
(b) room temperature
(c) critical temperature

4.19 In a P-type semiconductor, can the electrons (minority carriers) ever outnumber the holes (majority carriers)?

References

Branson, L. K., *Introduction to Electronics*. Englewood Cliffs, N. J.: Prentice-Hall, Inc., 1967.

Foster, J. F., *Semiconductor Diodes and Transistors*, Vol. 1. Beaverton, Oregon: Programmed Instruction Group, Tetronix, Inc., 1964.

Riddle, R. L. and M. P. Ristenbatt, *Transistor Physics and Circuits*. Englewood Cliffs, N. J.: Prentice-Hall, Inc., 1958.

Romanowitz, H. A. and R. E. Puckett, *Introduction to Electronics*. New York: John Wiley & Sons, Inc., 1968.

The P-N Junction

5.1.   Introduction

By themselves, the separate P- and N-type materials are of limited practical use to us, as previously stated. If a junction is made, consisting of a piece of P-type material joined to a piece of N-type material, so that the crystal structure is unbroken, a P-N *junction* is formed. Practically all semiconductors contain at least one P-N junction and for this reason it will be considered the basic building block in this study of semiconductor devices. A thorough discussion of the operation and properties of P-N junctions will be undertaken in an effort to establish a firm foundation on which to build up to devices with more than one P-N junction. The prime characteristic of the P-N junction, as we shall see, is its ability to conduct current easily in only *one* direction. The extreme usefulness of this property will readily become apparent.

5.2.   The P-N Junction

Before we look at the properties of a P-N junction, let us consider, first, the condition of the separate P-type and N-type materials just before they are joined together. (Actually we cannot just push the two pieces together; the crystal structure must remain intact at the junction of the two materials. We will not concern

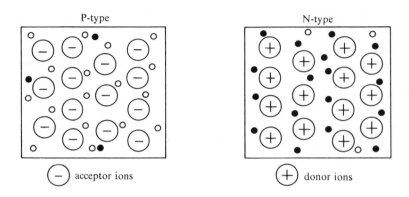

FIG. 5.1.   P-TYPE AND N-TYPE SILICON PRIOR TO FORMATION OF THE P-N JUNCTION

ourselves with the method of producing the P-N junction until later in the text.) In Figure 5.1, a small section of N- and P-type silicon is shown just prior to the formation of the P-N junction. The N-type material consists mainly of silicon atoms, a relatively small number of donor impurity atoms, free electrons (majority carriers) and a very few holes, due to thermal generation of hole pairs. In the figure, the silicon atoms are not shown and should be imagined as a continuous crystal structure in the background. The donor impurity atoms are shown as positive ions since at room temperature all of them have released one electron. These donor ions are fixed in the crystal structure and cannot move. The number of majority carriers is dependent on the number of donor atoms. The number of holes (minority carriers) depends on the temperature of the material. Similarly the P-type material consists mainly of silicon atoms, a relatively small number of acceptor atoms, holes (majority carriers) and a very few free electrons. The acceptor atoms are shown as negative ions since at room temperature all of them will have had a valence electron from a neighboring atom jump to fill its vacant covalent bond. These acceptor ions are fixed in the crystal and cannot move. The number of majority carriers is dependent on the number of acceptor atoms. The number of electrons (minority carriers) depends on the temperature of the material. Consider the situation at the moment when the P and N regions become joined together with a continuous crystal structure as in Figure 5.2. In the P region there is a high concentration of holes, the majority carrier. Across the junction in the N region there is a very low concentration of holes,

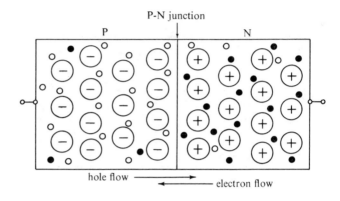

FIG. 5.2.   A P-N CRYSTAL IMMEDIATELY AFTER JOIN-
ING THE P AND N REGIONS

the minority carrier in that region. This difference in the concentration of holes in the semiconductor crystal (the joined P
and N regions are now one crystal) is precisely the condition which
brings about the flow of diffusion current as we discussed in
Section 2.6. Thus we can expect that the holes in the P region will
immediately begin diffusing from the region of high hole concentration across the junction into the region of low hole concentration. Similarly, in the N region there is a high concentration
of free electrons, the majority carrier, while across the junction
in the P region there is a very low concentration of free electrons,
the minority carrier in that region. Consequently, there is a
diffusion of electrons from the N region across the junction into
the P region.

As the holes diffuse from the P region across the junction they
encounter a multitude of free electrons in the N region. Due to
this great abundance of free electrons, each diffusing hole immediately recombines with a free electron and disappears. The
same thing occurs with regard to the electrons which are diffusing
across the junction from the N region. They encounter a great
number of holes in the P region and in doing so immediately recombine and disappear.

It might seem that eventually all the holes from the P side would
diffuse to the N side and all the free electrons from the N side
would diffuse to the P side, but this does not occur. Only those
majority carriers near the junction make it across. The reason
for this can be seen by considering Figure 5.3 which shows the

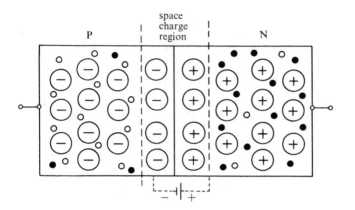

FIG. 5.3.   P-N CRYSTAL AFTER MAJORITY CARRIERS HAVE DIFFUSED, PRODUCING SPACE CHARGE REGION

status of the P-N crystal after some of the majority carriers have diffused across the junction and recombined.

Keep in mind that the negative acceptor ions in the P region are immobile. When the holes on the P side near the junction diffuse into the N region, they leave behind negative acceptor ions which have no corresponding hole. Thus, the P region is no longer electrically neutral because it has more negative charges (ions) than positive charges (holes).

Similarly, the N region near the junction becomes lined with fixed positive donor ions when free electrons in that region diffuse over to the P side. The N region is no longer electrically neutral because it has more positive charges (ions) than negative charges (electrons).

As shown in Figure 5.3, only the fixed ions remain near the junction, negative on the P side and positive on the N side, with no charge carriers in this region. These fixed charges near the junction, which have been built up as a result of majority carrier diffusion, tend to discourage and eventually prevent further diffusion. If a hole in the P side tries to diffuse across the junction it is repelled by the positive donor ions lining the N side of the junction and moves back into the P region where it belongs. At the same time, electrons in the N side trying to diffuse across the junction are repelled by the negative acceptor ions lining the P side of the junction.

Summarizing what has been covered thus far, diffusion of majority carriers across the junction results in a buildup of fixed

ionic charges lining the junctions. These fixed charges exert a
repelling force on any majority carrier diffusion. This force is
small at first but becomes greater as more charges diffuse across
the junction. Eventually, the repelling force becomes great enough
to stop further diffusion of the majority carriers. The region
near the junction which contains these fixed ionic charges and no
current carriers is called the *space charge region* as in Figure 5.3.
Also, because of the lack of current carriers in this region, it is
referred to as the *depletion region*.

The repelling force of the space charge region is an electrical
force. Actually the fixed charges on opposite sides of the junction
produce a *potential* barrier, the same as would be produced by a
battery. In fact, if we could put a volt-meter across the space
charge region we would measure a voltage equal to this potential
barrier. Typically, it is about 0.3 volt for germanium and 0.7
volt for silicon. This potential barrier is indicated in Figure 5.3
by a small battery across the space-charge region in dotted lines.

Outside the space charge region on either side of the junction,
the concentrations of charges are just as they were before the P
and N regions were joined, with positive and negative charges
equally distributed. The charge concentration profile of the P-N
crystal is shown in Figure 5.4. It shows the charge density plotted
against distance into the crystal. This charge density is approximately zero except at the space charge region. There, a large

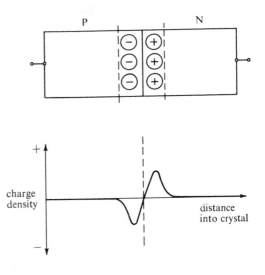

FIG. 5.4. CHARGE PROFILE OF A P-N CRYSTAL

negative charge density exists on the P side of the junction and a large positive charge density exists on the N side of the junction.

The space charge region in a P-N junction presents a potential barrier to any majority carriers which attempt to diffuse across the junction. This means that in order for a free electron in the N region to move to the P region, it must gain enough energy to overcome this potential barrier. Similarly, in order for a hole on the P side to move to the N region, a valence electron in the N side must climb the potential barrier in order to fill this hole and thus have the hole appear on the N side. At room temperature, due to the heat energy, a few majority carriers will be able to climb the potential barrier and cross the junction. A few of the holes in the P region and some of the electrons in the N region will acquire the energy to get over the barrier and diffuse across the junction. This small diffusion results in a *majority carrier diffusion current* (the sum of the hole current and electron current) across the P-N junction. However, this diffusion current is exactly balanced by a current in the opposite direction made up of minority carriers, electrons on the P side and holes on the N side. This minority carrier current is caused by the attraction of the space charge region. For example, in Figure 5.3, if an electron-hole pair is produced by thermal excitation in the space charge region, the electron will be accelerated toward the N side by the attraction of the positive ionic charges and the hole will be accelerated toward the P side by the negative ionic charges; this produces a *minority carrier drift current* across the junction in a direction

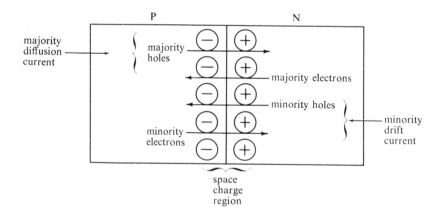

FIG. 5.5.   CURRENTS ACROSS A P-N JUNCTION WHICH HAS NO EXTERNAL CONNECTIONS (UN-BIASED). NET CURRENT IS ZERO.

opposite to that of the majority carrier diffusion current. When there are no external connections to the P-N crystal, as in Figure 5.3, these two currents cancel each other out to produce a net junction current of zero. This is illustrated in Figure 5.5.

A P-N junction with an external voltage applied between its terminals is said to be *biased*, and the applied voltage is called *bias voltage*. The P-N junction in Figures 5.3 to 5.5 have no external connections and are thus *unbiased*.

Briefly summarizing the material in this section, an unbiased P-N crystal will produce along its junction a space charge region which acts as a potential barrier to majority current flow across the junction. This potential barrier allows only a small number of majority carriers to diffuse across the junction. It also attracts the flow of minority carriers across the junction. These two currents are in opposite directions and cancel each other out in an unbiased P-N crystal.

5.3.   Reverse Biasing a P-N Junction

Applying a voltage source, such as a battery, across a P-N junction with the polarity as shown in Figure 5.6 is called *reverse biasing* the P-N junction. The positive terminal of the voltage source, V_R, is connected to the N side and the negative terminal of the voltage source is connected to the P side. With the P-N junction biased in this manner, holes in the P side will be attracted

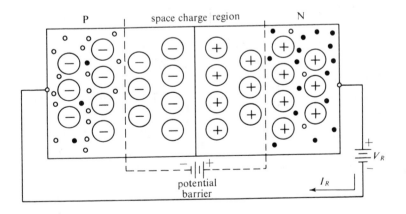

FIG. 5.6.   REVERSE-BIASED P-N JUNCTION

to the negative terminal of the battery, and electrons in the N side will be attracted toward the positive terminal of the battery.

Thus, the majority carriers are drawn away from the junction. As they are pulled away, more fixed donor and acceptor ions are left near the junction without a corresponding charge carrier, thus widening the space charge region as shown in Figure 5.6. (Compare this with the unbiased P-N junction in Figure 5.3.) This has the effect of increasing the potential barrier. In fact, the potential barrier is equal to V_R. This increase in the potential barrier makes it more difficult for majority carriers to diffuse across the junction. Actually, it takes only a very small reverse voltage, V_R, to completely halt the majority carrier diffusion current.

The increase in the potential barrier due to V_R has the opposite effect on the minority carriers since it aids their flow across the junction. They are now swept across the junction more easily, thus increasing the minority carrier drift current. As V_R increases, the minority current increases until eventually all the available minority carriers are crossing the junction. The minority carrier current cannot increase any further even though the reverse bias is increased.

Thus, reverse bias applied to a P-N junction produces only the flow of minority carriers, holes from N to P and electrons from P to N across the junction. This reverse current, of course, also flows in the external circuit as shown in Figure 5.7. Since it is the current flow under reverse bias, we will call it I_R. It should be

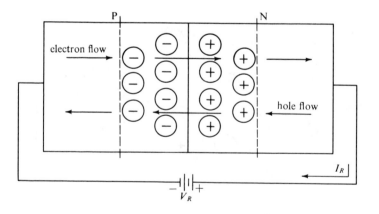

FIG. 5.7.   FLOW OF MINORITY CARRIERS IN REVERSE-
BIASED P-N JUNCTION

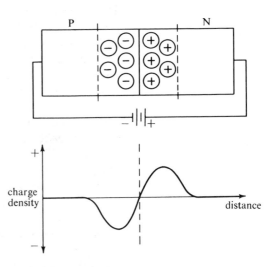

FIG. 5.8. CHARGE PROFILE OF A REVERSE-BIASED P-N JUNCTION

pointed out that because I_R depends on the number of minority carriers present in the P-N crystal it will be very sensitive to temperature. As the temperature of the junction is increased, more electron-hole pairs will be generated providing more minority carriers to the P and N regions. This of course will cause I_R to increase with temperature.

In practice, this reverse current can be as low as a few nano-amperes (10^{-9} amps) in silicon devices at room temperature and is typically around 100 nano-amperes. Germanium, since it has a smaller energy gap, has more minority carriers being generated at a given temperature than silicon. Consequently, it has reverse currents, typically about a few micro-amperes (10^{-6} amps) at room temperature. In both silicon and germanium P-N junctions, the resistance to current in the reverse direction is very high. The charge concentration profile of a P-N junction is greatly altered by reverse bias as can be seen by comparing Figure 5.8 with Figure 5.4.

5.4. Reverse Breakdown of a P-N Junction

We saw in the previous discussion that reverse biasing a P-N junction will stop all majority carrier flow, allowing only minority carriers to cross the junction producing a small reverse current.

This reverse current is limited by the number of minority carriers present in the P-N crystal and is usually very small.

This situation holds true as long as the reverse bias voltage, V_R, is not greater than a certain value. This certain value is called the *reverse breakdown voltage* of the P-N junction and is given the symbol V_{BD}. If the reverse bias exceeds this value the reverse current will increase very rapidly for a small increase in *reverse voltage* producing reverse breakdown of the P-N junction. When reverse breakdown occurs the P-N junction conducts heavily in the reverse direction, and unless the current is limited by a series resistor it may become damaged.

The phenomenon of reverse breakdown can easily be explained using the concepts we have learned thus far. Increasing the reverse voltage across a P-N junction causes the minority carriers to move across the junction at a higher speed. If this reverse voltage is high enough, the minority carriers move so rapidly that, on colliding with atoms of the crystal, they impart some of their energy to these atoms and if they have sufficient energy can knock valence electrons out of their covalent bonds. This creates more charge carriers (free electrons and holes) which can in turn be accelerated by the reverse voltage to speeds high enough to break the bonds of other atoms. This avalanching process will produce a great number of new current carriers causing a large increase in reverse current only when the reverse voltage is high enough to accelerate the minority carriers to the required energy. The necessary reverse voltage is V_{BD}, the reverse breakdown voltage. The process of reverse breakdown is also called avalanche breakdown because of the multiplying or avalanching of current carriers which takes place.

The reverse breakdown voltage, V_{BD}, of a P-N junction depends on many factors including junction temperature and impurity concentration. Both of these effects will be discussed later.

5.5.   Forward Biasing a P-N Junction

Applying a voltage across a P-N junction with the polarity as shown in Figure 5.9 is called *forward biasing* the P-N junction. The positive terminal of the voltage, V_F, is connected to the P side and the negative terminal to the N side.

With the P-N junction biased in this manner, holes in the P side are driven toward the junction by the positive terminal of the battery, and free electrons in the N side are repelled toward the junction by the negative terminal of the battery. The first effect

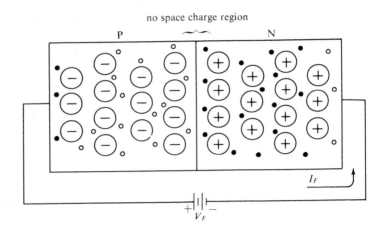

FIG. 5.9.   FORWARD-BIASED P-N JUNCTION

of this is to neutralize some of the donor and acceptor ions in the space charge region, thus reducing the potential barrier and allowing some diffusion of majority carriers across the junction. If the forward bias, V_F, is made large enough, the potential barrier is reduced to zero and the movement of majority carriers across the junction is unimpeded producing a relatively large *forward current*, I_F. Typical values of forward bias required to do so are

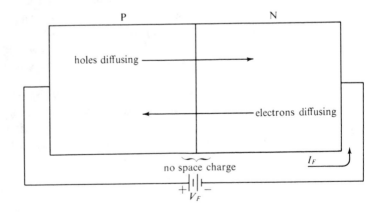

FIG. 5.10.   FLOW OF MAJORITY CARRIERS IN FOR-
                 WARD-BIASED P-N JUNCTION

0.3 volt for germanium and 0.7 volt for silicon, which are precisely the values of potential barriers in these materials. This forward current increases very rapidly for small increases in forward bias. The nature of this forward current is illustrated in Figure 5.10. It consists mainly of diffusing majority carriers. Figures 5.9 and 5.10 show that with sufficient forward bias, the space charge region is completely neutralized. The charge concentration profile of the forward-biased junction shown in Figure 5.11 also illustrates this.

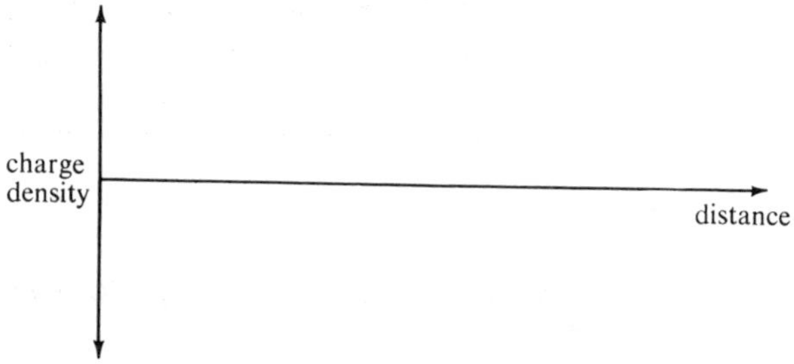

charge density

distance

FIG. 5.11.   CHARGE PROFILE OF A FORWARD-BIASED P-N JUNCTION

Let us briefly consider what happens to those majority carriers as they diffuse across the junction. The flow of holes in the P side approaching the junction encounters electrons that have crossed over from the N side and recombination occurs, becoming more frequent as the holes proceed across the junction until eventually some distance into the N side all the holes recombine and disappear. Similar action involving electron flow from the N side also takes place. These diffusing majority carriers, then, cross the junction, thus becoming minority carriers (since holes are now in the N region and electrons now in the P region) and eventually recombine. The forward current in the P-N crystal, then, is caused by majority carriers diffusing across the junction as minority carriers.

Briefly summarizing, forward biasing a P-N junction with a few tenths of a volt acts to completely neutralize the P-N junction potential barrier allowing majority carriers to diffuse freely across the junction. This produces a forward current, I_F, which increases sharply for small increases in this forward bias.

5.6.   *I-V* **Characteristic of a P-N Junction**

Having thoroughly discussed the physical operation of a P-N junction, we can now look at it as a two-terminal electronic device and examine its electrical characteristics. The previous sections of this chapter have dealt with the black box portion of this device. With this background we can determine the *I-V* characteristics of the P-N junction device, which we shall call a P-N *diode*.

Figure 5.12 shows the popular electronic symbol for a P-N diode, next to its physical structure. The P region of a P-N diode is called the *anode* and the N region is called the *cathode*. Since reverse current flows from P to N in the device, it flows *with* the arrow in the symbol. Forward current flows *against* the arrow in the symbol, since it flows from N to P.

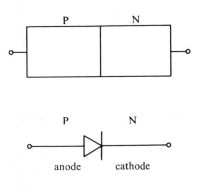

FIG. 5.12. SYMBOL FOR P-N DIODE

The *I-V* characteristic of a typical P-N diode is shown in Figure 5.13. Let us examine it carefully. Since a P-N diode is a two-terminal device we only need *one* *I-V* curve (Chapter 3). This consists of the relationship between cathode-to-anode (N side-to- P side) current, I_{CA}, and anode-to-cathode voltage, V_{AC}. When V_{AC} is positive, the anode is positive with respect to the cathode. This is forward biasing the P-N diode. Thus, forward current flows from cathode to anode and I_{CA} is positive. This is the forward bias region on the *I-V* curve in Figure 5.13. This portion of the curve shows that I_{CA} is very small until the forward voltage, V_{AC}, gets above the voltage V_{on}. V_{on}, the forward voltage needed to completely neutralize the potential barrier, is typically 0.3 volts for germanium diodes and 0.7 volts for silicon diodes. When V_{AC} is above this voltage, the forward current I_{CA} increases rapidly with increases in forward voltage. The P-N diode, then, when forward-biased conducts heavily, acting as a very low resistance.

When V_{AC} is made negative, the anode is negative with respect to the cathode. This is reverse biasing the P-N diode. Thus,

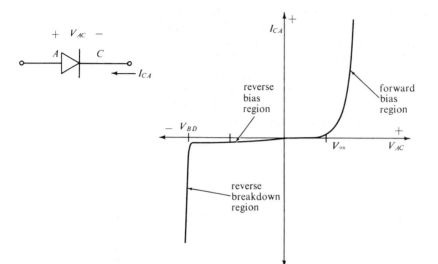

FIG. 5.13.   *I-V* CHARACTERISTIC OF A P-N DIODE

reverse current flows from anode to cathode and I_{CA} is negative. This is the reverse bias region in Figure 5.13. This portion of the *I-V* curve shows that the reverse current is very small until the reverse voltage reaches the reverse breakdown voltage, V_{BD}, after which reverse current increases rapidly. V_{BD} is usually fairly high ranging from about 30 volts up to thousands of volts in P-N diodes. The P-N diode, then, when reverse biased conducts very poorly (except at breakdown, which is usually avoided except in special P-N devices) acting as a very high resistance.

5.7.   P-N Diode Ratings

Ratings are the limiting values given to various parameters of a diode by the manufacturer. These values, if exceeded, can result in permanent damage to the diode or deterioration of its performance or life.

The ratings of a semiconductor diode are based on its ability to dissipate the heat generated by power losses. When this heat raises the junction temperature above the maximum specified by the manufacturer, the device may become damaged. The most important P-N diode ratings according to symbols and definition are shown in Table 5.1.

TABLE 5.1

TERM	SYMBOL	DEFINITION OF RATING
Peak reverse voltage	PRV	Maximum allowable *instantaneous reverse* voltage that may be applied across the diode. This rating is usually slightly below the reverse breakdown voltage of the diode.
Maximum reverse d-c voltage	V_{RDC}	Maximum allowable d-c reverse voltage- Usually less than PRV.
Maximum d-c forward current	$I_{F(max)}$	Maximum allowable d-c forward current which may flow at a stated temperature.

Other various diode parameters are also specified by the manufacturer. The two most usually supplied by the manufacturer are given in Table 5.2.

TABLE 5.2

TERM	SYMBOL	DEFINITION OF PARAMETER
Forward voltage drop	V_F	Value of anode-to-cathode forward voltage for a specified forward current at a given temperature
Reverse leakage Current	I_R	Value of reverse current at stated temperature and reverse voltage

A typical silicon diode *I-V* characteristic is shown in Figure 5.14 along with its ratings.

Specifications: (all at 25°C unless otherwise specified)
PRV: 290 volts
V_{RDC}:   250 volts
$I_{F(max)}$:   400 ma
V_F: 0.7v @ 100 ma; 0.64v @ 100 ma @ 55°C
I_R: 0.1 μa @ -200v; 1μa @ -200v @ 55°C

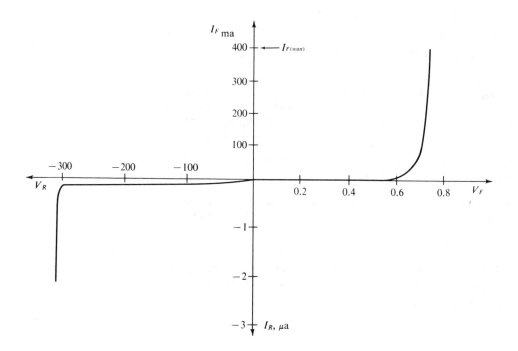

FIG. 5.14.   *I-V* CHARACTERISTIC AND SPECIFICATIONS
OF A TYPICAL SILICON DIODE

5.8.   Effects of Temperature on Diode Characteristics

Up to now, we have discussed the characteristics of P-N diodes at room temperature. We know semiconductor material is greatly affected by heat, so we can expect that a P-N diode will change its characteristics as its temperature changes. The primary effect of temperature on a semiconductor, as we learned in Chapter 1, is the generation of electron-hole pairs through the breaking of covalent bonds by thermally excited valence electrons. This means that at higher temperatures there are more free electrons and holes available in a semiconductor, whether it is an intrinsic or extrinsic semiconductor. These additional current carriers cause changes in a P-N junction's operation which are reflected in its *I-V* characteristic. We will study the principal changes closely.

In an unbiased P-N diode, the space charge region produces a potential barrier which limits the diffusion of majority carriers across the junction to that value which exactly balances out the flow of minority carriers across the junction in the opposite direction (Section 5.2). An increase in temperature makes available more minority carriers in both regions of the P-N diode. This dictates a decrease in potential barrier so as to allow the majority carrier diffusion to equal the minority carrier flow which would have increased. Thus, one effect of increased minority carriers due to increased temperature is that the space charge region (potential barrier) has decreased. This decrease in the junction potential barrier means that the forward voltage needed to cause current to flow is reduced. It also means that the reverse voltage needed to cause avalanche breakdown will increase since the minority carriers are accelerated through a narrower region and a higher voltage is needed to give them the energy needed to cause breakdown.

The second effect of increased minority carriers is that the reverse leakage current will be higher due to more available current carriers. This is very significant since P-N diodes are usually applied in circuits which depend on their ability to block current in the reverse direction.

The composite result of an increase in temperature can best be seen by comparing the *I-V* characteristics at two different temperatures. Figure 5.15 does this for a typical silicon diode. There are three main differences to be noted. First of all, in the forward bias region it takes less voltage to produce the same

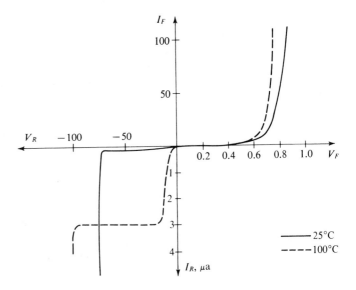

FIG. 5.15.   *I-V* CHARACTERISTIC OF A SILICON DIODE
AT 25°C AND 100°C

current at 100°C than at 25°C. For instance, at 25°C it takes 0.85 volt to produce 100 ma of current while at 100°C it only takes 0.75 volt to produce 100 ma. Secondly, in the reverse bias region the reverse leakage current is much higher at 100°C (3 μa) than at 25°C (0.1 μa). Finally, reverse breakdown occurs at 90 volts at 100°C and at 75 volts at 25°C. These changes with temperature occur for all semiconductor materials, although they occur in varying degrees. For example, the reverse leakage current in silicon doubles in value for every 11 degrees' rise in temperature while for germanium it doubles for every 9 degrees. The decrease in forward voltage, V_F, at a given forward current is typically around 2.2 mv/°C for both silicon and germanium devices. The increase in reverse breakdown voltage at higher temperatures is different for different devices, usually increasing more for higher-voltage (higher-PRV) diodes.

Thus, temperature changes cause significant changes in the *I-V* curves of P-N diodes and must be considered in the design of reliable circuits. These effects, which occur in each of the semi-conductor devices which we will study, should be thoroughly understood.

5.9.   P-N Diode Circuit Analysis: Load Line Method

The previous sections of this chapter have concentrated on the elements of the operation and characteristics of P-N diodes and their dependence upon temperature. With these elements now under our belts we can proceed to the practical aspect of employing semiconductor diodes in circuits. The basic problem consists of determining whether the diode is forward biased, reverse biased or in breakdown. There are several methods of doing this. The *load line method*, though rarely used for P-N diodes, brings out several important points. It is used for many other devices and is thus worth our attention at this point.

The simple P-N diode circuit shown in Figure 5.16 consists of a voltage source and resistor in series with the diode. The voltage source polarity is such that the diode is forward biased. Thus, we can expect that any current that will flow, as shown, will be forward current. The basic problem now is to find this current I_F, and the voltage drop across the diode, V_F. The values of I_F and V_F are called the *operating point* of the diode. In this circuit, the operating point is constant (does not change) since the source is constant. If the source were changing continuously, (as it

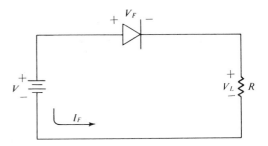

FIG. 5.16.   SIMPLE DIODE CIRCUIT

would with an a-c or time-varying source, then the operating point would also change continuously.

We have two unknown quantities, I_F and V_F. In order to determine the values of these quantities, then, two equations or relationships between I_F and V_F are needed. The first relationship can be obtained from the circuit by using Kirchhoff's voltage law. The input voltage source, V, must equal the sum of the voltages across R and across the diode. Stated in equation form,

$$V = V_L + V_F \qquad\qquad \textbf{(5.1A)}$$

and since the drop across R is simply $I_F \times R$, then

$$V = I_F \times R + V_F \qquad\qquad \textbf{(5.1B)}$$

Rewriting this and solving for V_F,

$$V_F = V - I_F \times R \qquad\qquad \textbf{(5.1C)}$$

The values of I_F and V_F must satisfy this equation at all times. It is a linear (straight line) equation relating I_F to V_F for given values of V and R. The second relationship can be obtained from the diode's *I-V* characteristic since it also relates I_F to V_F. This relationship is non-linear (not a straight line) and is in the form of a curve. The values of I_F and V_F must lie on the *I-V* characteristic curve. Since the values of I_F and V_F (the operating point) must lie on both the straight line (Equation 5.1C) and on the *I-V* characteristic curve, they must lie on the intersection of the two when plotted on $I_F - V_F$ axes. This is shown in Figure 5.17. The solid curve is the familiar *I-V* characteristic of a P-N diode. The dotted line is Equation 5.1C. In plotting this straight line, *two* points are needed. These two points are obtained by picking a value for either I_F or V_F and solving for the corresponding value of the other by using Equation 5.1C. The easiest values to use are $I_F = 0$ which gives $V_F = V$ according to Equation 5.1C, and

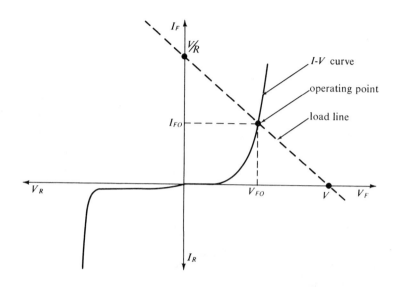

FIG. 5.17.   FINDING THE OPERATING POINT OF THE
CIRCUIT IN FIG. 5.16

$V_F = 0$ which gives $I_F = V/R$. These two points are indicated in Figure 5.17. The straight line is called the *load line* and the intersection of the load line and the *I-V* characteristic gives the operating point of the diode. The forward current at the operating point is I_{FO} and the voltage is V_{FO}.

▶ EXAMPLE 5.1

The circuit in Figure 5.16 uses a germanium diode with the *I-V* characteristic shown in Figure 5.18, a 3 volt source and a 1K resistor. The problem is to find the operating point of the circuit.

The equation of the load line as given by Equation 5.1C is

$$V_F = 3 - I_F \times 1K \qquad (5.2)$$

The two points used to plot this line are $I_F = 0$, $V_F = 3v$ and $V_F = 0$, $I_F = 3/1K = 3$ ma. The load line is shown in Figure 5.18 (solid line). The intersection of the load line and *I-V* curve gives the operating point as $I_{FO} = 2.75$ ma and $V_{FO} = 0.25$ volt. The drop across the resistor is $I_{FO} \times 1K = 2.75v$. Thus using Equation 5.2

$$0.25v = 3v - 2.75v = 0.25v \qquad ◀$$

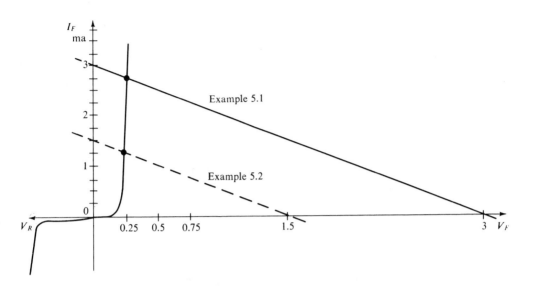

FIG. 5.18.   EXAMPLES 5.1 AND 5.2

► EXAMPLE 5.2

Repeating Example 5.1 using a source of 1.5 volts, the load line equation becomes

$$V_F = 1.5 - I_F \times 1K \qquad (5.3)$$

and is plotted in Figure 5.18 (dotted line). The intersection of the load line and the diode curve gives an operating point of $I_F = 1.26$ ma and $V_F = 0.24$v. Checking these values in Equation 5.3

$$0.24 = 1.5 - 1.26 \times 1K = 0.24$$

Thus, changing the voltage source from 3v to 1.5v changes the current from 2.75 ma to 1.26 ma but barely affects the voltage, V_F. This is a result of the diode's forward characteristics which produce large current changes for very small voltage changes. ◄

Let us now consider the simple diode circuit with the voltage source reverse biasing the diode as shown in Figure 5.19. We can expect that reverse current will flow as shown in the figure. The procedure for finding the operating point (I_R and V_R) in this case is exactly the same as in the previous circuit. First, the equation describing Kirchhoff's voltage law around the loop is written. The input voltage source, V, must equal the sum of the voltages across R and the diode. In equation form

$$V = V_L + V_R \qquad (5.4A)$$

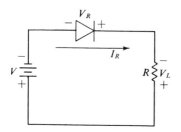

FIG. 5.19.   SIMPLE DIODE CIRCUIT WITH REVERSE
BIAS

Substituting $I_R \times R$ for voltages across R and solving for V_R we have

$$V_R = V - I_R \times R \qquad (5.4B)$$

The values of I_R, reverse current through the diode and V_R, the reverse voltage across the diode, must satisfy this equation at all times. They also must lie on the diode I-V characteristic curve. Thus, by plotting Equation 5.4B and the I-V characteristic on the same axes we can find their intersection, which will be the operating point. This is done in Figure 5.20. The straight line plot of

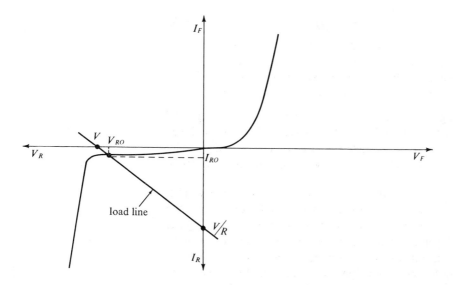

FIG. 5.20.   FINDING THE OPERATING POINT OF THE
CIRCUIT IN FIG. 5.19

Equation 5.4B is the load line. Two points are needed to plot the load line. From Equation 5.4B we can obtain the two points shown in the figure. When $V_R = 0$, $I_R = V/R$ and when $I_R = 0$, $V_R = V$ in Equation 5.4B. The load line between these two points intersects the diode characteristic at the circuit operating point. The reverse current at the operating point is I_{RO} and the reverse voltage at the operating point is V_{RO}.

▶ EXAMPLE 5.3

The diode used in Examples 5.1 and 5.2 is used in the circuit of Figure 5.19 with $V = 50$ volts and $R = 5$ megohms. The problem is to find the current and voltages in the circuit. The load line using $V = 50$v and $R = 5$ megohms is plotted along with the diode's characteristic curve in Figure 5.21. The intersection

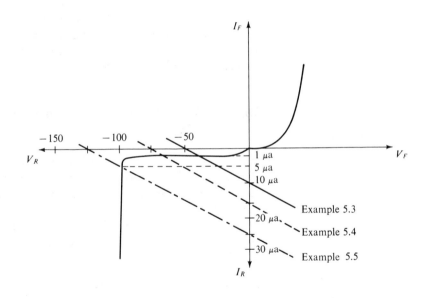

FIG. 5.21.   EXAMPLES 5.3, 5.4 AND 5.5

of the load line and characteristic curve give the operating point at $I_{RO} = 1\mu a$ and $V_{RO} = 45$ volts. We can check these values by using Equation 5.4B. The voltage across the resistor is $1\ \mu a \times 5$ megohms $= 5$ volts; across the diode the voltage is 45 volts. Thus using Equation 5.4B

$$45 = 50 - 5 = 45$$ ◀

▶ EXAMPLE 5.4

Repeat Example 5.3 for a voltage source of 75v. The load line for this case is shown as a dotted line in Figure 5.21. The intersection of this load line and the diode curve is $I_{RO} = 1$ μa and $V_{RO} = 70$ volts, the new operating point. Notice that changing the voltage source from 50v to 75v does not change the reverse current flowing through the diode. This is a result of the reverse current leveling off after all available minority carriers are flowing across the junction, until reverse breakdown occurs.   ◀

▶ EXAMPLE 5.5

Repeat the previous problem for $V = 125$v. The load line is plotted in Figure 5.21 (dot-dash line) and it obviously intersects the diode characteristic in its breakdown region with $V_{RO} = 100$ volts and $I_{RO} = 5$ μa. Actually any voltage source slightly above 100 volts will cause the diode to break down. In reverse breakdown the diode is capable of conducting large reverse currents and unless this current is limited, as it is in this example by the 5 megohm resistance, the diode may burn out.   ◀

5.10.   P-N Diode Circuit Analysis: Approximate Method

The previous examples illustrate the load line method for finding the operating point of a diode in a simple resistive circuit. This method is fairly easy to use for this simple circuit. However, it becomes virtually impossible to use in circuits which are only slightly more complicated. This makes it necessary to find a more suitable, though possibly less accurate, method of analyzing diode circuits.

We noticed in Examples 5.1 and 5.2 that with the diode forward-biased, changing the source voltage from 3 to 1.5 volts affected the voltage drop across the diode only slightly. This is typical of P-N diodes. Once the diode is "turned on," that is, forward biased enough so that current flows, its forward voltage changes very little for large changes in forward current. The diode is said to possess a low a-c *resistance*, this being its resistance to *changes* in current, once it is turned on. For instance, in Examples 5.1 and 5.2 the germanium diode's forward current changed from 2.75 ma to 1.26 ma while its forward voltage changed from 0.25v to 0.24v. Defining a-c resistance as the *change* in voltage divided by the *change* in current at a certain point on the diode's characteristics, we have

$$r_f = \frac{\Delta V_F}{\Delta I_F} = \frac{0.01\text{v}}{1.49\text{ ma}} = 6.7\Omega \qquad (5.5)$$

where r_f is the diode's a-c resistance in the *forward bias* region; ΔV_F is the change in voltage (Δ is the Greek letter delta); ΔI_F is the change in current; and Ω is the Greek letter omega, representing "ohms." Actually r_f is simply the reciprocal of the *slope* of the diode curve at the point of interest. Figure 5.22 shows how one

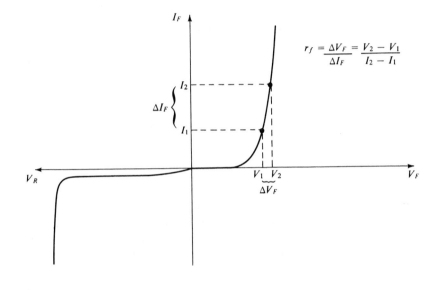

FIG. 5.22. OBTAINING r_f FROM THE DIODE CHARACTERISTIC

would determine r_f from a diode's characteristic. For most diodes r_f is very small in the forward bias region, usually only a few ohms. It changes depending on where on the characteristic it is measured. The value of r_f decreases as the forward current increases and the curve gradually gets steeper.

The relative constancy of the diode's forward voltage once it is turned on is a useful property for analyzing diode circuits such as the one in Figure 5.16. Since the diode voltage is essentially constant for varying current, the current in the circuit is primarily determined by the voltage source and the series resistance. The current in the circuit varies directly with the voltage source and inversely with the series resistance.

The *approximate method* of calculating the operating point of the diode in a circuit such as Figure 5.16 is as follows: First, calculate the approximate forward current by estimating the forward voltage of the diode and using Kirchhoff's law (Equation 5.1). Then use this approximate current to find the forward voltage of the diode on its characteristic curve. Now using this value of forward voltage, calculate the actual forward current. This last step is frequently unnecessary if the estimated forward voltage across the diode is close to the actual voltage.

▶ EXAMPLE 5.6

Use the approximate method to find I_{FO} and V_{FO} for the circuit in Example 5.1.

From the diode's characteristic in Figure 5.18 we can estimate the diode's voltage at 0.25v since it is forward biased. Using $V_{FO} = 0.25$v we can calculate from Equation 5.1C the approximate value of forward current. That is

$$0.25\text{v} = 3\text{v} - I_{FO} \times 1\text{K}$$

or

$$I_{FO} = \frac{2.75\text{v}}{1\text{K}} = 2.75 \text{ ma}$$

Now, looking at the diode characteristic at a current of 2.75 ma we read a voltage of 0.25v. Thus our original estimate of V_{FO} was a good one. These results agree exactly with those obtained by the load line method in Example 5.1.   ◀

▶ EXAMPLE 5.7

Use the approximate method to find I_{FO} and V_{FO} for the circuit in Example 5.2.

From the diode's characteristic in Figure 5.18 we can again estimate the diode's voltage at 0.25v. Using $V_{FO} = 0.25$v the approximate value of forward current is given by

$$0.25\text{v} = 1.5\text{v} - I_{FO} \times 1\text{K}$$

or

$$I_{FO} = \frac{1.25\text{v}}{1\text{K}} = 1.25 \text{ ma}$$

Now, looking at the diode characteristic at a current of 1.25 ma we read a voltage of 0.24v. This is very close to our original estimate of 0.25v. Thus, we can accept these results as a very good *approximation to those calculated in Example 5.2.*   ◀

In many cases, a circuit designer or analyst does not have the I-V characteristic or specifications for the diode readily available and he must base his approximations on experience. He usually estimates V_{FO} at about 0.7v for a silicon diode and about 0.3v for a germanium diode unless he knows the diode's characteristics. This is usually accurate enough for most purposes; for some purposes, however, the diode's characteristics or specifications must be known.

▶ EXAMPLE 5.8

Repeat Example 5.6 assuming $V_{FO} = 0.3$v, since the diode is germanium. Using $V_F = 0.3$v the approximate value of I_{FO} is given by

$$0.3v = 3v - I_{FO} \times 1K$$

or

$$I_{FO} = \frac{2.7v}{1K} = 2.7 \text{ ma}$$

Compare this with the results of Example 5.6. ◀

An approximate method can also be used for solving circuits such as the one in Figure 5.19 where the diode is reverse-biased. The method takes advantage of the diode's characteristic in the reverse-bias region where its reverse current is fairly constant, until reverse breakdown is reached.

The procedure is to obtain the reverse current from the diode's characteristic or specifications and to use it to calculate the diode voltage with Kirchhoff's law (Equation 5.4B). In most cases most of the supply voltage, V, will be dropped across the diode since in reverse bias the current is very small and the drop across the series resistor will be small.

▶ EXAMPLE 5.9

Use the method outlined above to find the operating point of the circuit in Example 5.3.

From the diode's characteristic in Figure 5.21 we can estimate the reverse current, I_{RO}, at 1μa since this is the reverse current at 50 volts reverse voltage. Using this value of current in Equation 5.4B, we can calculate V_{RO}.

$$V_{RO} = 50v - 1\mu a \times 5 \text{ megohms} = 45v$$

These values agree exactly with those in Example 5.3 obtained using the load line method.

The procedure is somewhat different if the supply voltage V is greater than the diode's reverse breakdown voltage. In this case the diode will almost always be broken down and its voltage will be approximately equal to its reverse breakdown voltage. Using this value for V_{RO}, the value of I_{RO} can be calculated using Kirchhoff's law (Equation 5.4B). ◄

▶ EXAMPLE 5.10

Find V_{RO} and I_{RO} for the circuit of Example 5.4.

Since $V = 125$ volts and the diode breaks down at 100 volts, we can assume the diode is in breakdown and $V_{RO} = 100$ volts. Using this value in Equation 5.4B and solving for I_{RO} we have

$$100\text{v} = 125\text{v} - I_{RO} \times 5 \text{ megohms}$$

or

$$I_{RO} = 25\text{v}/5 \text{ megohms} = 5\mu\text{a}$$

These values agree exactly with Example 5.4. ◄

In most circuits such as Figure 5.19 the voltage across the resistance, R, will be very small unless R is large (as in our examples). This voltage can usually be ignored and all of the supply voltage can be considered to be across the diode (unless $V > V_{BD}$)

▶ EXAMPLE 5.11

If the value of R is changed to 10K find V_L, the voltage drop across the resistor if V is 50 volts.

Using $I_{RO} = 1\mu\text{a}$, as in Example 5.9, the voltage across R is given by

$$V_L = I_{RO} \times R = 1\mu\text{a} \times 10\text{K} = 0.01 \text{ volts}$$

Thus, essentially no voltage is dropped across the resistor meaning $V_{RO} = V = 50$ volts. ◄

These approximate methods of analysis are the most widely used and we shall employ them in the next section as we look at some typical applications of the P-N diode.

5.11.   Applications of P-N Diodes

A basic characteristic of P-N diodes is that they conduct current much more readily in the forward-biased state than in the reverse-biased state unless they are broken down. When forward biased, current in the circuit is essentially limited by the resistance in series with the diode, while in a reverse-biased circuit the diode's small reverse current is all that flows. Any device which possesses this property is called a rectifying device. A P-N diode, then, is often referred to as a P-N *rectifier*.

A figure of merit, M, for rectifiers is based upon its resistance to current in both its regions of operation. It is simply the ratio of the diode's reverse resistance to its forward resistance. That is

$$M = R_R/R_F \qquad (5.6)$$

where R_R and R_F are the d-c *resistance* of the diode in the reverse direction and forward direction, respectively. R_R is equal to the d-c reverse voltage across the diode divided by its reverse current and R_F is equal to the forward voltage drop divided by its forward current.

For example, the diode used in the examples of the previous section had a reverse current of $1\mu a$ at reverse voltages up to 100 volts. Thus R_R at $V_R = 100$ volts would be

$$R_R = 100v/1\mu a = 100 \text{ megohms}$$

The same diode had a forward current of 2.75 ma at a forward voltage of 0.25v. Thus R_F at $I_F = 2.75$ ma would be

$$R_F = 0.25v/2.75ma = 90 \text{ ohms}$$

This gives a figure of merit of

$$M = R_R/R_F = 100 \text{ megohms}/90 \text{ ohms} = 1.1 \times 10^6$$

This is considered a good ratio although some P-N diodes, especially silicon types, have ratios well above ten times this value. Note that the values of R_R and R_F can vary depending on where on the diode's characteristics you take the measurements. Figure 5.23 shows the general method of finding these quantities. The main application of rectifiers is to convert an input a-c voltage to a pulsating d-c voltage across a load. This is illustrated in Figure 5.24 where a silicon rectifier is placed in series with an a-c voltage source and a load resistance. The a-c voltage source, in this case, is simply a voltage which alternates between $+50$ volts and -50 volts periodically. When the input voltage E_{in} is at $+50$ volts, the diode is forward-biased and when E_{in} is at -50 volts, the diode

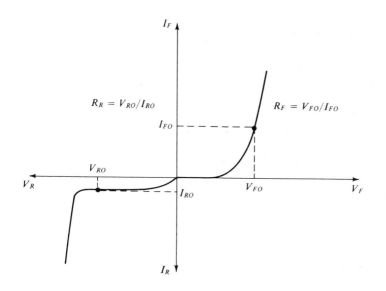

FIG. 5.23.   CALCULATION OF R_R AND R_F FROM DIODE CHARACTERISTIC

is reverse-biased. When forward-biased, the diode will have V_F equal to 0.7v dropped across it. This means that the remainder of the +50 volt from the input must appear across the 1K load re-

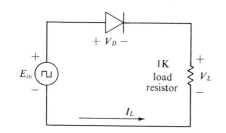

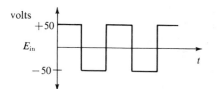

FIG. 5.24.   RECTIFICATION OF AN A-C VOLTAGE

sistor. That is 49.3 volts, which produces $49.3/1K = 49$ ma of current flow, will be across the load resistor. When reverse biased, the diode will allow a small reverse leakage current to flow which develops only a very small voltage across the load. Essentially all of the -50 volts from the input appear as reverse voltage on the diode. That is, V_D will equal -50 volts. Figure 5.25 shows the voltage waveforms of the circuit, including E_{in}.

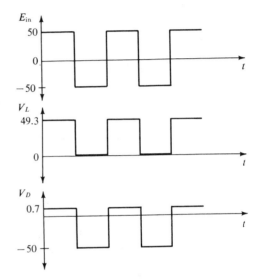

FIG. 5.25.   VOLTAGE WAVEFORMS FOR CIRCUIT IN FIG. 5.24.

Note that at all times $E_{in} = V_D + V_L$ satisfying Kirchhoff's voltage law. Although E_{in} alternates between a positive and a negative voltage, the voltage across the load resistor has a positive portion only. The rectifier has allowed forward current to flow and develop a positive voltage across the load, while blocking reverse current so that no voltage appears across the load when E_{in} is negative. Thus, the a-c input has been rectified producing pulsating d-c* across the load.

It is important to note that in this type of circuit the rectifier must be able to withstand a reverse voltage equal to the peak negative voltage of the input, in this case 50 volts. The rectifier must have a PRV (see Section 5.7) rating of at least this amount.

---

*Pulsating d-c is simply current which flows in one direction only but is not necessarily a constant current such as pure d-c.

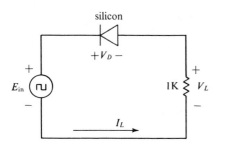

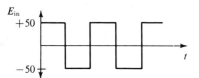

FIG. 5.26.　　RECTIFIER CIRCUIT WITH DIODE REVERSED

▶ EXAMPLE 5.12

For the rectifier circuit in Figure 5.26 sketch the voltages V_D and V_L. Determine a safe PRV rating for this rectifier.

This circuit is similar to the one in Figure 5.25 except that the diode connections have been reversed. With the diode connected

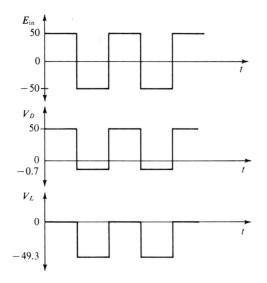

FIG. 5.27.

as such, it will become forward-biased when E_{in} is at -50 volts and reverse-biased when E_{in} is at $+50$ volts. Thus, forward current will flow through the diode when E_{in} is at -50 volts. The voltage V_D will be about -0.7 volts since the diode is forward-biased. This leaves a voltage of -49.3 volts across the load. When E_{in} is at $+50$ volts the diode is reverse-biased, V_L will be essentially zero, and V_D will be 50 volts reverse voltage on the diode. The voltage waveforms are shown in Figure 5.27. This time the a-c input has been rectified so that only negative pulsating d-c appears across the load. Since the diode has 50 volts reverse voltage across it when E_{in} is positive it must have a PRV rating of at least 50 volts. ◀

There are many applications of P-N diodes in electronic cir-
cuitry. Almost all of them, however, take advantage of the diode's rectifying property. Some other diode circuits will be left as problems at the end of the chapter.

5.12.   Power Dissipation in P-N Diodes

The power dissipated in P-N diodes as a result of current flow ($P = IV$) contributes to the temperature rise at the P-N junction in the same way as an increase in the ambient (surrounding) temperature. The power dissipation must never go above the value which causes the junction to rise above its maximum allowable temperature. If it does the device may become permanently damaged.

The power dissipation, P_D, is simply equal to the diode's voltage multiplied by its current. The diode dissipates power in all of its operating regions: forward bias, reverse bias and reverse breakdown.

The product of power dissipation, P_D and the *thermal re-
sistance* of the diode, θ_{JA} (where θ is the Greek letter theta), gives the rise in junction temperature due to power dissipation. Adding this rise in temperature to the ambient temperature, T_A, gives the junction temperature, T_J. That is

$$T_J = T_A + P_D \theta_{JA} \tag{5.7}$$

The thermal resistance θ_{JA} is a physical property of the diode and its casing. It is a measure of the diode's ability to lose its heat to the surrounding air. A lower value of θ_{JA} indicates a diode which can safely dissipate more power. The units of θ_{JA} are usually °C/w or °C/mw.

▶ EXAMPLE 5.13

A silicon diode conducts a forward current of 100 ma while its forward voltage is 0.7v. Find the temperature at its junction if its thermal resistance θ_{JA} is 0.4°C/mw and the ambient temperature, T_A, is 25°C. Repeat for a T_A of 55°C.

The temperature at the junction is given by Equation 5.7. In this case P_D is 0.7 volt × 100 ma or 70 mw. Thus at $T_A = 25$°C

$$T_J = 25°C + (70 \text{ mw})(0.4°C/\text{mw}) = 53°C$$

and at $T_A = 55$°C

$$T_J = 55°C + (70 \text{ mw})(0.4°C/\text{mw}) = 83°C$$

This example shows us that the junction temperature will increase as the ambient temperature increases indicating an important point: the maximum allowable power dissipation of a diode is lower at higher ambient temperatures.   ◀

▶ EXAMPLE 5.14

The silicon diode of Example 5.13 has a maximum allowable junction temperature $T_{J(\text{max})}$ of 150°C. Find the maximum allowable power dissipation, $P_{D(\text{max})}$, at 25°C ambient temperature. Repeat for an ambient temperature of 55°C.

Stated differently, the problem is to find what value of P_D causes T_J to rise above 150°C. At 25°C we have

$$T_J = 25°C + P_{D(\text{max})}(0.4°C/\text{mw})$$

Setting $T_J = T_{J(\text{max})} = 150$°C, we have

$$150°C = 25°C + P_{D(\text{max})}(0.4)$$

which gives

$$P_D = 313 \text{ mw}$$

Thus, at 25°C ambient temperature a diode power dissipation of 313 mw causes T_J to rise to 150°C.

At 55°C ambient, we have

$$150°C = 55°C + P_{D(\text{max})}(0.4)$$

or

$$P_{D(\text{max})} = 238 \text{ mw}$$

Thus, the diode is allowed to dissipate only 238 mw at 55°C.   ◀

The power that the diode can safely dissipate decreases with ambient temperature. This is a very important consideration in the design of circuits which may be subjected to temperatures above room temperature. We will find this to be true of all semiconductor devices.

A diode may be operated above the maximum power dissipation if *heat sinks* are used. Heat sinks are large metal bases of copper and aluminum upon which the diodes may be mounted. The heat sinks may have their outside surfaces formed as fins to radiate heat more readily. The overall effect is to reduce θ_{JA} so as to allow more power dissipation without exceeding $T_{J(max)}$.

Forward current in a diode is limited only by the allowable power dissipation; this depends on the type of construction, the size of the junction, the diode material and the mounting used in assembling the device. There are various processes used to manufacture P-N junctions, most of which are also employed in the production of transistors. As such, these processes will be discussed later along with transistor fabrication methods.

5.13.   Comparison of Diode Materials

The basic concepts previously discussed apply to all diodes and diode devices. There are, however, some basic differences among the different types of semiconductor materials which make one type more suitable for a particular application. For example, diode devices used for high-power rectifier applications are now primarily made of silicon as the basic material with the doping impurities added by the process of diffusion (to be discussed later). Selenium rectifiers, germanium diodes and some copper oxide devices are sometimes used for high-power rectifiers; however, silicon is by far the most popular. The silicon diode can tolerate higher temperatures than other devices. Semiconductor diodes other than silicon have maximum operating temperatures of around 100°C whereas silicon can typically operate at 150°C. Silicon has the added advantage of a lower reverse current, at a given temperature and voltage, than other diode devices. It also has a much higher reverse breakdown voltage (up to perhaps several thousand volts), and the ability to handle much greater forward currents. Silicon does have a disadvantage in that its forward voltage drop is higher than some of the other devices (0.7 volt versus 0.3 volt for germanium) and, therefore, dissipates a little more power for a given forward current. Electron and hole mobilities are higher in germanium and gallium arsenide than in silicon. If speed is a consideration, the use of germanium or gallium arsenide as the basic material might be warranted. All things considered, the use of silicon devices has thus far predominated for most of the reasons mentioned above.

5.14.   P-N Junction Capacitance

A reverse-biased P-N junction can be compared to a charged capacitor. This is illustrated in Figure 5.28. The N and P regions (away from the space charge region) are essentially low resistance areas due to the high concentration of majority carriers, while the space charge region, which is depleted of majority carriers, is essentially an area of effective insulation between the N and P regions. The N and P regions act as the plates of the capacitor while the space charge region acts as the insulating dielectric. The reverse-biased junction thus has an effective capacitance, shown in dotted lines in the figure. The value of this capacitance depends on the width of the space charge region (distance between capacitor plates). Thus, it depends on reverse voltage. As reverse voltage increases, the space charge region becomes wider, effectively increasing the plate separation and decreasing the capacitance. A device known as a voltage variable capacitor (also called a Varactor) uses this property of P-N junctions in communications circuitry. This junction capacitance affects the speed of operation

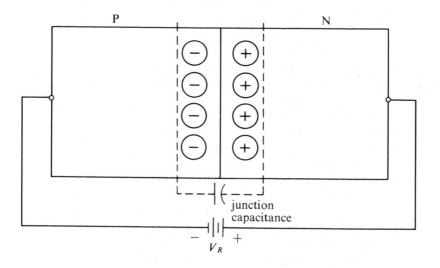

FIG. 5.28.   P-N JUNCTION CAPACITANCE

of P-N diodes and, in fact, all P-N junction devices as will be pointed out in subsequent work.

GLOSSARY

P-N junction: the joining of a P region and an N region in a single crystal structure

Space charge region (depletion region): the area on either side of a P-N junction which contains impurity ions, and is depleted of carriers

Potential barrier: the electrical force exerted by the space charge region on charge carriers

Majority carrier diffusion current: the current flow across a P-N junction carried by diffusing majority carriers

Minority carrier drift current: the current flow across a P-N junction carried by minority carriers accelerated by the potential barrier

Reverse bias: voltage applied to a P-N diode so as to increase the potential barrier (positive voltage on N region, negative on P region)

Forward bias: voltage applied to a P-N diode so as to neutralize the potential barrier (positive voltage on P region, negative on N region)

Reverse current: the current flow across a P-N junction when it is reverse-biased

Forward current: the current flow across a P-N junction when it is forward-biased

Reverse breakdown: the process of minority carrier avalanching when sufficient reverse voltage is applied

Anode: P region of a P-N diode

Cathode: N region of a P-N diode

$PRV, V_{RDC}, I_{F(max)}, V_F, I_R$: See Tables 5.1 and 5.2.

Load line: the line representing a plot of the Kirchhoff voltage law equation in a diode circuit

A-c resistance: a P-N diode's resistance to *changes* in current at a given operating point

Rectification: the process of changing an a-c voltage to a d-c voltage

Rectifier: a device which performs rectification

Thermal resistance: measure of a device's ability to lose heat to its surroundings

Junction capacitance: effective capacitance of a P-N junction

Questions

5.1 Briefly describe the charge situation of a P-type region at room temperature. Repeat for an N-type region.

5.2 What causes majority carriers to flow at the moment a P- and N-region are brought together?

5.3 Why doesn't this flow continue until all carriers have recombined?

5.4 Describe the formation of the "space charge region" in a P-N junction.

5.5 In an unbiased P-N junction what currents are continually flowing across the junction?

5.6 Sketch the charge concentration profile of an unbiased P-N junction.

5.7 Compare the potential barriers in silicon and germanium P-N junctions.

5.8 Explain the effect of reverse bias on the space charge region.

5.9 Which carriers conduct current when a P-N diode is reverse-biased? Draw the symbol for a P-N diode showing the direction of reverse current flow.

5.10 What limits the number of reverse current carriers?

5.11 Why is the reverse current in a silicon diode much smaller than in a comparable germanium diode?

5.12 Describe the process of avalanche breakdown in a P-N diode.

5.13 What limits the reverse current in a diode which is in reverse breakdown?

5.14 Explain the effect of forward bias on the space charge region.

5.15 Which carriers conduct forward current in a diode? Draw the symbol for a P-N diode showing the direction of forward current.

5.16   Roughly how much forward voltage is needed to cause current to flow in silicon? In germanium?

5.17   Draw the charge concentration profile for a reverse-biased P-N diode. Repeat for a forward-biased diode.

5.18   How many *I-V* curves are needed to characterize a P-N diode?

5.19   Draw the *I-V* characteristic of a typical diode. Label all significant points and regions.

5.20   In Figure 5.29, indicate the type of bias in each case.

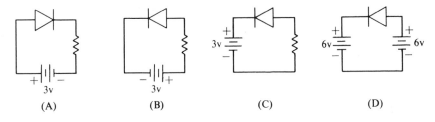

(A)   (B)   (C)   (D)

FIG. **5.29.**

5.21   A germanium diode has the following ratings and specifications at 25°C:

PRV:	200 volts	V_F:	0.3v @ 100 ma
V_{RDC}:	150 volts	I_R:	10 @ 100 volts
$I_{F(max)}$:	500 ma		

     (a) What is the maximum allowable d-c reverse voltage for this diode?

     (d) What is the maximum allowable forward current for this diode?

     (c) Should a reverse voltage of 180 volts be applied to this diode under any condition?

5.22   What is the primary effect of temperature on a semiconductor material?

5.23   What effect does an increase in temperature have on a diode's potential barrier? How does this affect a diode's forward characteristic? Its reverse characteristic?

5.24   A silicon diode has a reverse current of $1\mu a$ at 25°C. What will be its approximate reverse current at 36°C? At 47°C?

5.25   Using the load line method, find the operating point of the circuit shown in Figure 5.30.

5.26   The diode of Question 5.25 is used in the circuit of Figure 5.31. Find the operating point of the circuit using the approximate method.

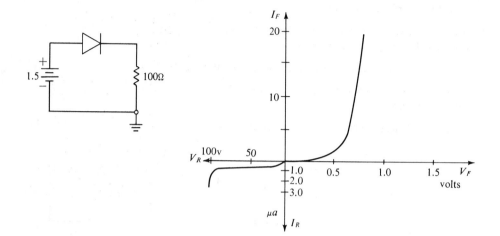

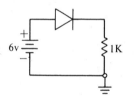

FIG. 5.30.

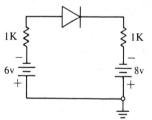

FIG. 5.31.

5.27   Replace the battery in 5.26 by a −50 volt battery and find the voltage across the 1K resistor. Repeat for a −150 volt battery.

FIG. 5.32.

5.28   Will the diode in Figure 5.32 conduct forward current?

5.29   A certain diode has an a-c resistance, r_f, of 10 ohms at $I_F = 10$ ma, $V_F = 0.6$ volt. What would be the value of I_F at $V_F = 0.59$ volt? At 0.61 volt?

5.30   Find the value of R_F, d-c forward resistance, for the diode of Figure 5.30 at 10 ma. Find R_R, d-c reverse resistance, at $V_R = 100$ volts. What is the figure of merit, M, for this diode?

5.31   A silicon diode is used as a rectifier in the circuit of Figure 5.33. Sketch the voltage across the resistor.

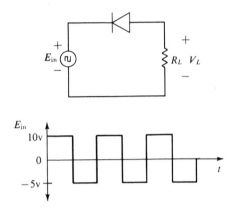

FIG. 5.33.

5.32   What is the lowest PRV which the diode in Question 5.31 can have for safe operation?

5.33   The diode in Figure 5.34 is employed as a *voltage limiter*. Its function is to limit the maximum output voltage, V_{out}, to a value of around 6.7 volts no matter how high V_{in} becomes. V_{out} can go below 6.7 volts, but not above, since the diode will become forward-biased when V_{in} equals 6.7 volts; increases in V_{in} will merely serve to supply more current to the diode whose voltage will change only slightly.

   (a) Find V_{out} when $V_{in} = -2$ volts if the diode is silicon and $I_R = 1\mu a$.
   (b) Find V_{out} for $V_{in} = 2$ volts.
   (c) Find V_{out} for $V_{in} = 4$ volts.
   (d) Find V_{out} for $V_{in} = 6.7$ volts.
   (e) Find V_{out} for $V_{in} = 10$ volts.
   (f) Plot V_{out} versus V_{in}.
   (g) What limits the maximum *positive* value of V_{in} which can be applied to this circuit? Maximum *negative* value?

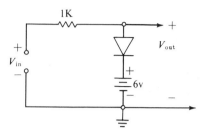

FIG. 5.34.

5.34 Design a diode limiter to limit the output voltage to 10.3 volts, using a germanium diode. If the input can go as high as 100 volts what value of series resistor must be used? Assume $I_{F(\text{max})} = 100$ ma.

5.35 What is the power dissipation of the silicon diode in Figure 5.35?

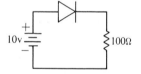

FIG. 5.35.

5.36 The diode in Question 5.35 has a thermal resistance, θ_{JA}, of $0.2°C/mw$. Find the diode's junction temperature if T_A is 25°C.

5.37 If a diode has an $I_{F(\text{max})}$ of 1 amp at $V_F = 1$ volt, what is its maximum allowable power dissipation, $P_{D(\text{max})}$ at $T_A = 25°C$?

5.38 The same diode has $\theta_{JA} = 0.1°C/mw$. What is its maximum allowable junction temperature? What is its $P_{D(\text{max})}$ at $T_A = 55°C$?

5.39 Compare silicon and germanium diodes as to the following:
(a) maximum operating temperature
(b) reverse breakdown voltages
(c) reverse leakage current
(d) forward voltage drop
(e) current handling capabilities
(f) speed

5.40 Indicate whether junction capacitance increases or decreases with the following:
(a) decrease in reverse bias
(b) increase in temperature
(c) increase in forward bias

5.41 The P-N diode whose characteristic is shown in Figure 5.36 has a maximum allowable junction temperature $T_{J(max)}$ of 125°C.
(a) Calculate the diode's thermal resistance if $P_{D(max)} = 500$ mw at $T_A = 25°C$.
(b) What is $I_{F(max)}$ at a T_A of 25°C?
(c) Find the minimum value of R that can be used in the circuit shown at 25°C ambient.
(d) Calculate $P_{D(max)}$ at T_A equals 40°C and repeat (b) and (c) for 40°C. (Assume the diode's *I-V* characteristic does not change appreciably.)

5.42 The diode in Figure 5.37 has a reverse breakdown voltage of 100 volts and a maximum power rating of 400 mw. What is the minimum value of R that can be used in this circuit?

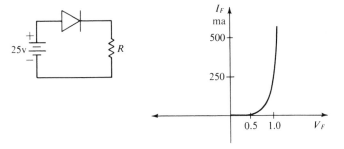

FIG. 5.36.

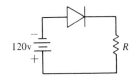

FIG. 5.37.

References

Foster, J. F., *Semiconductor Diodes and Transistors*, Vol. 2. Beaverton, Oregon: Programmed Instruction Group, Tetronix, Inc., 1964.

Romanowitz, H. A. and R. E. Puckett, *Introduction to Electronics*. New York: John Wiley & Sons, Inc., 1968.

6

Zener Diodes

6.1.   Introduction

Reverse breakdown of a P-N diode can take place due to avalanche breakdown, *zener breakdown* or a combination of both. Avalanche breakdown having already been discussed in Chapter 5, the mechanism of zener breakdown will be explained in this chapter, including the effects of impurity concentration and temperature. Both types of reverse breakdown are employed in *zener diodes*, which are P-N diodes specifically designed to operate in the reverse breakdown region. Studying the principal applications of zener diodes will help to explain their widespread usage in electronic circuitry.

6.2.   Zener Breakdown

When a reverse-biased diode goes from a low conduction state to a state of high conduction, either zener breakdown or avalanche breakdown, or a combination of both, takes place. Avalanche breakdown, as we have seen, is a result of the ionization of covalent bonds by minority carriers accelerated across the reverse-biased junction. This results in a multiplication of carriers crossing the junction, causing reverse current to increase rapidly with reverse voltage. When reverse breakdown in a diode occurs at a voltage greater than 5 volts, it is probably due to avalanche breakdown. When it occurs below 5 volts, it is due to zener breakdown. Zener breakdown is a result of the ionization of covalent bonds due to the high-intensity electric field that inherently exists across the narrow space charge region. If the space charge region is sufficiently narrow, increasing the potential difference across it will eventually develop an electric field (recall that electric field strength is inversely proportional to the distance over which a potential difference exists) which is strong enough to literally yank valence electrons out of their covalent bonds thereby producing extra conduction electrons and holes. These additional carriers drift across the junction under the influence of reverse voltage causing reverse current to increase rapidly and bringing about zener reverse breakdown. In order for zener breakdown to occur the width of the space charge region must be made very narrow. This can be accomplished by increasing the doping in both the P and N regions, as can be seen by comparing the two silicon P-N junctions shown in Figure 6.1. In the P-N junction in part (A) of the figure,

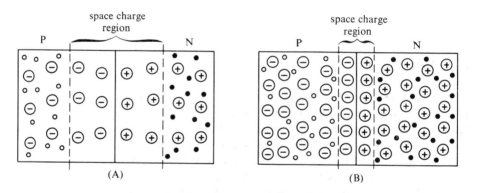

FIG. 6.1.   EFFECT OF DOPING ON SPACE CHARGE REGION

the space charge region produces a potential barrier of 0.7 volt. This potential barrier is produced by a certain number of impurity ions residing near the junction. If we increase the density of the impurities in both regions, the P-N junction in part (B) of the figure results. Since there are now more impurity ions per unit volume, the width of the space charge region needed to produce a 0.7-volt potential barrier is reduced. If the amount of doping is great enough, space charge regions as narrow as a few millionths of an inch can result making it possible for zener breakdown to occur at a few volts reverse bias.

The amount of reverse voltage needed to cause zener breakdown decreases as the space charge region becomes narrower. Thus, zener breakdown voltage decreases as the amount of doping increases. The effect of an increase in temperature on zener breakdown is to cause the zener breakdown voltage to *decrease*. This is opposite to what happens in avalanche breakdown where *increasing* temperature *increases* breakdown voltage.

As mentioned previously, zener breakdown occurs at voltages below 5 volts while avalanche breakdown occurs above 5 volts. Breakdown at around 5 volts is probably a combination of both mechanisms.

6.3.   Zener Diodes

When dealing with P-N diodes as rectifiers, the entrance of the diode into its reverse breakdown region was undesirable. If a diode is purposely constructed to operate in the reverse breakdown region, the voltage across the diode's terminals will remain fairly constant over a wide range of currents if the diode is in the breakdown condition. For a diode which is designed to operate in the reverse breakdown mode, the amount of doping and the junction's geometry can be varied to cause the diode to break down at a certain reverse voltage, and handle a given range of reverse currents.

The name *zener diode* is given to these diodes, which may be misleading since they encompass both types of reverse breakdown mechanisms, zener and avalanche breakdown. Other names like *reference diodes* or *breakdown diodes* are sometimes used but zener diode is the most widely accepted and we shall use it here. Zener diodes are designed to operate in the reverse breakdown portion of their characteristics. By careful control of impurity concentration and junction geometry, close tolerances on the reverse breakdown voltage can be obtained. Zener diodes with breakdown voltages below around 5 volts are affected by zener breakdown; zener diodes with breakdown voltages above 5 volts are affected by avalanche breakdown.

Figure 6.2 shows the *I-V* characteristic of a typical zener diode. It is not much different from that of a conventional P-N diode. However, a significant difference is the sharpness of the curve at the boundary of the breakdown region; compare this curve with the dotted curve for a conventional P-N diode. This extremely sharp curve is a desirable characteristic as we shall see when we investigate circuit applications of zener diodes. The electronic symbol for a zener diode is illustrated in Figure 6.3 alongside that of a

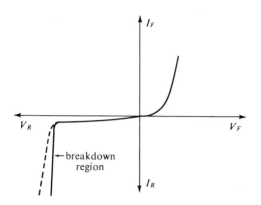

FIG. 6.2.   TYPICAL ZENER DIODE CHARACTERISTIC

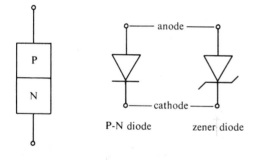

FIG. 6.3.   ZENER DIODE SYMBOL

conventional diode. Before proceeding, it should be re-emphasized that a zener diode is a P-N diode specially constructed to operate in the reverse breakdown region and whose *I-V* characteristics are essentially those of a P-N diode.

6.4.   Zener Diode Specifications and Ratings

The *I-V* characteristic of a typical zener diode is repeated in Figure 6.4 showing some of the important points on the characteristic curve. Note that reverse current is labelled I_Z, zener current; reverse voltage is labelled V_Z, zener voltage, since this is common practice. Zener diodes are meant to operate in their breakdown region, and as such, this is the most important region on the zener curve. The portion of the reverse characteristic where the device just begins going into breakdown is called the "zener knee". The zener current at the zener knee is labelled I_{ZK}. This is the minimum value of zener current which must be supplied in order to assure that the zener diode is operating in its breakdown region.

Once the zener diode reaches breakdown (below the knee) the zener current increases sharply with voltage. In this region (the zener region) the voltage across the zener is fairly constant over a wide variation in current. Manufacturers stipulate a test point on the zener breakdown curve somewhere below the knee. The current at this point is labelled, I_{ZT}, zener test current. The zener voltage at this point is labelled V_{ZT}. V_{ZT} is called the nominal zener voltage and is measured at the zener test current. For a given type of zener diode manufacturers usually place a tolerance of 5, 10 or 20 per cent on the value of V_{ZT}, similar to the tolerances on resistors. For example, if a zener diode type has a nominal value of V_{ZT} of 10 volts with a 10 per cent tolerance, we can expect zener diodes of this type will have values of V_{ZT} of 10 volts ± 10 per cent that is, anywhere from 9 to 11 volts.

The maximum allowable zener current is labelled I_{ZM} and is the maximum zener current which can be safely conducted by the zener diode. I_{ZM} is determined by the maximum power dissipation rating of the zener diode, $P_{Z(\text{max})}$. As with ordinary P-N diodes, this maximum power dissipation is determined by the maximum

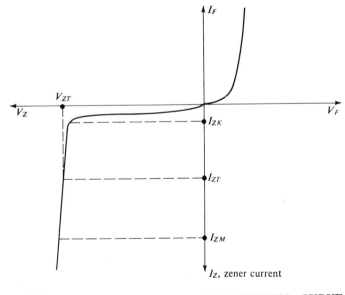

FIG. 6.4.   ZENER DIODE CHARACTERISTIC CURVE

allowable junction temperature, $T_{J(\max)}$. Exceeding this rating can lead to destruction of the zener diode.

Another important parameter of zener diodes is called zener impedance, Z_Z. The zener impedance is essentially the a-c resistance (impedance) of the zener diode (similar to a-c resistance of an ordinary P-N diode; see Section 5.10). It is simply the slope of the zener curve. Zener impedance is usually measured just above the knee in the zener region, Z_{ZK}, and at the zener test point, Z_{ZT}. Zener impedance decreases with increases in zener current, since the slope of the zener curve gets steeper as current increases. Thus, Z_{ZT} is always much smaller than Z_{ZK}. Zener impedance is important since it is a measure of the steepness of the zener region and, as such, indicates how much the reverse voltage across the zener diode will change for a change in zener current. That is

$$Z_Z = \frac{\Delta V_Z}{\Delta I_Z} \tag{6.1}$$

and is obtained from the zener curve in the same manner as was the a-c resistance of a P-N diode in Section 5.10.

The effect of temperature on the breakdown voltage of zener diodes was qualitatively discussed in Section 6.2. It is usually important in circuit design and analysis to know quantitatively what this effect will be. For this reason manufacturers often supply a typical *zener voltage temperature coefficient* as part of the zener diode specifications. The zener voltage temperature coefficient, denoted K_T, indicates the percentage change in nominal zener voltage, V_{ZT}, for each degree centigrade of change in junction temperature. For a zener diode which has a K_T of 0.05 per cent per °C, each degree of *increase* in junction temperature will *increase* the value of V_{ZT} by 0.05 per cent of its nominal value. A K_T of -0.05 per cent per °C means that each degree of *increase* in temperature will *decrease* the value of V_{ZT} by 0.05 per cent of its nominal value. Zener diodes which break down due to zener breakdown (see Section 6.2) have a *negative* temperature coefficient while those which break down due to avalanche breakdown have a *positive* value of K_T. The value of K_T increases as the nominal zener voltage increases.

A typical zener diode specification which contains values of all these parameters is shown in Figure 6.5. Much valuable information about this zener diode can be ascertained from these specifications. In fact, with this information one could make a fairly accurate sketch of this zener's *I-V* curve. Let us take a look at some of the information which can be derived from these specs.

This particular zener diode has a maximum power rating, $P_{Z(max)}$ of one watt at an ambient temperature of 25°C and has a nominal zener voltage, V_{ZT}, of 20 volts with a 10 per cent tolerance. Thus, a zener diode of this type can have a value of V_{ZT} anywhere in the range of 18 to 22 volts at 25°C. Its temperature coefficient, K_T, is 0.075 per cent per °C and can be used to determine the value of V_{ZT} at elevated junction temperatures.

ELECTRICAL CHARACTERISTICS (@ 25°C AMBIENT)

V_{ZT}:	20 volts ± 10% (measured at I_{ZT})
I_{ZT}:	12.5 ma
I_{ZK}:	0.25 ma
I_{ZM}:	32 ma
Z_{ZT}:	22 ohms max. (measured at I_{ZT})
Z_{ZK}:	750 ohms max. (measured at I_{ZK})
K_T:	0.075 %/°C
$P_{Z(max)}$:	1 watt: θ_{JA} — 100°C/watt
I_R:	1μa @ V_R = 6 volts

FIG. 6.5.   TYPICAL ZENER DIODE SPECS

▶ EXAMPLE 6.1

If a zener diode with the specs given by Figure 6.5 has its junction temperature increased from 25°C to 75°C, find the value of V_{ZT} at the higher temperature.

Since K_T gives the percentage change per degree, it is advisable to first use K_T to calculate the voltage change per degree and then multiply by the number of degrees *change* in temperature. Thus, the voltage change per degree is given by

$$\frac{K_T}{100\%} \times V_{ZT} = \text{v/°C} \qquad \textbf{(6.2)}$$

which for this zener diode becomes

$$\frac{.075\%/°C}{100\%} \times 20\text{v} = .015 \text{ v/°C}$$

Multiplying this by the change in temperature, in this case 50°C (75°C − 25°C), we have the total voltage change, ΔV_{ZT}, given by

$$\Delta V_{ZT} = (0.015\text{v/°C}) \times (50°C)$$
$$= 0.75\text{v}$$

Adding this change in voltage to the nominal V_{ZT} gives the value of V_{ZT} at 75°C. That is

$$V_{ZT}(\text{at } 75°C) = V_{ZT}(\text{at } 25°C) + \Delta V_{ZT}$$
$$= 20\text{v} + 0.75\text{v}$$
$$= 20.75\text{v}$$

The general formula for calculating the zener voltage at temperatures other than 25°C is given by Equation 6.3,

$$V_{ZT}(\text{at } T_1) = V_{ZT}(\text{at } 25°C) + \frac{K_T}{100} \times V_{ZT}(\text{at } 25°C) \times (T_1 - 25)$$

(6.3)

where T_1 is the temperature of interest. Note that if T_1 is *less* than 25°C, then V_{ZT} at T_1 will be *less* than V_{ZT} at 25°C since K_T is positive. The opposite is true if K_T is negative. ◀

Zener diode junction temperature depends on ambient temperature and power dissipation exactly as discussed in Section 5.11 and given by Equation 5.6 for the P-N diode. Essentially all the material in Section 5.11 can be applied to the zener diode as well, since it is, after all, a special type of P-N diode.

▶ EXAMPLE 6.2

For the zener diode with specs given by Figure 6.5, determine the maximum allowable junction temperature.

The maximum junction temperature occurs when the maximum rated power is being dissipated. Thus

$$T_{J(\text{max})} = T_A + P_{Z(\text{max})} \times \theta_{JA}$$ (6.4)

For this zener diode

$$T_{J(\text{max})} = 25°C + (1 \text{ watt}) \times (100°C/\text{watt})$$
$$= 125°C$$

The knee current, I_{ZK}, for the zener diode of Figure 6.5 is given as 0.25 ma indicating that at least this amount of zener current must be flowing to assure that the zener is operating on the good portion of its characteristic curve.

The maximum zener current, I_{ZM}, is given as 32 ma for this zener diode. The manufacturer cannot guarantee operation of this zener diode at currents above this value.

Also given as part of the zener diode specs is the value of reverse current, I_R, at some value of reverse voltage much less than V_{ZT}. This is 1μa at 6 volts for the zener of Figure 6.5 indicating a reverse leakage current of $1\mu a$ before the zener reaches breakdown.   ◄

More detailed zener specifications than those in Figure 6.5 are usually the case. Information on the physical characteristics and markings, as well as additional electrical specifications, are included. Appendix II contains a typical manufacturer's zener diode spec sheet.

6.5.   The Zener Diode as a Circuit Element

The zener diode is a special type of P-N diode and, as such, the methods of analyzing its operation in circuits are the same as those covered in Chapter 5. Both the load-line method and the approximate method can be used for zener diodes; however, the latter is usually employed because of its simplicity. The load-line method will be used in some circuits to help explain the zener diode's operation.

Before turning to specific zener diode applications, let us consider the simple circuit of Figure 6.6. The zener diode in this circuit has the *I-V* characteristic depicted in this Figure. This circuit is similar to one studied in Section 5.9. The polarity of the voltage, E_{in}, is such that the zener diode is reverse biased. Looking

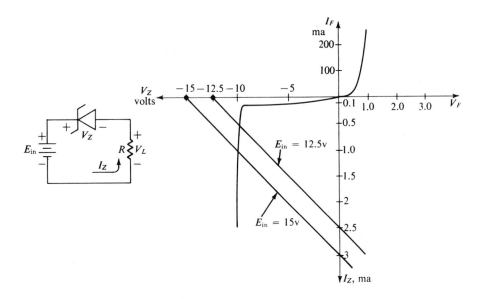

FIG.   6.6.   SIMPLE ZENER DIODE CIRCUIT AND ZENER CHARACTERISTIC CURVE

at the *I-V* characteristic, the zener breakdown voltage is around 10 volts. Thus, for values of E_{in} below 10 volts only a small reverse current will flow. The voltage across the zener diode will be equal to E_{in} and across the load resistor it will be essentially zero (Example 5.11). For values of E_{in} greater than 10 volts, the zener diode will be in its breakdown region if the zener current, I_Z, is above the knee current, I_{ZK}, which is 0.1 ma for this zener.

Consider an input voltage of 12.5 volts and a load resistor of 5K. The procedure for finding the exact operating point of the zener diode starts with drawing the circuit load-line (Section 5.9) which is shown in Figure 6.6. It is a straight line connected between $V_Z = 12.5v$ and $I_Z = 12.5v/5K = 2.5$ ma. The point at which this load-line intersects the zener characteristic is the operating point of the zener, which in this case is $V_Z = 10$ volts and $I_Z = 0.5$ ma. The 12.5-volt input is sufficient to cause the zener to operate in its breakdown region with $V_Z = 10$ volts. The voltage V_L, across the 5K load resistor, accounts for the other 2.5 volts of the input. That is, since

$$E_{in} = V_Z + V_L \tag{6.5}$$

the input voltage must equal the sum of the voltage across the zener diode and the load. Since $I_Z = 0.5$ ma at the operating point and this current flows through the 5K load, we have

$$V_L = I_Z \times 5K = 2.5v$$

If we change E_{in} to 15 volts and repeat the above procedure, we find the operating point to be the intersection of the 15-volt load line and the zener characteristic. The zener is still operating in its breakdown region but at a greater zener current. From the figure, it can be seen that $V_Z = 10.1$ volts and $I_Z = 0.98$ ma at the operating point. Also, $V_L = 4.9$ volts.

Let us now compare these two cases which are summarized in Table 6.1 below. The main point to be noticed in this com-

TABLE 6.1

E_{in}	V_Z	I_Z	V_L
12.5v	10v	0.5 ma	2.5v
15v	10.1v	0.98 ma	4.9v

parison is the relative constancy of the voltage across the zener diode as the zener current increases. The increase in input voltage from 12.5 volts to 15 volts results in a change in current from 0.5 ma to 0.98 ma (almost double). This change in current produces only a 0.1 volt increase in the voltage across the zener (a 1 per cent change). Most of the 2.5 volt change in the input voltage is dropped across the load resistor. The ability of a zener diode to maintain a nearly constant voltage for varying currents arises from the shape of its characteristic in the breakdown region. The more nearly this portion of the characteristic approaches a perfectly vertical line, the more constant the zener voltage will be for varying zener currents. A measure of this constant-voltage property of zener diodes is the zener impedance, Z_Z. A small value of Z_Z indicates that a change in zener current will result in a small change in zener voltage. From Table 6.1 we can calculate the value of Z_Z for this zener diode in the region of its operation. The current I_Z changes 0.48 ma resulting in a 0.1 volt change in V_Z. Thus

$$Z_Z = \frac{\Delta V_Z}{\Delta I_Z} = \frac{0.1v}{0.48 \text{ ma}} = 208.3\Omega$$

This value is somewhat high since some zener diodes operate with zener impedances of less than 100 ohms and as low as a fraction of an ohm. Actually the value of Z_Z decreases with increases in I_Z. For this reason, zeners should be operated well above the zener knee current if a better constant voltage property is desired.

Most applications of zener diodes make use of their constant-voltage characteristic in the breakdown region. This will be pointed out in the following sections where we will examine some of the standard zener diode circuits.

6.6.   The Zener Diode as a Voltage Regulator

Probability the most popular application of zener diodes is in producing a *regulated* output voltage from a practical d-c power supply; that is, from a source having internal resistance.

To help understand how a zener diode achieves *voltage regulation* requires a brief study of a practical d-c voltage supply. Figure 6.7 shows a practical d-c source represented by an ideal source E and a series internal resistance, R_{int}. The output terminals of the source are labelled *xx*, and these are the terminals accessible to the user. In other words, these terminals are connected to the load to which d-c power is being applied. The internal resistance R_{int} is internal to the power supply and generally cannot be modified by the user.

Consider the case where $E = 10$ volts and $R_{int} = 100\Omega$. If we

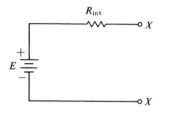

FIG. 6.7.   PRACTICAL VOLTAGE SOURCE

measure the voltage at the terminals of the voltage source with no load connected, we will measure 10 volts. This no-load voltage is represented by E_{NL}. Thus $E_{NL} = 10$ volts. Consider now a load resistor, R_L, connected to the voltage source terminals as in Figure 6.8. The load resistor will draw current, I_L, from the voltage source developing an output voltage, E_L. This voltage can be easily calculated using Ohm's law in Equation 6.6. The load current, I_L, is given by

$$I_L = E/(R_{int} + R_L) \qquad (6.6)$$

The load voltage, E_L, is then given by

$$E_L = I_L R_L = E\left(\frac{R_L}{R_L + R_{int}}\right) \qquad (6.7)$$

It can be seen from Equation 6.7 that the voltage across the load is dependent on the load resistance. For example, with $R_L = 400\Omega$ we have, from Equation 6.7,

$$E_L = 10\left(\frac{400}{400 + 100}\right) = 8 \text{ volts}$$

Thus, the output voltage has dropped from 10 volts at no load to 8 volts at a 400Ω load. The drop in output voltage due to loading is caused by R_{int}; that is, the load current develops a voltage drop across it equal to $I_L \times R_{int}$. This voltage drop

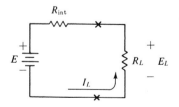

FIG. 6.8.   LOADED VOLTAGE SOURCE

leaves less voltage available to the load causing the load voltage to decrease.

The percentage change in output voltage from no-load condition to a loaded condition on the power supply is called the *percentage regulation* of the power supply and is determined by applying

$$\text{percentage regulation} = \left(\frac{E_{NL} - E_L}{E_{NL}}\right) \times 100 \qquad \textbf{(6.8)}$$

For the case under consideration we can use this equation to calculate

$$\text{percentage regulation} = \left(\frac{10 - 8}{10}\right) \times 100 = 20\%$$

This indicates a 20 per cent change in output voltage going from a no-load to loaded condition. This is typical for an unregulated power supply. The task of a regulated power supply is to maintain a nearly constant output voltage over the range of load current (no-load to full-load current). The zener diode accomplishes the necessary regulation in the circuit shown in Figure 6.9.

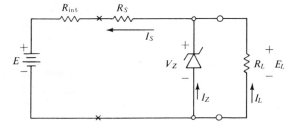

FIG. 6.9.   ZENER REGULATED SUPPLY

In this circuit a series resistor, R_S, and a zener diode are connected to the terminals of the unregulated supply. The output is taken across the zener diode and the terminals labelled *oo* are the output terminals of the regulated supply. The function of the zener diode is to keep the output voltage fairly constant over a wide variation in load current. This is accomplished by operating the zener in its breakdown region where its voltage varies only slightly with changes in zener current. The zener breakdown voltage must, of course, be less than E in order to insure operation of the zener in its breakdown region. The resistor R_S is necessary to keep the zener current limited to a value below I_{ZM} (see Section 6.4).

Circuit operation may best be described by assuming some circuit values. Let $E = 10$ volts, $R_{int} = 100\Omega$, $R_S = 100\Omega$, $V_{ZT} = 6$ volts. With these values for the circuit, consider the case with no load; that is, $R_L = \infty$. In this case $I_L = 0$ and the current supplied by the voltage source all flows through the zener, that is, $I_Z = I_S$. To calculate I_S, we can use Kirchhoff's voltage law

$$E = I_S \times (R_{int} + R_S) + V_Z \qquad (6.9)$$

If we assume that the zener diode is in breakdown (it should be if $I_S > I_{ZK}$), then V_Z will be approximately equal to $V_{ZT} = 6$ volts. The output voltage, which is equal to V_Z, is $E_{NL} = 6$ volts. Substituting for R_{int}, R_S, E and V_Z, we have, using Equation 6.9

$$10\text{v} = I_S \times (200\Omega) + 6\text{v}$$

Solving for I_S,

$$I_S = 4\text{v}/200\Omega = 20 \text{ ma}$$

Thus, the current flowing through the zener is 20 ma. This is the maximum current which will flow through the zener in this regulator circuit, since there is no load resistor to shunt some of the current away from the zener. The I_{ZM} rating of this zener should then be greater than 20 ma to insure safe operation

If we now connect a load resistor across the output terminals of the regulated supply, it will draw current depending on its resistance. This current is subtracted from the 20 ma being supplied by the voltage source, leaving less available for the zener current. However, V_Z will change very slightly with changes in I_Z as long as I_Z is sufficiently above the value I_{ZK}. If we assume a value of $I_{ZK} = 1$ ma for this zener, then we can consider that V_Z will remain at approximately 6 volts as long as I_Z is kept greater than 1 ma. Consider a load resistor $R_L = 600\Omega$ in the circuit which is redrawn in Figure 6.10. With 6 volts across the zener, the load voltage is also 6 volts as indicated. The load current is therefore $6\text{v}/600\Omega = 10$ ma. The current supplied by the voltage source is still 20 ma as calculated previously. This means that 10 ma of this current is being supplied to the load leaving $I_Z = 10$ ma. This is a result of applying Kirchhoff's current law at the output terminals. That is

$$I_S = I_L + I_Z \qquad (6.10)$$

The 10 ma of zener current is well above the knee current, so that the zener is definitely in its breakdown region where $V_Z = 6$ volts.

If we calculated the percentage regulation of this circuit using Equation 6.8, the result would be zero, indicating perfect regulation, since $E_L = E_{NL} = 6$ volts. In practice, however, the output

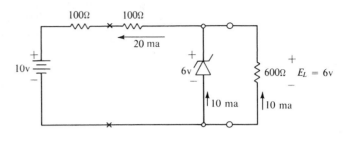

FIG. 6.10.

voltage does drop slightly when a load is connected since V_Z is not perfectly constant as I_Z changes. Just how much V_Z changes depends on the slope of the zener breakdown curve; that is, the change depends upon the zener impedance. A low value of zener impedance will result in a small variation in V_Z as the regulated supply is loaded giving a percentage regulation generally close to zero per cent.

There is a limit to how much load current can be supplied before the circuit of Figures 6.9 and 6.10 begins to lose regulation. As mentioned previously, at least 1 ma of current must be supplied to the zener to keep it operating in its breakdown region. This means that of the 20 ma supplied by the voltage source, no more than 19 ma can be drawn by the load if good regulation is to be maintained. This stipulation, of course, determines the minimum value of R_L which can be used. That is

$$R_{L(min)} = E_L/I_{L(max)} \qquad \textbf{(6.11)}$$

which in this case becomes

$$R_{L(min)} = 6v/19 \text{ ma} = 315\Omega$$

Any value of R_L below 315Ω would draw more than 19 ma of current, and thus pull the zener out of its breakdown region.

▶ EXAMPLE 6.3

A zener diode with the following specifications is used in the voltage regulator circuit of Figure 6.9 with $E = 20$ volts and $R_{int} = 100\Omega$.

$$V_{ZT} = 10 \text{ volts } @ I_{ZT} = 24 \text{ ma}$$
$$I_{ZK} = 1 \text{ ma}; I_{ZM} = 80 \text{ ma}$$

(a) Calculate the value of R_S required to insure that I_Z stays below I_{ZM}. The no-load case gives the most current flow through the zener; that is, $I_Z = I_S$. If we use Equation 6.9 and set $I_S = I_{ZM} = 80$ ma, we can solve for the value of R_S which will produce 80 ma of current flow. Substituting our values in this equation, we have

$$20v = 80 \text{ ma} \times (100\Omega + R_S) + 10v$$

Solving for R_S, we obtain

$$R_S = \frac{10v}{80 \text{ ma}} - 100\Omega = 25\Omega$$

Any value of R_S below 25Ω would cause more than 80 ma of current to flow through the zener in the no-load case.

(b) Using $R_S = 25\Omega$, calculate the minimum load resistor, $R_{L(min)}$, which can be used and still have voltage regulation maintained. Since $I_{ZK} = 1$ ma, the maximum load current will be 80 ma $-$ 1 ma $=$ 79 ma. Using Equation 6.11, $R_{L(min)}$ is given by

$$R_{L(min)} = 10v/79 \text{ ma} = 126.6\Omega \qquad \blacktriangleleft$$

To summarize this discussion, it can be stated that the addition of a zener diode to an unregulated power supply will generally improve the output voltage regulation. This improvement is a direct result of the zener diode's ability to maintain a relatively constant voltage for a wide range of zener current when operated in its breakdown region.

6.7.   The Zener Diode as a Reference Element

There are many applications in which it is desirable to maintain a constant voltage between two points in a circuit and use this voltage as a reference to which another circuit voltage may be compared. The difference between the compared voltage and the reference voltage is usually amplified and used to perform some control function. Elaborate power supply voltage regulator circuits, measurement circuits and servomechanism circuits use this type of arrangement which is shown in Figure 6.11.

A zener diode of an appropriate voltage rating can be advantageously used as the reference element. Its constant-voltage characteristic in the breakdown region makes it desirable for this application. The circuit of Figure 6.11 is redrawn in Figure 6.12 using a zener diode as the reference element. The reference voltage, E_{ref}, in this circuit is equal to the zener breakdown voltage. Current is supplied to the zener by the main circuit power supply,

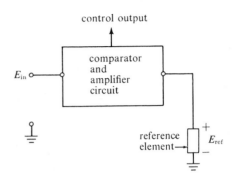

FIG. **6.11.** COMPARISON CIRCUIT

E_S, through a series resistor, R_S. Obviously E_{ref} must be less than E_S. The value of R_S is chosen to insure that the zener is operating well below the knee on the good part of its characteristic.

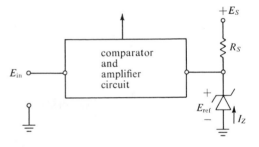

FIG. **6.12.** ZENER DIODE AS THE REFERENCE ELEMENT

▶ EXAMPLE 6.4

The circuit of Figure 6.12 is to use the zener diode specified in Example 6.3. The supply voltage, E_S, is +24 volts. Calculate a value for R_S to use in this circuit. The value of R_S must be small enough to assure that I_Z is greater than $I_{ZK} = 1$ ma and yet not so small that I_Z is greater than $I_{ZM} = 80$ ma. In this circuit, since $E_S = 24$v and $E_{ref} = 10$ volts, the voltage drop across R_S is 14 volts. Thus we have

$$I_Z \times R_S = 14\text{v}$$

For $I_Z = I_{ZK} = 1$ ma we can calculate $R_{S(max)}$, the maximum value of R_S we can use.

$$R_{S(max)} = 14v/1 \text{ ma} = 14K$$

For $I_Z = I_{ZM} = 80$ ma we can calculate $R_{S(min)}$, the minimum value of R_S we can use.

$$R_{S(min)} = 14v/80 \text{ ma} = 175\Omega$$

In practice a value of R_S somewhere between these limits would be used.   ◀

There are, of course, many more applications for the zener diode in today's vast complexity of electronic circuits. Most of these applications take advantage either of the zener's constant-voltage characteristic or of its ability to block current in the reverse direction until the applied voltage is greater than the breakdown voltage. Use of the zener diode in conjunction with other semiconductor devices will be covered in the course of this text.

GLOSSARY

Zener breakdown: onset of heavy current conduction in the reverse direction due to the high-intensity electric field across a narrow space-charge region

Zener diode: a P-N diode designed to operate in the reverse breakdown region (also called reference diode or breakdown diode)

Zener knee: region of the zener diode characteristic curve at point where breakdown just begins

I_Z, V_Z: zener current and voltage

I_{ZK}:   zener knee current

I_{ZT}:   zener test current

I_{ZM}:   maximum allowable zener current

V_{ZT}:   nominal zener voltage measured at I_{ZT}

$P_{Z(max)}$:   maximum allowable zener power dissipation

Z_Z: zener impedance

K_T: zener voltage temperature coefficient

Voltage regulation: ability to maintain a nearly constant voltage over a wide range of current levels

Percentage regulation: percentage decrease in output voltage of a power supply from no-load to loaded conditions

Reference voltage: a constant voltage used as a reference to which another voltage is compared

Questions

6.1 Name the *two* types of reverse breakdown which can occur in P-N diodes. Which occurs at lower voltages?

6.2 How does increased doping of both sides of a P-N junction affect the space charge region? How does it affect reverse breakdown voltage?

6.3 Would you expect the breakdown voltage of a 4-volt zener diode to increase with an increase in temperature? Why?

6.4 What is the principal difference between the *I-V* characteristics of a zener diode and those of an ordinary P-N diode?

6.5 Consider the zener diode *I-V* characteristic in Figure 6.13. From this characteristic
(a) estimate the value of I_{ZK}.
(b) determine V_{ZT}, nominal zener voltage, if $I_{ZT} = 30$ ma.

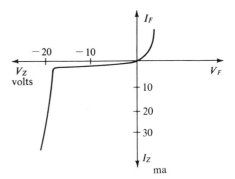

FIG. 6.13.

6.6   Data taken on a certain zener diode is given in the table below. From this data determine
(a) approximate zener impedance, Z_{ZK}, at $I_{ZK} = 1$ ma
(b) approximate zener impedance, Z_{ZT}, at $I_{ZT} = 10$ ma

I_Z ma	V_Z volts
0.0	0.00
0.5	7.50
0.9	8.99
1.0	9.00
1.1	9.01
5.0	9.20
9	9.24
10	9.25
11	9.26
12	9.27
15	9.30
20	9.33
40	9.38

FIG. 6.14.

6.7   The zener diode of Question 6.6 is specified to have a nominal zener voltage of 9.1v $\pm$ 5 per cent. Does the zener of Figure 6.14 fall within specifications?

6.8   Refer to the silicon zener diode specification sheet in Appendix II. From this spec sheet determine the following:
(a) Which zener diode of this series is least dependent on temperature?
(b) Which is most dependent on temperature?
(c) What is the maximum junction temperature, $T_{J(max)}$?
(d) What is the maximum power dissipation, $P_{Z(max)}$?

6.9   From the zener spec sheet in Appendix II, determine the value of V_{ZT} for the 1N3827 at the following temperatures:
(a) $T_J = 25°C$
(b) $T_J = 100°C$
(c) $T_J = 175°C$

6.10   Repeat Question 6.9 for the 1N3824 diode.

6.11   The zener diodes specified in Appendix II have a $P_{Z(max)}$ of 1 watt. The spec also indicates that this value should be derated by 6.67

mw for each degree that ambient temperature is above 25°C.
(a) Calculate $P_{Z(\text{max})}$ at $T_A = 50°C$
(b) Calculate $P_{Z(\text{max})}$ at $T_A = 100°C$

6.12   A 1N3826 zener diode (Appendix II) is used in the circuit below.
Determine the maximum value of E_{in} which should be used for
safe operation.

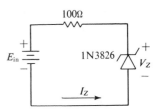

FIG. 6.15.

6.13   In the circuit of Figure 6.15 calculate the voltage across the
resistor for $E_{\text{in}} = 15$ volts; $E_{\text{in}} = 3$ volts.

6.14   A particular unregulated 30-volt d-c source has its output voltage
drop to 27 volts when loaded with 100Ω. Calculate the percentage regulation for this source.

6.15   A zener regulated voltage supply employs a 1N3830 zener diode
(Appendix II) and a 15-volt unregulated supply with an internal
resistance of 50 Ω. The regulated voltage must supply current to
a minimum load resistance of 100Ω. Calculate the largest value
for series resistance, R_S, which could be used.

6.16   Why is it advantageous to operate a zener diode at high current
levels (somewhat higher than necessary to keep it operating in
its breakdown region) if it is to be used as a voltage regulator?

6.17   It is desired to convert a 15-volt unregulated d-c power supply
into a zener regulated power supply with *two* separate output
voltages of 7.5 volts and 12.6 volts. Design a circuit which will
accomplish this using the zener diode series in Appendix II.

6.18   The 1N3821 zener diode is to be used as a reference voltage for a
circuit such as Figure 6.12. Calculate the limits on series resistor
R_S. What value of R_S should be used to keep $E_{\text{ref}} = V_{ZT}$?

References

Foster, J. F., *Semiconductor Diodes and Transistors*, Vol. 2. Beaverton, Oregon: Programmed Instruction Group, Tetronix, Inc., 1964.

Silicon Zener Diode and Rectifier Handbook. Phoenix: Motorola, Inc., 1961.

Sowa, B. A. and M. M. Toole, *Special Semiconductor Devices*. New York: Holt, Rinehart and Winston, Inc., 1968.

Tunnel Diodes

7.1.   Introduction

A revolutionary, relatively new semiconductor device developed from the P-N junction is the *tunnel diode* invented in 1958 by Dr. Leo Esaki. The principles of operation of the tunnel diode are remarkably different from those of other semiconductor devices. A detailed explanation of these principles will not be presented here as they are not necessary to understand the action of a tunnel diode in a circuit. The tunnel diode will be used mainly as a vehicle for introducing the student to the concept of *negative resistance* which he will encounter in later circuit work. Some of the important applications of this device require more background than the student is expected to have at this time and will be passed over in favor of simpler circuits which illustrate the use of negative resistance. For a more detailed and higher-level discussion of tunnel diodes the student is advised to consult the references listed at the end of this chapter.

7.2.   The Tunnel Diode

As was discussed in the previous chapter, increasing the amount of doping impurities added to the P and N regions of a P-N junction reduces the voltage at which the diode enters a reverse break-

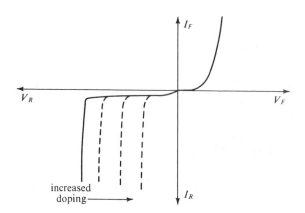

FIG. 7.1.   EFFECT OF DOPING ON REVERSE BREAK-
DOWN VOLTAGE

down condition. This is illustrated in Figure 7.1. It might be
thought that there would be a limiting case when the reverse
breakdown voltage is reduced to zero volts. However, experiments
have shown that it is possible to dope many semiconductor materials heavily enough to cause reverse breakdown to occur at a
slight forward bias. When a larger forward bias is applied, the
device goes out of reverse breakdown and the current falls to a
small value until forward bias turn-on occurs.

The breakdown mechanism in these devices is known as the
tunnel effect; this is a process whereby electrons, with apparently
insufficient energy to do so, can surmount a potential barrier.
In this case, the barrier is the space charge potential barrier.
Because of the heavy doping, the space charge region in a tunnel

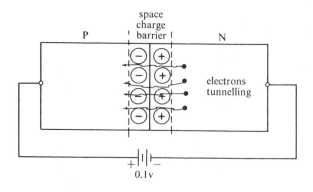

FIG. 7.2.   ILLUSTRATION OF ELECTRONS TUNNELLING

diode is very narrow (less than a millionth of an inch) which is why
electrons can tunnel through the barrier. This tunnelling gives
rise to an additional current across the P-N junction at very small
forward bias which disappears as forward bias is increased.
Figure 7.2 is an illustration of electrons tunnelling through the
space charge barrier.

A typical tunnel diode *I-V* characteristic curve (solid curve) is
shown in Figure 7.3 along with that of a conventional P-N diode
(dotted curve). Notice that with no applied voltage there is no
current flow through the tunnel diode (point *A*). With the application of reverse voltage, reverse current begins to flow immediately
since the device is very heavily doped. This is completely different
from what occurs in the conventional P-N diode where reverse
current is very small for values of reverse voltage below the relatively high reverse breakdown voltage. As forward voltage is
applied to the tunnel diode, forward current immediately begins
to flow until a point is reached where the current starts to decrease
as forward voltage is increased (point *B*). This region of decreasing
current (point *B* to point *C*) is called a *negative resistance region*
since the a-c resistance (r_F in Chapter 5) is negative; that is, a
positive ΔV_F produces a negative ΔI_F. Further increase in voltage
past point *C* causes the tunnel diode to enter the normal forward
conduction mode of the conventional P-N diode. The entire
region of the tunnel diode curve from point *A* to point *C* is due
to the tunnelling effect which occurs as a result of heavy impurity
doping. This effect is not present to the right of point C, where
normal P-N diode operation takes place.

A detailed discussion on the nature of the tunnel current

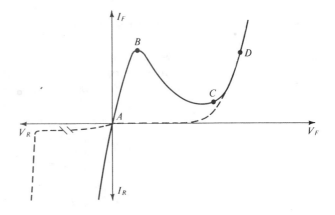

FIG. 7.3.   TUNNEL DIODE *I-V* CURVE

(point *A* to point *C*) would require some understanding of quantum mechanics and will not be presented here. It should be noted, however, that the speed of the electrons which tunnel through the space charge barrier is much faster than the speed of electrons which diffuse from the N side to the P side (normal forward current in a P-N diode). In fact, the tunnelling electrons travel very close to the speed of light across the P-N junction. For this reason tunnel diodes are particularly suited for use at very high frequencies (theoretically as high as 10^7 meghz). The principal applications of the tunnel diode take advantage of its fast operating speed. Figure 7.4 shows some symbols that indicate a tunnel diode. The first symbol is the one which will be used from this point on.

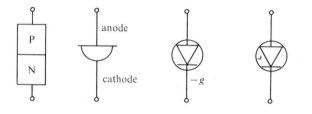

FIG. 7.4.   TUNNEL DIODE SYMBOLS

7.3.   Tunnel Diode Specifications

The *I-V* curve of a typical germanium tunnel diode is drawn in Figure 7.5 showing the important tunnel diode parameters (I_P, I_V, V_P, V_V and V_{FP}). The *peak current*, I_P, is measured at the point where the current starts decreasing with voltage (point *B*) and *peak voltage*, V_P, is the corresponding voltage at that point. The *valley current*, I_V, is measured at the point where current begins increasing again (point *C*) and *valley voltage*, V_V, is the corresponding voltage at that point. The *forward point voltage*, V_{FP}, is measured in the region of normal P-N diode conduction at a forward current equal to I_P (point *D*). In the area of negative resistance between points *B* and *C* the value of a-c resistance or of a-c *conductance* can be calculated. Most often a-c conductance is used for the tunnel diode and is given the symbol *g*. It is given by

$$g = \frac{\Delta I_F}{\Delta V_F} \text{ mhos } (\text{ohms}^{-1}) \tag{7.1}$$

and is calculated in the negative resistance region at the point

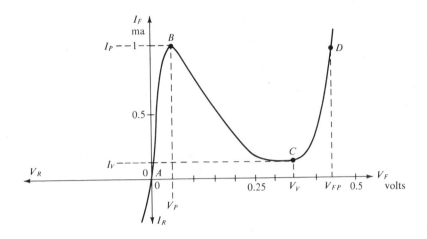

FIG. 7.5.   *I-V* CURVE FOR GERMANIUM TUNNEL DIODE

where the curve is the steepest. Thus, g is always a negative quantity. An approximate value of g can be obtained using

$$g = \frac{-2(I_P - I_V)}{(V_V - V_P)} \qquad (7.2)$$

The values of peak voltage, valley voltage and forward point voltage are determined primarily by the semiconductor material used in construction of the tunnel diode. Peak current is determined by the geometry of the junction. Valley current and the a-c conductance depend on a number of factors. Typical values of these parameters for germanium tunnel diodes are $V_P = 55$ mv, $V_V = 350$ mv and $V_{FP} = 500$ mv. For gallium arsenide tunnel diodes, $V_P = 150$ mv, $V_V = 500$ mv and $V_{FP} = 1100$ mv. These voltages are typical at room temperature. Typical values of I_P, I_V and g can be obtained from Figure 7.5 as $I_P = 1$ ma, $I_V = 0.125$ ma and $g = -0.01$ mhos.

Temperature affects each of these parameters. Peak voltage, valley voltage, a-c conductance and forward voltage all decrease with increasing temperatures while the valley current increases with increasing temperature. The peak current may increase or decrease with temperature depending on the doping level and the semiconductor material. For a typical germanium tunnel diode, V_P decreases 60 μv for each degree increase in temperature, V_V and V_{FP} decrease 1 mv per degree. Note that this is less than for a conventional diode (Section 5.8), whose forward voltage decreases typically 2.2 mv per degree. In general, tunnel diodes are less sensitive to temperature than P-N diodes and other semiconductor devices. Tunnel diodes may operate at temperatures as high as 340°C whereas conventional silicon diodes stop working at 200°C and germanium at about 100°C.

There are other important tunnel diode parameters which will not be covered here but are thoroughly discussed in this chapter's references.

7.4.   The Tunnel Diode as a Circuit Element

The many features of tunnel diodes make it a very useful circuit element. The negative resistance characteristic makes it possible to use the tunnel diode as an amplifier, an oscillator and an extremely rapid switching device. It can operate at speeds and temperatures at which other semiconductor devices cannot function. Besides these features it also is relatively insensitive to the damaging effects of nuclear radiation environments which are very harmful to other semiconductors. This gives it a priority in space vehicles and missile circuitry and in applications related to nuclear power production and control.

As the first step in understanding the tunnel diode's operation in a circuit consider the circuit shown in Figure 7.6 along with the *I-V* characteristic for the tunnel diode used in the circuit. The 0.5 volt battery in series with the tunnel diode and 100Ω resistor forward-biases the tunnel diode. In order to find I_F, tunnel diode

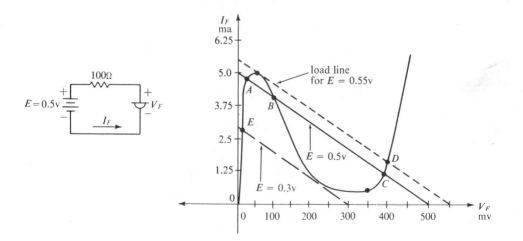

FIG. 7.6.   SIMPLE TUNNEL DIODE CIRCUIT

forward current, and V_F, tunnel diode voltage, the load-line procedure is used as in the two previous chapters. The equation of the load-line in this case is

$$0.5v = I_F \times 100 + V_F \qquad (7.3)$$

Superimposing this load-line (solid line) on the *I-V* curve should give us the operating point of the tunnel diode. However, a remarkable situation has occurred. The load line intersects the tunnel diode curve at *three* separate points. The question now becomes: if all three points *A*, *B* and *C* lie on both the load-line and the *I-V* curve, which point is the actual operating point of the circuit? It certainly cannot be all three points at the same time. Consider point *B*. It lies on the negative resistance portion of the tunnel diode *I-V* curve. This circuit cannot operate at point *B* since it is an *unstable point*. That is, even if the circuit were somehow made to operate at this point, any little circuit fluctuation or spurious noise would cause the circuit to immediately move to point *A* or point *C* and remain there. This instability is analogous to a ball resting on the peak of a hill as in Figure 7.7(A). With

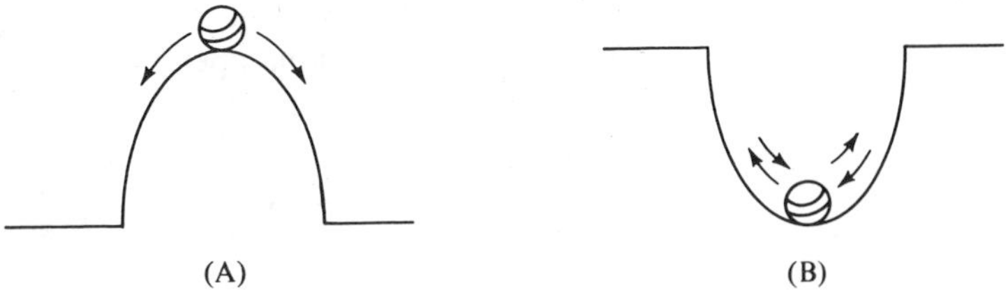

(A)   (B)

FIG. 7.7.   A. UNSTABLE POINT; B. STABLE POINT

the ball in this position, any small disturbance will cause it to roll down either side of the hill and come to rest at the bottom. Point *A*, on the other hand, is a *stable* point of operation. That is, small circuit fluctuations will not cause the operating point to shift. It will always return to point *A*. Point *C* is also a *stable* operating point. These stable points are analagous to a ball resting in a bowl as in Figure 7.7(B). Small disturbances may cause the ball to move up the side of the bowl, but it will always come back to rest at the bottom.

Points which lie on positive resistance portions of the tunnel diode curve, such as points *A* and *C*, are always stable points. Points which lie on negative resistance portions of the curve, such as point *B*, are unstable if the load-line also intersects the curve at stable points.

In the circuit under consideration, point *A* is at I_F = 4.75 ma and V_F = 25 mv; point *C* is at I_F = 1.0 ma and V_F = 400 mv. The circuit can operate stably at either point. Before the circuit is connected both V_F and I_F are zero. After the circuit is connected the circuit will move up the *I-V* curve to the stable operating point at point *A*. In order for the circuit to operate at point *C*, the load-line must be momentarily moved *above* the *peak-point*. This can be done by momentarily increasing the battery voltage to 0.55 volt causing the load-line to move to a new position (shown by a dotted line) where it now intersects the *I-V* curve only at point *D*, a stable point. The circuit will remain at point *D* as long as the input voltage is kept at 0.55 volt. However, if the battery voltage is reduced back to 0.5 volt, the circuit will not return to point *A* but rather will move along the *I-V* curve to point *C* and remain there. Operation will return to point *A* only if the load-line is momentarily moved *below* the valley-point by reducing the input voltage to, say, 0.3 volt (shown by a dashed line). This will cause the operating point to shift to point *E*, a stable point. When the battery is increased back to 0.5 volt the operating point will move up the *I-V* curve to point *A*. Thus, it can be seen that this circuit does not have a unique operating point, but will operate at either *A* or *C* depending on what has previously occurred. Since this circuit has two stable operating points it is considered a *bi-stable* circuit. This property, unlike any circuit or device we have yet studied, results from the tunnel diode's negative resistance.

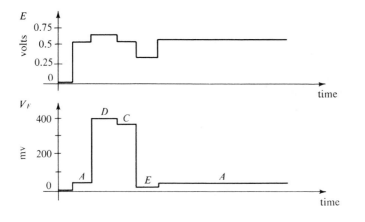

FIG. 7.8.   VARIATION OF V_F AS BATTERY VOLTAGE CHANGES

Figure 7.8 summarizes the variation of tunnel diode voltage in this circuit as the battery voltage is varied from zero to 0.5 volt, up to 0.55 volt, back to 0.5 volt, down to 0.3 volt and back up to 0.5 volt.

It is possible for the circuit of Figure 7.6 to have a load-line which intersects the tunnel diode curve in its negative resistance region and nowhere else. For example, a battery voltage of 0.2 volt and a resistance of 20 ohms would produce such a load-line. This is exactly the manner in which tunnel diodes are biased when they are used in amplifier or oscillator circuits. The operating point in this situation would be on the negative resistance portion of the tunnel diode curve. Such an operating point is *conditionally stable;* that is, it will be stable if care is taken to keep circuit inductance to a very low value; otherwise, undesirable circuit oscillations will take place and the circuit will never stabilize. For this reason, design of tunnel diode amplifiers is critically dependent on the physical circuit layout.

7.5.   Tunnel Diode Switching Circuits

In the previous section we saw that with the proper load-line the tunnel diode circuit is bistable and the circuit can be made to switch from one stable operating point to another. For purposes of our discussion we will refer to the two possible operating points as the *low-voltage point* and the *high-voltage point*. In Figure 7.6, point A would be the low voltage point and point C would be the high voltage point. The low voltage point is always at a value of V_F which is less than V_P and the high voltage point is always at a value of V_F which is greater than V_V.

In the circuit of Figure 7.6 we switched the circuit operating point from A to C by increasing the input voltage. A more commonly used procedure is to increase the input current until it is at a value greater than the peak-point current. This causes the tunnel diode to switch to its high-voltage region (to the right of the valley point) since in the low-voltage region (to the left of the peak point) the tunnel diode current can only go as high as I_P. Consider the circuit of Figure 7.9 which employs the tunnel diode used in Figure 7.6. Assume, to start, that $E = 0$ volts and that the tunnel diode is in its low-voltage state with $V_F \approx 0$. We now can calculate I_F to see whether the tunnel diode is actually in its low-voltage state. We have

$$I_F = I_1 + I_2 \tag{7.4}$$

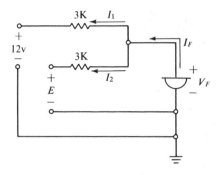

FIG. 7.9.   TUNNEL DIODE SWITCHING CIRCUIT

The current I_1 is approximately

$$12v/3K = 4\ ma$$

since $V_F \approx 0$. The current I_2 is essentially zero since $E = 0$.
Thus, from Equation 7.4

$$I_F = 4\ ma + 0\ ma = 4\ ma$$

This is less than the peak-current for this tunnel diode which is
given as 5 ma in Figure 7.6. Thus, the tunnel diode actually is in its
low-voltage state with $V_F \approx 0$ (to be exact it is a few millivolts, but
for our purposes we can call it zero). In order to get the tunnel
diode into its high-voltage state, the total input current $I_1 + I_2$
must, at least momentarily, exceed I_P. If E is increased to 3.3
volts, then I_2 will be approximately

$$3.3v/3K = 1.1\ ma$$

and I_F will then be 5.1 ma. This is greater than I_P, which means
that the tunnel diode must be in its high voltage state. In this
state we can usually approximate V_F by V_{FP} volts which is 0.425
volt for this diode. Since V_F is now approximately 0.425 volt,
we must recalculate I_1 using this value. I_1 is given by

$$I_1 = \frac{(12 - 0.425)v}{3K} = 3.86\ ma$$

and I_2 is given by

$$I_2 = \frac{(3.3 - 0.425)v}{3K} = 0.96\ ma$$

resulting in $I_F = 4.82$ ma. Notice that this is less than I_P, but the
diode has already switched to the high-voltage state. It will remain
in this state with $V_F \approx 0.425$ volt until I_F is reduced below the

valley current (0.5 ma for this diode). This is because the tunnel diode high-voltage state exists only for currents greater than I_V (see I-V curve). When I_F goes below I_V the tunnel diode switches back to its low-voltage state with $V_F \approx 0$.

▶ EXAMPLE 7.1

For the circuit of Figure 7.9 determine the variation of V_F as the voltage E is varied according to the waveform in Figure 7.10. One

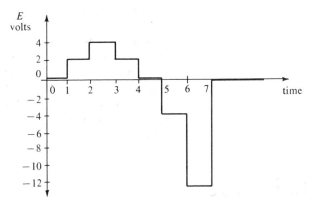

FIG. 7.10.

procedure is to calculate I_F each time the value of E changes. If the tunnel diode is initially in the low-voltage state and I_F is increased above I_P, the tunnel diode then switches to its high-voltage state. If the tunnel diode is initially in the high-voltage state and I_F is decreased below I_V, the tunnel diode then switches to its low-voltage state. A simpler procedure would be to determine what value of E is needed to cause the tunnel diode to switch to the high-voltage state and what value of E is needed to get the tunnel diode back to the low-voltage state.

If the diode is initially in the low state, then $I_1 = 4$ ma as calculated previously. Thus, I_2 must increase to just above 1 ma for I_F to go above $I_P = 5$ ma and cause switching. This necessitates a value of E greater than 1 ma $\times$ 3K = 3 volts to cause the tunnel diode to switch from its low state to its high state. If the diode is initially in the high state, then $V_F = V_{FP} = 0.425$ volt and $I_1 = 3.86$ ma as calculated previously. Since I_F must drop below $I_V = 0.5$ ma for switching to occur, I_2 must be made to flow in the opposite direction shown in Figure 7.9 so as to subtract from I_1. That is,

$$I_1 + I_2 = 0.5 \text{ ma}$$
$$3.86 \text{ ma} + I_2 = 0.5 \text{ ma}$$

or

$$I_2 = -3.36 \text{ ma}$$

Thus, E must be negative and is given by

$$E = 3K \times (-3.36 \text{ ma}) + 0.425\text{v} = -9.675\text{v}$$

The value of E must be more negative than this value in order to switch the diode from its high state to its low state. Looking at the waveform above, $E = 0$ initially and the tunnel is initially in its low state with $V_F = 0$. It will stay there until E jumps to 4 volts whereupon it goes to its high state with $V_F \approx 0.425$ volt. The diode remains in its high state until E drops to -12 volts whereupon it switches to $V_F \approx 0$ and remains there. The waveform of V_F corresponding to the input voltage, E, waveform is shown below.   ◀

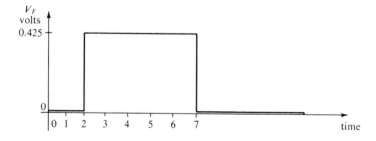

FIG. 7.11.

The chief advantage of tunnel diodes in switching circuits lies in their high operating speed. This property, inherent in the tunnelling process, makes them a likely candidate for increased application in high speed computers and computer systems.

GLOSSARY

Tunnel effect: a process whereby electrons, with apparently insufficient energy to do so, can surmount a potential barrier (tunnel through the barrier)

Negative resistance region: that portion of the tunnel diode *I-V* curve where increases in V_F cause I_F to decrease

I_P: peak point current

V_P: peak point voltage

I_V: valley current

V_V: valley voltage

g: a-c conductance

V_{FP}:   forward point voltage

Unstable operating point: a possible circuit operating point at which the circuit cannot stably exist

Bi-stable circuit: a circuit with two possible stable operating points

Low-voltage point or region: that region of the tunnel diode characteristic for values of V_F less than V_P

High-voltage point or region: that region of the tunnel diode characteristic for values of V_F greater than V_V

Questions

7.1   What condition is necessary for the tunnel effect to occur in a P-N junction?

7.2   Sketch the *I-V* characteristics of a tunnel diode and a P-N diode on the same set of axes.

7.3   Why can't a tunnel diode be used as a rectifier?

7.4   Why are tunnel diodes particularly useful at high frequencies?

7.5   From the tunnel diode *I-V* curve in Figure 7.12 determine (a) I_P (b) V_P (c) I_V (d) V_F (e) V_{FP} and (f) g (use Equation 7.2).

7.6   How is a tunnel diode affected by temperature in comparison to a conventional P-N diode?

7.7   Can a tunnel diode be biased so that the load-line intersects the *I-V* curve in only *two* points both of which are stable?

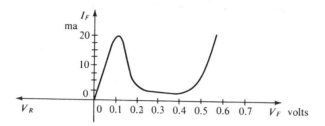

FIG. 7.12.

7.8 A 1N3150 tunnel diode has the specifications listed in Appendix II. In Figure 7.13, what will be the value of I_F and V_F if $E = 6$ volts? If $E = 24$ volts?

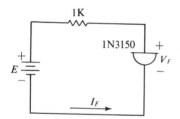

FIG. 7.13.

7.9 In the circuit of Figure 7.13, sketch the waveform of V_F if E has the waveform shown in Figure 7.14.

7.10 The circuit in Figure 7.15 uses a 1N3150 tunnel diode. Inputs E_1 and E_2 can be either 6 volts or 0 volts and are controlled by switches S_1 and S_2.

(a) Choose values of R_1 and R_2 so that the tunnel diode will go to the high-voltage state only if E_1 *and* E_2 are both at $+6$ volts. This is called an "and" circuit.

(b) Choose values of R_1 and R_2 so that the tunnel diode will switch to the high-voltage state if either E_1 *or* E_2 or both are at 6 volts. This is an "or" circuit.

(c) Add another branch to this circuit with input E_3. Choose resistor values so that the diode switches when 2 out of 3 inputs are 6 volts. This is a "majority" circuit.

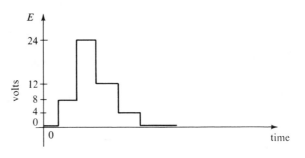

FIG. **7.14.**

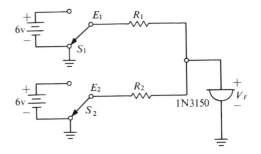

FIG. **7.15.**

7.11   The 1N3150 tunnel diode is used in Figure 7.16. The current, I_1, which is supplied by the 6-volt source, serves to keep the tunnel diode current above the valley current level at all times. The current, I_2, is supplied by the input E_{in}. This input voltage is monitoring a certain manufacturing process. It is normally at zero volts. However, when a momentary irregularity occurs in the process, E_{in} becomes 6 volts for the duration of the malfunction. The duration may be very short and unless someone monitors E_{in} continuously, a malfunction may go undetected. This tunnel diode circuit is designed to *detect* when E_{in} goes to 6 volts and *store* this information. It does this by remaining in its low-voltage state while E_{in} is zero and then switching to its high-voltage state when E_{in} becomes 6 volts. If E_{in} returns to zero volts, the tunnel diode will remain in its high-voltage state since I_1 will supply enough current to keep $I_F > I_V$. Thus, the tunnel diode remains in its high state even if E goes to 6 volts only momentarily. The tunnel diode essentially *remembers* that the input was 6 volts. It is said to have a *memory*. This memory comes about due to its negative resistance characteristics.

Choose values of R_1 and R_2 to insure that the circuit operates as explained above.

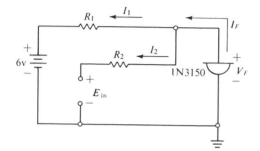

FIG. 7.16.

References

Chow, W. F., *Principles of Tunnel Diode Circuits*. New York: John Wiley & Sons, Inc., 1964.

Sowa, W. A. and J. M. Toole, *Special Semiconductor Devices*. New York: Holt, Rinehart and Winston, Inc., 1968.

Tunnel Diode Manual. Syracuse, New York: General Electric Company, 1964.

Photoelectric Devices

8.1. Introduction

Up to now we have discussed the electrical properties of semiconductor devices and considered the influence of temperature
(heat energy) on these properties. Another physical quantity,
light, also exerts a considerable influence on these electrical properties. Devices which are specially designed for operation under the
influence of light energy are called *photoelectric devices*. The role
that photoelectric devices play in today's technology is ever increasing. Missile and satellite systems, computer systems and
even oil burners and clothes dryers use light sensitive devices.
The input to these devices is a light beam, and before any study
of the devices can be made, a brief and somewhat simplified discussion of light and its properties is necessary. This discussion
will by no means be thorough, as such a treatment might be beyond
the scope of the student's background at this time. It is assumed
that a detailed coverage of light energy will be included in the
student's physics studies. The topic of photoelectric devices will
be categorized into two groups and a study of each group will be
made.

8.2. The Nature of Light

In order to explain certain phenomena, some of which are
present in photoelectric devices, it is necessary to think of light

as being made up of minute particles of concentrated energy that strike all objects in machine-gun bullet fashion. Each particle, or bundle, of energy is called a *photon*. The energy content of these photons depends on the color* of the light. Figure 8.1 shows the

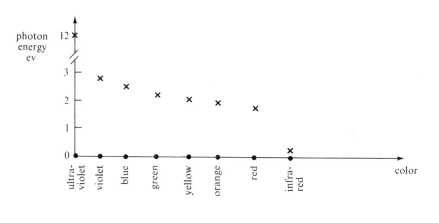

FIG. 8.1.   PHOTON ENERGY OF VARIOUS COLORS OF LIGHT

photon energy for the different colors of visible light as well as for infra-red and ultra-violet light. In view of the fact that photon energy (light energy) is different for different colors we can expect that photoelectric device operation will be to some extent sensitive to color. This principle is utilized in cameras and color film processors.

Before attempting to understand properly the operation of photoelectric devices we should be familiar with a measure of illumination, that is, the amount of light present or the number of photons present. We will use the quantity called a *foot-candle* to describe illumination. One *foot-candle* of illumination is a standard of illumination kept by the U. S. Bureau of Standards.

8.3.   Photoconductive Cells

This category of photoelectric devices is a broad category which includes devices fabricated from germanium, silicon, selenium and cadmium compounds. The effect of light on these substances is to

---

*The photon energy is a function of the light frequency only. Different light frequencies affect the eye as different color.

decrease the resistivity of the material. For this reason they are
sometimes referred to as *photoresistors*. Photoconductive cells
generally consist of a thick film of photosensitive semiconductor
material deposited on an insulating substratum with metallic
leads attached to each end of the semiconductor. This structure
is illustrated in Figure 8.2.

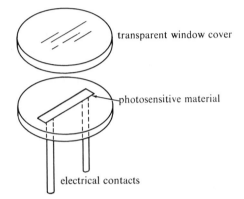

transparent window cover

photosensitive material

electrical contacts

FIG. 8.2.   STRUCTURE OF A TYPICAL PHOTOCONDUC-
TIVE CELL

When light strikes the semiconductor material, the photons
may impart their energy to valence electrons through collisions.
If this energy is sufficient, these valence electrons can break their
covalent bonds, jump the energy gap into the conduction band
and become free electrons, producing hole-electron pairs. The
amount of incident light (illumination) determines the number of
hole-electron pairs and the resulting resistance of the photoconductive cell.

The most sensitive photoconductor materials are those which
are essentially insulators in the dark, so that the additional carriers
generated by the absorption of light energy cause the greatest
possible change in resistivity of the cell. For this reason, semiconductor materials which have practically no thermally-generated
current carriers at room temperature are used as photoconductors.
These materials, which include cadmium sulfide (CdS), cadmium
selenide (CdSe) and cadmium telluride (CdTe), have wider energy
gaps than silicon and germanium. Thus, they do not contain very
many thermally-generated electron-hole pairs. Because of their
different energy gaps (2.45 ev for CdS, 1.74 ev for CdSe, 1.45 ev
for CdTe), the response of each of these materials to the different
colors of light will be different. CdS is most sensitive to green

light, CdSe to red light and CdTe to infra-red light (invisible to the human eye).

CdS photocells currently enjoy the widest application among photoconductive devices due mainly to their high sensitivity. The resistance of a CdS crystal in the dark may be 10,000 to 100,000 times greater than its resistance when illuminated with 100 foot-candles of light. However, the protective enclosure of commercial photocells absorbs some light, thus lowering this range to about 600 to 1. The smallest CdS cells respond to light intensities as low as 0.0001 foot-candle. The CdS crystal may be pure, but more often it contains a small amount of impurity, called an activator, which adds to the device's sensitivity. The activator employed is usually silver, antimony or indium.

One of the most important parameters of the photoconductive cell is its resistance at different levels of illumination. Cell resistance as a function of illumination for a typical CdS cell is shown in Figure 8.3 along with the electronic symbol for photo-

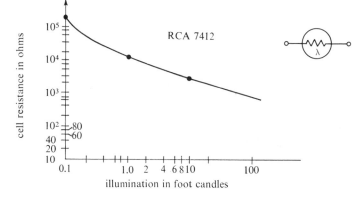

FIG. 8.3.   SYMBOL AND RESISTANCE VERSUS ILLUM-
                   INATION PLOT FOR TYPICAL CDS CELL

conductive or photoresistive devices. Note that the scales used in the plot are log scales. The curve is close to being a straight line, indicating that resistance decreases approximately proportional to some power of illumination. That is,

$$R = R_1 L^{-\gamma} \tag{8.1}$$

where R_1 is the resistance at 1 foot-candle, L is the illumination in foot-candles and γ (gamma) is a constant. For the cell of Figure 8.3, R_1 is 20,000Ω and γ is approximately 0.75.

▶EXAMPLE 8.1

Using the photocell described in Figure 8.3 in the circuit Figure 8.4 below, calculate the circuit current for $E = 10$ volts and $E = -10$ volts if the cell is subjected to 10 foot-candles of illumination.

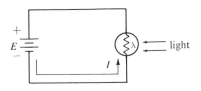

FIG. 8.4.

From the curve in Figure 8.3, the cell resistance at 10 foot-candles is 3000Ω. With $E = 10$ volts and using Ohm's Law, I is easily calculated as 3.33 ma flowing in the direction shown. If the 10 volt battery is reversed so that $E = -10$ volts, then I is simply -3.33 ma. That is, the current is the same only in the opposite direction. The photoconductive cell conducts the same in both directions. After all, it is simply a resistor whose resistance value depends on illumination. This is probably the only semiconductor component a technician will encounter which does not contain a P-N junction.   ◀

The resistance of a photoconductive cell is often indirectly expressed in terms of the current drawn through the cell at a given voltage across the cell and at a given light level. For example, the cell of Example 8.1 would be rated at 3.33 ma at 10 volts under 10 foot-candles of illumination.

The resistance of CdS cells does not change rapidly with rapid changes in incident illumination but requires some time to reach its steady-state* value. This is, in part, due to the activator impurity, and is the price paid for added sensitivity. This effect is illustrated in the circuit of Figure 8.5 using the photocell with the characteristics of Figure 8.3. If 10 foot-candles are applied instantaneously at time = 0 sec, the photocell will not respond immediately but will gradually drop in resistance until its resistance is 3000Ω. When the cell is dark its resistance is above 10 megohms or 10 million ohms; from Figure 8.5 we see that it takes approxi-

_____
*Steady-state value is the value the resistance eventually reaches under a constant illumination.

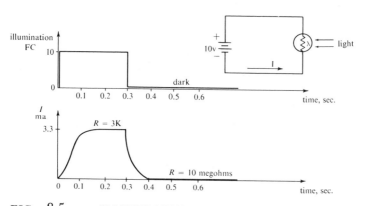

FIG. 8.5.   ILLUSTRATION OF TYPICAL RESPONSE TIME
OF CDS PHOTOCELL

mately 0.1 sec for the current in the circuit to increase from zero
to 3.3 ma after the light is applied. On the other hand, when the
illumination is instantaneously removed, it takes some time for
the photocell to return to its high resistance state. The current in
the circuit gradually decays to zero about 0.1 sec after light is
removed.

This relatively slow buildup and decay of current upon the
application or removal of illumination limits the use of CdS
photocells to applications where the light levels are not changing
any faster than around 100 times per second (100HZ). For applications at higher speeds, CdS photocells give way to other types,
most popular of which is CdSe. CdSe photocells can operate at
speeds 100 times greater than CdS photocells but are roughly 100
times less sensitive. Thus, the CdS cell is used where a large resistance change for a given variation of light is important, and the
CdSe cell is used where fast action is necessary.

Semiconductor photocells are adversely affected by increases
in temperature which produce electron-hole pairs. These thermally-
generated current carriers cause the cell resistance to decrease.
This lowers the cell's sensitivity to light energy. CdS cells are not
affected as much as other types because of its wide energy gap.
CdSe, with a smaller energy gap, is more temperature-sensitive.

8.4.   Photoconductive Cell Ratings and Specifications

In addition to the resistance-versus-illumination curve of
Figure 8.3, manufacturers normally supply certain ratings and
specifications. Figure 8.6 contains some typical ratings and
specifications for a CdS photocell. The ratings are maximum
values of cell voltage, current and power dissipation which should

CdS Photoconductive Cell

Type: RCA 7412
Maximum voltage: 200 volts
Maximum power dissipation: 50 mw
Maximum current: 5 ma
Photocurrent at 12 volts and 1 foot-candle: 65 to 275 μa
@ 25°C

Decay current: 1 μa (10 seconds after removal of above illumination) @ 25°C

FIG. 8.6.   TYPICAL RATINGS AND SPECIFICATIONS FOR A CDS PHOTOCELL

not be exceeded. One specification given is the *photocurrent* at a given voltage (12 volts) under a given illumination (1 foot-candle). It ranges between 65 and 275 μa at 25°C for this particular cell. Also given is the value of *decay current* which is the current flowing through the photocell a certain time (10 seconds) after the illumination (1 foot-candle) is removed. The decay current is essentially the d-c current through the cell when it has been in the dark for greater than 10 seconds. It is also called the *dark current*.

8.5. Applications of Photoconductive Cells

The photoconductive cell can be used in many applications that require the control of a certain function or event according to the absence, presence, color or intensity of light. Its numerous applications include door openers, burglar alarms, flame detectors, smoke detectors, and lighting control for street lamps in residential and industrial areas. It has been used in automatic business machines to read holes on cards or punched tape, in X-ray measurements and in photographic equipment. Many of the above applications require the use of the photocell in conjunction with a relay. The circuit of Figure 8.7 is a very useful circuit of this type. In this circuit the relay will not be energized as long as the photocell resistance is high enough to keep the current, I, below the pull-in current of the relay. As the cell is illuminated its resistance decreases causing I to increase thus energizing the relay. The relay contacts control the desired function. In a garage door opener the relay would control the power applied to the motor mechanism. In this circuit, the photocell must have a current rating greater than the value needed to energize the relay and a voltage rating greater than the supply voltage.

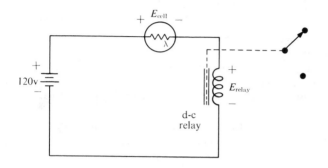

FIG. 8.7.   PHOTOCELL-RELAY CIRCUIT

▶ EXAMPLE 8.2

A relay with a pull-in current of 2 ma and a d-c resistance of 10K is used in the circuit of Figure 8.7. The cell is a type 7412 (Figures 8.3 and 8.6).

(a) Find the current, I, when the cell is dark.

(b) Determine the illumination needed on the cell to just energize the relay.

When this cell is in the dark it has a resistance equal to 12 megohms. This is determined from the cell specifications in Figure 8.6 where 12 volts produces 1 μa of decay or dark current. Thus,

$$R_{\text{dark}} = 12\text{v}/1\mu\text{a} = 12 \text{ megohms}$$

To find I in this case using Ohm's law we have

$$I = \frac{120\text{v}}{R_{\text{dark}} + R_{\text{relay}}} = \frac{120\text{v}}{12 \text{ megohms}} = 10 \ \mu\text{a}$$

This is not enough to energize the relay.

The relay requires 2 ma to be energized. The supply voltage must supply this amount of current to just energize the relay. The current, I, is given by

$$I = \frac{120\text{v}}{R_{\text{cell}} + R_{\text{relay}}} = \frac{120\text{v}}{R_{\text{cell}} + 10\text{K}}$$

In order to get $I = 2$ ma, the total resistance of relay and cell must be 60K. Thus, R_{cell} must be 50K. The amount of light needed to produce a cell resistance of 50K is obtained from Figure 8.3 as approximately 0.3 foot-candles.   ◀

▶ EXAMPLE 8.3

Repeat the previous example for a relay with pull-in current of 10 ma and a d-c resistance of 1K.

According to the specs on the 7412, it can handle a maximum current of only 5 ma and thus cannot be used in this circuit with this particular relay. A higher current photocell must be used. ◀

▶ EXAMPLE 8.4

Repeat Example 8.2 using a 240 volt battery.

According to the specs on the 7412, it can handle a maximum voltage of 200 volts. Thus, it cannot operate in this circuit since in the dark condition the total supply voltage of 240 volts would be dropped across it. A higher voltage cell must be used. ◀

The circuit of Figure 8.7 can also operate on a-c voltage, using an a-c relay, since the photocell acts as a bilateral resistor (it conducts equally in both directions). Much more sophisticated circuits utilize photocells in conjunction with other semiconductor devices. A number of these circuits will be brought out in the problems at the end of this chapter and in subsequent chapters.

8.6.   Photovoltaic Cells

Photovoltaic devices are devices that develop an electromotive force when illuminated. That is, they convert light energy directly to electrical energy. No outside source of electrical energy is required to produce current flow as in photoconductive devices. Figure 8.8 represents the basic construction of a *junction photovoltaic cell*. It consists of a silicon P-N junction as in a normal P-N diode. With no light applied to the junction, the circuit shown will produce no current flow (no bias on the P-N diode). However, if the space charge region near the junction is illuminated an interesting phenomenon can be observed. In the circuit there will be a flow of current caused by a voltage appearing at the terminals of the photovoltaic cell. This voltage is labelled V_{PH}, photovoltage, and the resulting current I_{PH}, photocurrent. The photovoltage arises from the generation of electron-hole pairs in the space charge region due to light energy. The electrons are swept into the N side by the positive space charge and the holes are swept into the P side by the negative space charge. This movement charges the N side negatively and the P side positively, with the

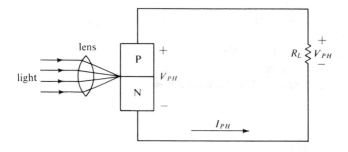

FIG. 8.8. JUNCTION PHOTOVOLTAIC CELL

resultant potential difference between the two sides being V_{PH}. The illuminated P-N junction acts like a source of electrical energy similar to a battery. It can supply electrical power to a load. As with any source of electrical energy the output voltage is a maximum when the load is an open circuit ($R_L = \infty$). This is the open circuit voltage V_{OC}. The output current is a maximum when the load is a short circuit ($R_L = 0$). This is the short circuit current I_{SC}.

In Figure 8.9 the *I-V* characteristic of a typical silicon photovoltaic cell is drawn, along with the symbol for photovoltaic devices, for various values of illumination. If we consider the curve for 100 foot-candles, we see that under no load (with $I_{PH} = 0$) the output voltage of the cell is 0.42 volts. This is the open circuit

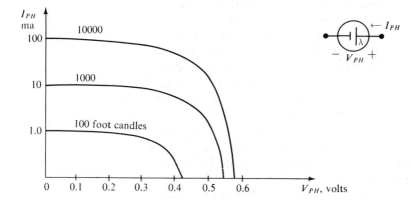

FIG. 8.9. TYPICAL PHOTOVOLTAIC CELL *I-V* CHARACTERISTIC AT 25°C

voltage V_{OC}, and is the maximum output voltage which the cell can supply at 100 foot-candles. If the cell is supplying current to a load, its output voltage will drop as can be seen from this *I-V* curve until with the cell short-circuited ($V_{PH} = 0$), I_{PH} is 1 ma. This is the short circuit current, I_{SC}, and is the maximum current the cell can supply at 100 foot-candles. Increasing the illumination on the cell to 1000 foot-candles causes the *I-V* curve for the cell to move upward. V_{OC} increases to 0.55 volts and I_{SC} increases to 10 ma. At 10,000 foot-candles V_{OC} increases to 0.58 volts and I_{SC} to 100 ma. Thus, the amount of current and voltage which the cell can supply increases as the illumination increases. For most photovoltaic cells the short circuit current, I_{SC}, is directly proportional to illumination. That is,

$$I_{SC} = K \times L \qquad (8.2)$$

where L is the illumination in foot-candles and K is the constant of proportionality. For the cell of Figure 8.4

$$I_{SC} = 10^{-5} \times L$$

with I_{SC} given in amps. For example, at $L = 100$ foot-candles, this equation gives

$$I_{SC} = 10^{-5} \times 100 = 10^{-3}a = 1 \text{ ma}$$

The open circuit voltage, V_{OC}, also increases with illumination but it eventually levels off at high values of illumination to typically 0.5v to 0.7v for silicon cells.

A photovoltaic cell acts as a *power converter*. It can supply electrical power to a load when light power is applied to the cell. The efficiency with which it transforms light power to electrical power is given by

$$\% \text{ efficiency} = \frac{\text{electrical power output}}{\text{light power input}} \times 100 \qquad (8.3)$$

A high efficiency is, of course, desirable since it indicates a higher electrical power output for a given light power input. The most efficient type of photovoltaic cell on the market today is the silicon P-N junction photovoltaic cell. It can have efficiencies of 10 to 15 per cent and, for this reason, is widely used in space applications where sunlight is the only source of light. When used in this application, these cells are called *solar cells*, or *solar batteries*.

Despite the high efficiency of silicon cells many commercial photovoltaic cells use selenium as the semiconductor since it gives more stable characteristics with temperature and age. Selenium cells have an efficiency usually around 1 per cent. Its *I-V* characteristics are similar to those in Figure 8.9.

The speed of response of photovoltaic cells is considerably greater than for CdS photoconductive cells. Typically, they can respond to light levels which are changing 10,000 to 50,000 times per second (10 KHZ to 50 KHZ).

The effect of temperature on the characteristics of photovoltaic devices is illustrated in Figure 8.10. The open circuit

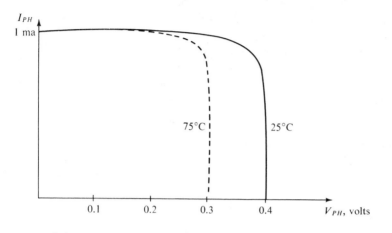

FIG. 8.10.   EFFECT OF TEMPERATURE ON PHOTOVOLTIAC CELL CHARACTERISTIC

voltage decreases as temperature increases from 25°C to 75°C. Thus, the cell cannot supply as much voltage, and consequently as much power, at 75°C as it can at 25°C. Note that the short circuit current is practically independent of temperature.

8.7.   Photovoltaic Cells as Circuit Elements

Figure 8.11 is a typical photovoltaic cell circuit. The cell is acting as the electrical power source supplying voltage and current to the load. Obviously, in this circuit the voltage across the load resistor is equal to the output voltage of the cell. That is,

$$V_L = V_{PH} \tag{8.4}$$

And since $V_L = I_{PH} \times R_L$, we have

$$I_{PH} \times R_L = V_{PH} \tag{8.5}$$

This equation is a straight line equation relating I_{PH} to V_{PH}. If we plot this line on the $I_{PH} - V_{PH}$ coordinates, its intersection with the cell's characteristic curve will give us the operating point

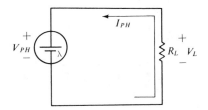

FIG. 8.11.   PHOTOVOLTAIC CELL SUPPLYING POWER
TO A LOAD

of the circuit. This is illustrated in Figure 8.12 for a 1000Ω resistor.
The operating point becomes $V_{PH} = 0.4$v and $I_{PH} = 0.4$ ma. The
power being supplied by the cell is given by the product $V_{PH} \times I_{PH}$.
In this case it is 0.16 mw of power which is being supplied to the
1000Ω load.

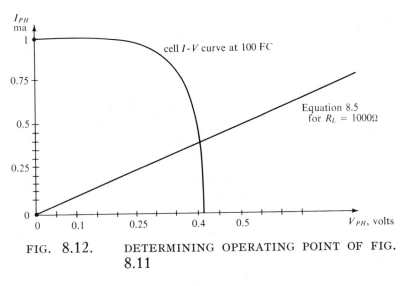

FIG. 8.12.   DETERMINING OPERATING POINT OF FIG.
8.11

8.8.   Applications of Photovoltaic Cells

The principal applications of photovoltaic cells are in the
fields of (1) photographic exposure meters, (2) foot-candle meters,
(3) lighting control, and (4) automatic iris control on cameras.
All of these take advantage of using no electrical power source
other than the cell itself. Typical of these is the foot-candle meter

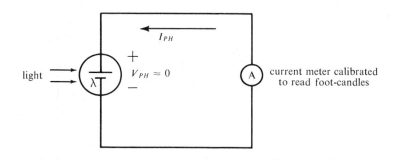

FIG. 8.13.   FOOT-CANDLE METER CIRCUIT

circuit shown in Figure 8.13. In this circuit the photovoltaic cell is in series with a current meter. The current meter is usually a very low resistance and essentially the cell is operating into a short circuit. Thus, the photocurrent flowing in the circuit will be the cell's short circuit current, I_{SC}. This current, we know, will vary proportionately with illumination, as will the reading of the current meter. The current meter can be calibrated to read foot-candles, thus serving as an extremely simple, yet very practical and popular, light meter.

As far as space and missile systems are concerned, *solar cells* find their greatest application here. Solar cells are usually made up of many silicon photovoltaic cells in series in order to obtain high enough voltages; each cell contributes only a few tenths of a volt. In space vehicles, solar cells are used as secondary power sources which can supply electrical power when the vehicle is illuminated by sunlight. When the vehicle is in the dark the solar cells do not operate and storage batteries provide the vehicle power. The solar cells serve to recharge the storage batteries during the light hours. Solar cells can be constructed to supply large amounts of power by increasing the area exposed to sunlight.

GLOSSARY

Photoelectric devices: devices designed to operate under the influence of light

Photon: particles of light energy

Foot-candle: quantity of illumination

**Photoconductive
(photoresistive) devices:** devices whose resistivity varies with illumination

Photocurrent: current flowing through a photoelectric device

**Decay current
(dark current):** current flowing through a photoelectric device under zero illumination

Photovoltaic devices: devices which can supply electrical power when illuminated

Open circuit voltage (V_{OC}): voltage supplied by an unloaded photovoltaic cell

Short circuit voltage (I_{SC}): current supplied by a short-circuited photovoltaic cell

Solar cell (solar battery): photovoltaic cell which operates under solar illumination

Questions

8.1 Why do the various colors of visible light have different effects on photoelectric devices?

8.2 How does light affect photoconductive cells?

8.3 Why are photoconductive cells of CdS, CdSe and CdTe used more widely than Si or Ge?

8.4 An RCA-7412 photoconductive cell is used in Figure 8.14. Determine the photocurrent at an illumination of 20 foot-candles.

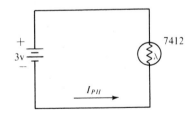

FIG. 8.14.

8.5   Why are CdS cells unsuitable for applications where light levels change rapidly?

8.6   How does heat affect the sensitivity of semiconductor photocells?

8.7   Refer to the specifications for the 7412 photocell (Figure 8.6). What is the maximum illumination which should be applied to the cell in the circuit of Figure 8.14?

8.8   Change the 3v battery to 12v in Figure 8.14. Calculate the maximum allowable illumination.

8.9   The *dark resistance* of a photoconductive cell is obtained from its specifications (Figure 8.6) by dividing applied voltage (12v in this case) by the decay (dark) current. What is the dark resistance of the 7412 cell?

8.10   For the circuit in Figure 8.15, calculate E_{out} for the following values of illumination: 0, 1, 10, 100 foot-candles. Plot E_{out} versus L.

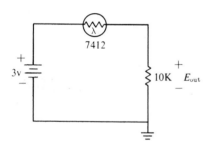

FIG. 8.15.

8.11   Design a simple circuit, similar to Figure 8.15, in which E_{out} *decreases* as illumination increases.

8.12   The circuit in Figure 8.16 energizes the relay when the cell is in the dark and de-energizes it when the cell is illuminated. The relay pulls in at 3 ma, drops out at 2 ma and has a resistance of 3K. Determine the value of R needed to insure that the relay drops out at exactly 10 foot-candles.

8.13   The circuit in Figure 8.17 utilizes *two* 7412 cells. Output voltage will be high only if both cell A *and* cell B are illuminated at the same time. Calculate E_{out} for the following conditions:
(a) Cell A dark; cell B dark
(b) Cell A dark; cell B at 10 foot-candles
(c) Cell B dark; cell A at 10 foot-candles
(d) Cell B and cell A both at 10 foot-candles
This is a photocell *and* circuit.

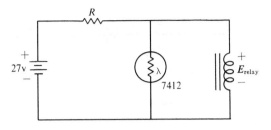

FIG. 8.16.

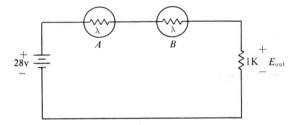

FIG. 8.17.

8.14   Design a simple *or* circuit, using *two* 7412 cells, in which the output voltage is high if either cell *A or* cell *B or* both are illuminated (10 foot-candles).

8.15   The circuit in Figure 8.18 uses a 7412 cell and 1N3150 tunnel diode. The tunnel diode voltage is low when the cell is dark. When the cell is illuminated the tunnel diode switches to its high state. Calculate the value of R such that the tunnel diode switches to its high state when the illumination is 10 foot-candles or above.

8.16   Briefly explain the photovoltaic effect in a junction photovoltaic cell.

8.17   A particular photovoltaic cell delivers 12 mw of power to a load when it is supplied with 98 mw of light power. What is this cell's efficiency?

8.18   For the circuit of Figure 8.11 determine the following, using the cell characteristic in Figure 8.12:
(a) The operating point using $R_L = 500\Omega$
(b) The power supplied to the load
(c) Repeat (*a*) and (*b*) for $R_L = 250\Omega$.
(d) Plot power output versus R_L for $R_L = 250\Omega$, 500Ω and 1000Ω.

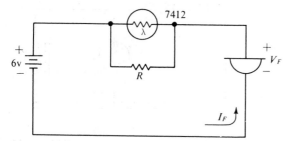

FIG. 8.18.

References

Brophy, J. J., *Semiconductor Devices.* New York: McGraw-Hill Book Company, 1964.

Phototubes and Photocells. Lancaster, Pa.: Radio Corporation of America, 1963.

Sowa, W. A. and J. M. Toole, *Special Semiconductor Devices.* New York: Holt, Rinehart and Winston, Inc., 1968.

Basic Junction Transistor Operation

9.1.   Introduction

The junction transistor is a *two-junction*, three-terminal device whose operation can be understood from our previous study of the P-N junction diode. Since the invention of the transistor in 1948 there has been a rapidly expanding effort to utilize and develop many types of semiconductor devices. Transistors themselves have replaced bulky vacuum and gas tubes in performing many jobs. Transistors offer several advantages over tubes. Among them are: (1) they have a much smaller size; (2) no heater or filament is required; (3) very low operating voltages can be used; (4) they consume low power, resulting in greater circuit efficiency; (5) they have long life with essentially no aging effects; (6) they are essentially shock-proof.

The material in this chapter describes the physical structure, theory of operation and the electrical characteristics of junction transistors. The basic behavior of the transistor as a circuit element will be emphasized. However, actual applications of transistors will be deferred until after Chapter 10 in which amplifier theory will be introduced.

9.2.   Junction Transistor Structure

Figure 9.1 shows the symbolic structure of an NPN *junction transistor*. It contains *three* separate extrinsic regions present in

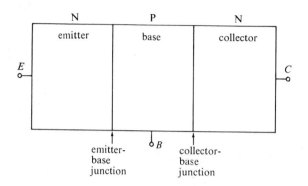

FIG. 9.1.   NPN TRANSISTOR STRUCTURE

one crystal structure. The two outside regions are doped so they are N-type and the center region is doped so it is P-type. For reasons which will become clear later the center P-region is called the *base*, the first N-region is called the *emitter* and the second N-region is called the *collector*. There are two P-N junctions present. The P-N junction formed by the emitter and base regions is called the *emitter-base (E-B) junction*. The P-N junction formed by the collector and base regions is called the *collector-base (C-B) junction*. A terminal or lead is connected to each region making the transistor a three-terminal device.

Figure 9.2 shows a similar structure for the PNP *junction transistor*. In a PNP transistor the doping is just the opposite

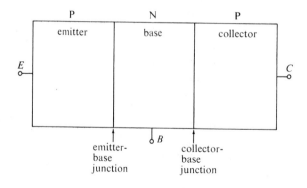

FIG 9.2.   PNP TRANSISTOR STRUCTURE

of that in an NPN type. We shall study both types of transistor since each is widely used. The operation of each type is essentially the same except for differences in voltage and current polarities.

For this reason, the discussion will concentrate on the NPN type, pausing periodically to relate the discussion to the PNP type.

9.3.   Junction Transistor Operation

Consideration of Figures 9.1 and 9.2 will reveal that there are four possible ways of biasing the two transistor junctions. These are enumerated in table form in Table 9.1. Of these four possible combinations, only one interests us at the moment: Condition I where the *E-B* junction is forward-biased and the *C-B* junction is reverse- (or un-) biased. Let us consider this condition of operation, which is referred to as *active operation*, by modifying the drawing of Figure 9.1 as in Figure 9.3. In this circuit arrange-

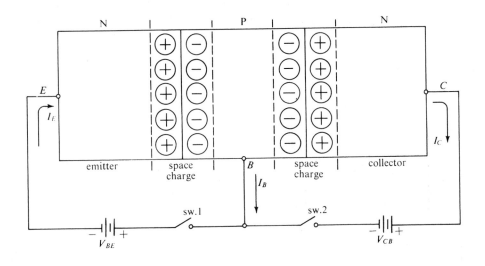

FIG. **9.3.**   BIASING THE NPN TRANSISTOR FOR ACTIVE
OPERATION

ment the battery V_{BE} acts to forward-bias the *E-B* junction and the battery V_{CB} acts to reverse-bias the *C-B* junction. The currents flowing through each terminal have been labelled I_E (emitter current), I_B (base current) and I_C (collector current). The directions indicated are the assumed directions for an NPN transistor.

    If only sw. 1 is closed the *E-B* junction will be forward biased. Since the emitter and base regions are essentially just like a P-N diode we can expect that a relatively large current will flow across

TABLE 9.1

	E-B Junction	C-B junction	Region of Operation
Condition I	Forward-biased	Reverse- (or un-) biased	Active
Condition II	Forward-biased	Forward-biased	Saturation
Condition III	Reverse-biased	Reverse- (or un-) biased	Cut-off
Condition IV	Reverse-biased	Forward-biased	Inverted

the *E-B* junction. This current will consist of majority carriers from the emitter and base diffusing across the junction. This case is summarized in Figure 9.4. The total current flow across the *E-B*

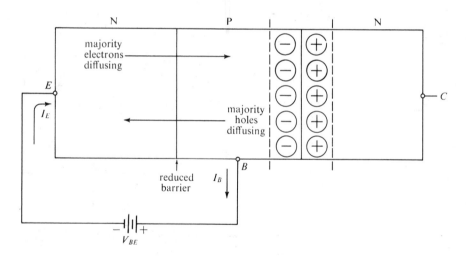

FIG. 9.4.   SW. 1 CLOSED, SW. 2 OPEN

junction is the sum of the electron diffusion current and hole diffusion current. In junction transistors the base region is de- liberately doped *very lightly* compared to the emitter region. Because of this, the electrons diffusing from the emitter usually make up over 99 per cent of the total current. Another effect of the light base doping is that many of the electrons which have entered from the emitter will move through the base region toward the positive terminal of the battery without finding a hole to recombine with. Only a very small number of the diffusing electrons will find a hole to recombine with in the base region. We should note in Figure 9.4 that large equal currents flow into the emitter lead and out of the base lead ($I_E = I_B$) and no collector current flows ($I_C = 0$).

Referring again to Figure 9.3, if only sw. 2 is closed the *C-B* junction will become reverse-biased. This case is summarized in Figure 9.5. With reverse bias, the only current flow across the

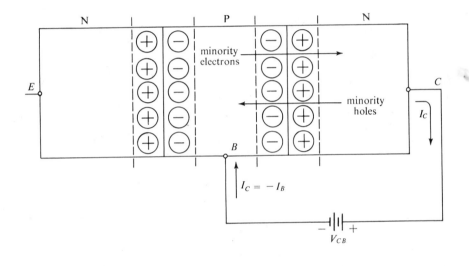

FIG. 9.5.   SW. 2 CLOSED, SW. 1 OPEN

C-B junction will be the reverse-leakage current made up of thermally-generated minority carriers which are accelerated by the potential barrier. It will be relatively small and, of course, dependent on temperature. We should note in Figure 9.5 that the current will actually flow into the base terminal. Thus, I_B will be negative since it actually flows opposite to the assumed direction. In this case very small currents flow out of the collector lead and into the base lead ($I_C = -I_B$) and no emitter current flows ($I_E = 0$). The small collector current in this case is given a special symbol, I_{CBO}. It represents the *collector leakage current* which flows when $I_E = 0$ and the *C-B* junction is reverse biased.

Referring again to Figure 9.3, what should we expect to occur if both sw. 1 and sw. 2 are closed? It would seem from the previous

two discussions that both I_E and I_B would be rather large currents
and I_C would be a very small current. However, the results of
closing both switches are almost entirely unexpected. I_E is a large
current, as expected, but I_B turns out to be a very small current and
I_C turns out to be a large current. The reason for I_C being large,
while I_B is small, must be investigated. The drawing in Figure
9.6 depicts this situation. Some of the holes and electrons have
been numbered to facilitate the following description of transistor
action.

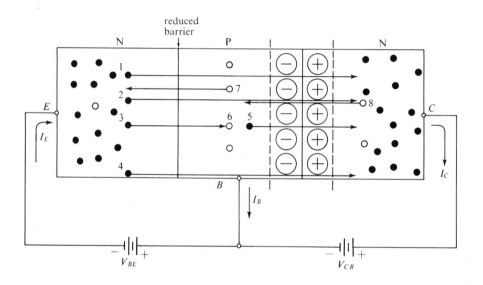

FIG. 9.6.   SW. 1 AND SW. 2 CLOSED; NPN TRANSISTOR
OPERATING IN THE ACTIVE REGION

Consider first the *E-B* junction. It is, of course, still forward-
biased by the voltage V_{BE}. As such, majority carriers will diffuse
across the junction as exemplified by electrons no. 1, 2, 3 and 4
from the emitter to base and hole no. 7 from base to emitter.
Since the base is very lightly doped, most of this majority diffusion
current is carried by the electrons and very little by the holes.
Now let us consider the *C-B* junction. It is still reverse-biased by
the voltage V_{CB}. As such, only minority carriers will cross the
junction as exemplified by electron no. 5 from base to collector
and hole no. 8 from collector to base. These minority carriers are
thermally generated and their current is essentially the I_{CBO} discussed previously. However, there are minority electrons in the
base region which are not a result of heat but have diffused from

the emitter. These are electrons no. 1 to no. 4 which become minority carriers once they enter the base. These electrons diffuse through the base region and toward the *C-B* junction. Many of them diffuse as far as the space-charge region where they are then accelerated by the potential barrier into the collector in the same way as the thermally-generated electrons. In this diagram electrons no. 1, 2 and 4 make it through to the collector. These additional electrons crossing the *C-B* junction add to the normal reverse leakage current I_{CBO} to give a larger collector current. Electron no. 3 however, does not cross through the base to the collector since it meets hole no. 6 in the base region and recombines with it. In general, it is desirable to have most of the electrons coming from the emitter reach the collector. For this reason, the base region is deliberately made *very narrow* (0.001 in.) so that the diffusing electrons will reach the collector before encountering a hole to recombine with. The light doping in the base also contributes to the difficulty of recombination in the base region.

It should now be apparent how the terms *emitter* and *collector* come about. With forward bias applied to the *E-B* junction, the emitter *emits* or injects its majority carriers into the base region. Many electrons are injected, many more than can find a hole in the base to recombine with. The electrons that cannot find a hole diffuse toward the *C-B* junction and upon reaching it are accelerated by the potential barrier there and *collected* by the collector region. In a good transistor only a small percentage of the injected electrons recombine in the base. The greater part of them reach the collector. This is accomplished by making the base very narrow and doping it very lightly. Since most of the emitter-injected electrons reach the collector, the collector current will be large; normally, it is approximately the same as the emitter current. The base current, then, will be very small.

The amount of emitter current which will flow in the transistor is essentially determined by the magnitude of forward bias V_{BE}. The base thickness and its degree of doping effectively determine how much of the emitter current will reach the collector and become collector current. The value of reverse bias V_{CB} on the *C-B* junction has a slight effect on collector current. There has to be a space charge region surrounding the *C-B* junction in order to attract the diffusing electrons into the collector region. Increasing this space charge region will cause more emitter electrons to reach the collector, since the diffusing electrons will not have as far to go. This is illustrated in Figure 9.7 which shows how increasing V_{CB} essentially narrows the effective base width which the electrons must traverse before reaching the space charge region.

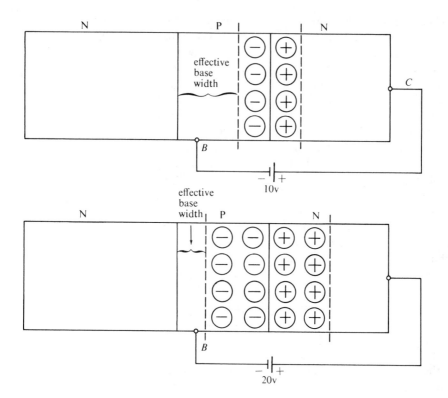

FIG. 9.7. EFFECT OF V_{CB} ON THE EFFECTIVE BASE WIDTH

Thus, we can expect for a given value of I_E that I_C will increase slightly and I_B will decrease slightly as V_{CB} is increased.

At this point we can begin writing down some of the relationships among the various transistor currents. First of all, invoking Kirchhoff's current law we can state that

$$I_E = I_B + I_C \qquad (9.1)$$

This equation is a simple statement of what has been said up to now about the emitter current distributing itself as collector current and base current. Secondly, from the discussions above we can state that the collector current is made up of two parts: normal reverse leakage current, I_{CBO}, and the fraction of emitter current which reaches the collector. In equation form this becomes

$$I_C = \alpha_{\text{d-c}} I_E + I_{CBO} \qquad (9.2)$$

where $\alpha_{\text{d-c}}$ is the fraction of emitter current, I_E, which reaches the collector. Solving for $\alpha_{\text{d-c}}$ in the above equation we obtain

$$\alpha_{\text{d-c}} = \frac{I_C - I_{CBO}}{I_E} \qquad \text{(9.3A)}$$

In cases where I_{CBO} is very small compared to total collector current, it can be neglected in the above equation to give

$$\alpha_{\text{d-c}} \approx \frac{I_C}{I_E} \qquad \text{(9.3B)}$$

Here it is given as simply the ratio of d-c collector current to d-c emitter current in the transistor. For typically good transistors $\alpha_{\text{d-c}}$ is usually in the range of 0.900 to 0.999, indicating that most of the emitter current becomes collector current.

If we now use Equations 9.1 and 9.2 to solve for I_B in terms of I_E we will obtain

$$I_B = (1 - \alpha_{\text{d-c}})\, I_E - I_{CBO} \qquad \text{(9.4)}$$

This equation along with Equation 9.2 allows us to determine I_C and I_B for given values of I_E.

▶ EXAMPLE 9.1

A certain transistor has a value of $\alpha_{\text{d-c}}$ of 0.98 and a collector leakage current I_{CBO} of 1 μa. Calculate base and collector currents when $I = 1$ ma. Repeat for $I_E = 0$ μa.

(a) With $I_E = 1$ ma and using Equation 9.2 we can solve for I_C.

$I_C = 0.98 \times 1 \text{ ma} + 1\mu\text{a}$

$I_C = 0.98 \text{ ma} + 0.001 \text{ ma} = 0.981 \text{ ma} = 981\mu\text{a}$

Using Equation 9.4 for I_B we obtain

$I_B = (1 - 0.98) \times 1 \text{ ma} - 1\mu\text{a}$

$\qquad = 0.02 \text{ ma} - 0.001 \text{ ma}$

$\qquad = 0.019 \text{ ma} = 19\mu\text{a}$

The sum of I_B and I_C should equal I_E. Checking this, we have

$$I_E = I_B + I_C$$
$$1 \text{ ma} = 0.019 \text{ ma} + 0.981 \text{ ma} = 1 \text{ ma}$$

We could have used equation 9.1 to calculate I_B once we had I_C and obtained the same result. Note that I_C and I_E are almost equal and I_B is very small. This is usually the case when the transistor is operating in the *active region*.

(b) With $I_E = 0$ and using Equation 9.2 we obtain for I_C

$$I_C = 0.95 \times 0 + 1\mu a$$
$$= 1\mu a = I_{CBO}$$

and using 9.1 to find I_B we have $I_B = -1 \ \mu a$

These results should be expected, since with no emitter current flowing the only current present across the *C-B* junction is leakage current.   ◄

▶ EXAMPLE 9.2

Measurements on a certain transistor produce the following data

I_E	I_C	I_B
0	0.01 μa	−0.01 μa
10 μa	9.91 μa	0.09 μa

From this data determine (a) I_{CBO}, (b) $\alpha_{d\text{-}c}$ and (c) I_C when $I_E = 20 \ \mu a$.

(a) From the measurements at $I_E = 0$ the value of I_C is seen to be 0.01 μa. Thus $I_{CBO} = 0.01 \ \mu a$.

(b) Using Equation 9.3B and substituting the values $I_E = 10 \ \mu a$ and $I_C = 9.91 \ \mu a$ we obtain

$$\alpha_{d\text{-}c} \approx \frac{9.91 \ \mu a}{10 \ \mu a} = 0.991$$

(c) Using the values of $\alpha_{d\text{-}c}$ and I_{CBO} just obtained we can calculate I_C using Equation 9.2 with $I_E = 20 \ \mu a$.

$$I_C = 0.991 \times 20 \ \mu a + 0.01 \ \mu a = 19.83 \ \mu a$$

Again note that I_C is almost equal to I_E.   ◄

Everything which has been said thus far is also applicable to PNP transistor operation. The only differences are the following for the PNP type:

(a) The emitter injects *holes* into the base region since the emitter is P-type.

(b) The bias voltages have the opposite polarity of those for the NPN transistor.

(c) The current directions for I_B, I_C and I_E are also the reverse of those for the NPN type.

The operation of the PNP transistor in the active region is summarized in Figure 9.8. Compare it with Figure 9.6 for the

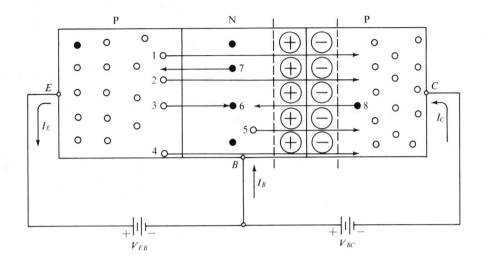

FIG. 9.8.   PNP TRANSISTOR OPERATING IN THE ACTIVE
REGION

NPN transistor. Note that the holes and electrons have interchanged. In the NPN transistor, electrons were the principal
carrier, while in the PNP type it is the holes which have this role.
The Equations 9.1 to 9.4 developed previously for the NPN transistor are equally valid for the PNP transistor. Thus, Examples
9.1 and 9.2 could just as easily have used PNP transistors.

To summarize what has been said thus far concerning transistor
operation in the *active* region, the following points should be re-
emphasized:

(a) When the *E-B* junction is forward-biased, the emitter injects
its majority carriers (electrons for NPN, holes for PNP)
into the base region.

(b) Since the base region is lightly doped and very narrow,
most of these injected carriers diffuse to the *C-B* junction
without recombining in the base region.

(c) If the *C-B* junction is reverse biased, the space charge
region at the junction serves to accelerate these carriers
into the collector region. These carriers which are added
to the normal reverse leakage current, I_{CBO}, at the *C-B*
junction contribute to a large collector current.

(d) The base current is typically very small since most of the
injected carriers reach the collector.

At this point a brief description of the other conditions of operation given in Table 9.1 should be given. Conditions II and III, *saturation* and *cutoff*, are extremely important and must be completely understood if intelligent use of transistors is to be accomplished. Condition IV, *inverted operation*, is used only in certain special circuits and, as such, will not be stressed here.

Referring to Table 9.1, it is seen that operation in the *saturation region* occurs when both transistor junctions are forward-biased. In this condition, the *C-B* junction space charge region has almost completely diminished and the ability of the collector to collect the emitter injected carriers is greatly reduced. In fact, if the forward bias on the *C-B* junction is sufficient the collector will stop collecting carriers and will begin emitting carriers into the base in exactly the same way as the emitter. Much more will be said about saturation in the following sections.

Operation in the *cutoff region* occurs when both transistor junctions are reverse biased. In this condition, the emitter will *not* inject majority carriers into the base region. The only emitter current flowing will be a reverse leakage current and consequently the collector current will also consist of a reverse leakage current. The cutoff region also includes the case where the emitter circuit is open, that is, $I_E = 0$. In any case, with no injected emitter current, the transistor is said to be cut off and only very small leakage currents flow. More will be said about cutoff in the following sections.

Inverted operation is simply using the transistor's collector as the emitter and vice-versa. This operation is quite different from the normal operation (Condition I, active) since the emitter and collector are not doped exactly the same. The emitter is the most heavily doped region of the three. The base is the most lightly doped and the collector is doped at some intermediate level. Interchangeability of collector and emitter is therefore not possible. However, some transistor applications utilize this type of operation for reasons which need not be discussed here.

9.4.   The Common Base Configuration

The electronic symbols for both the NPN and PNP transistor are shown in Figure 9.9. The arrow on the emitter of each type indicates the direction of emitter current flow when the *E-B* junction is reverse-biased. In other words, it is opposite to the direction of forward-bias current through the emitter.

Recall from our discussion in Chapter 3 that when analyzing a three-terminal device, such as a junction transistor, one of the

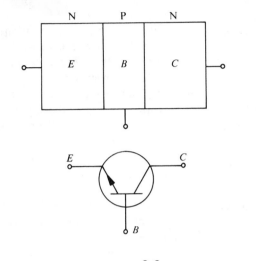

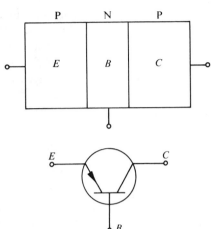

FIG. **9.9.**　　ELECTRONIC SYMBOLS FOR NPN AND PNP TRANSISTORS. ARROW ON THE EMITTER INDICATES THE DIRECTION OF CURRENT FLOW WHEN *E-B* JUNCTION IS REVERSE BIASED.

terminals is chosen as the *common* terminal, one as the *input* and one as the *output*. Let us first consider here the *base* as the *common* terminal, the *emitter* as the *input* terminal and the *collector* as the *output* terminal. This configuration is called the *common-base*

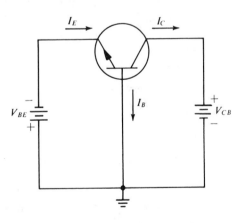

FIG. **9.10.**　　NPN TRANSISTOR IN COMMON BASE CON-FIGURATION AND BIASED IN THE ACTIVE REGION

configuration. An NPN transistor in the *common-base* configuration is shown in Figure 9.10 with the bias voltages applied for operation in the active region. The *E-B* junction is forward-biased producing I_E and I_B in the direction shown. The *C-B* junction is reverse-biased producing I_C in the direction shown. In the common base configuration (abbreviated Com. B) the emitter terminal is considered the input. The emitter current is the input current and the collector current is the output current. For a particular I_E input there will be a corresponding I_C output.

▶ EXAMPLE 9.3

The *E-B* junction of the transistor in Figure 9.10 is forward biased so that an emitter current of 10 ma flows. Determine I_C and I_B under these conditions if $\alpha_{d-c} = 0.99$.

     (a) Using Equation 9.2 and neglecting I_{CBO}; $I_C = 0.99 \times 10$ ma = 9.90 ma

     (b) Using Equation 9.1 we have $I_B = I_E - I_C = 10$ ma − 9.90 ma = 0.10 ma = 100 μa

In the Com. B configuration the parameter α_{d-c} is called the *common base* d-c *current gain* since it relates the d-c output current, I_C, to input current I_E. The term *gain* seems to imply an increase in current from input to output. However, since α_{d-c} is always less than one, the output current in Com. B is *always less* than the input current. That is, the *current gain* is always less than one. In Example 9.3 above, the output current was 99 per cent of the input current since α_{d-c} was 0.99.

    A summary of the basic transistor equations for the Com. B configuration is presented in Figure 9.11.   ◀

$$I_C = \alpha_{d-c} I_E + I_{CBO}$$

$$I_B = (1 - \alpha_{d-c}) I_E - I_{CBO}$$

$$\alpha_{d-c} = \frac{I_C - I_{CBO}}{I_E}$$

FIG. **9.11.**   COMMON BASE TRANSISTOR EQUATIONS

9.5.   Common Base Characteristic Curves

The equations above do not, by any means, completely describe the transistor behavior. For one thing, the value of α_{d-c} is not constant but varies with I_C and V_{CB}. α_{d-c} increases as I_C *increases* up to a point and then *decreases* for further increases in I_C. It also *increases* as V_{CB} increases. Secondly, these equations assume I_E is known. To find I_E, the variation of I_E with V_{BE} must be available. For these reasons the transistor characteristic curves are often utilized in analysis and design.

Recall from Chapter Three that for a three-terminal device *two* sets of *I-V* characteristics are needed to completely describe its static operation: the *input characteristics* and the *output characteristics*. For the NPN transistor in the Com. B configuration, typical input characteristics are as shown in Figure 9.12. These

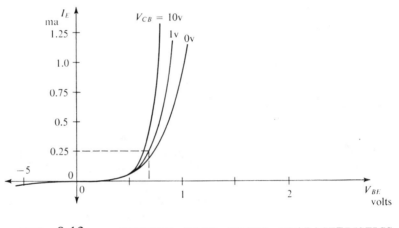

FIG. 9.12.   COMMON BASE INPUT CHARACTERISTICS
                  FOR A TYPICAL NPN SILICON TRANSISTOR

are the *common base input characteristics* and they relate the input current, I_E, to the voltage between the emitter and base, V_{BE}, for different values of collector-base reverse voltage, V_{CB}. For a given value of V_{CB}, the curve relating I_E to V_{BE} is essentially that of a P-N junction diode, which is, of course, the *E-B* junction. The *E-B* junction becomes a better diode as V_{CB} increases. That is, there will be a greater I_E for a given V_{BE} as V_{CB} increases. The effect of V_{CB} comes about as the result of the increased space-charge region at the *C-B* junction as V_{CB} is increased. This effectively increases the ease with which majority carriers diffuse from the emitter to base by exerting a greater force on them once they enter the base. It can be seen from Figure 9.12 that this effect is slight except for small values of V_{CB} and, as will be shown, in many cases can be neglected.

Note that for negative values of V_{BE}, the NPN transistor *E-B* junction is reverse-biased and only a small leakage current flows through the emitter. This is the condition for *cutoff* when $I_E = 0$. For the same NPN transistor in the Com. B configuration, a set of output characteristics are shown in Figure 9.13. These are

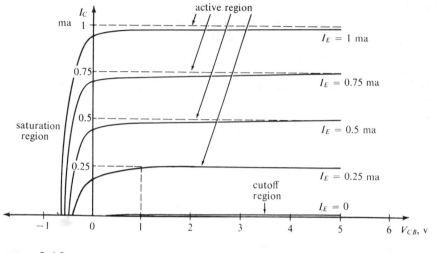

FIG. 9.13.   COMMON BASE OUTPUT CHARACTERISTICS
FOR NPN SILICON TRANSISTOR

the *common base output characteristics* and they relate the output current, I_C, to the voltage between collector and base, V_{CB}, for various values of input current, I_E.

A study of these output characteristics reveals several interesting points.

(a) The collector current is approximately equal to the emitter current for positive values of V_{CB} (*C-B* junction reverse-biased). This is the *active* region.

(b) All the curves have a slight slope for positive values of V_{CB}, indicating that I_C increases slightly as V_{CB} increases for a given I_E. This indicates that α_{d-c} increases slowly with V_{CB}.

(c) The collector current is not zero when I_E is zero but has a value of I_{CBO}. That is, when the transistor is in *cutoff* only a very small value of I_C flows.

(d) As V_{CB} becomes negative (*C-B* forward biased) I_C begins to decrease for a given I_E. This is the *saturation* region.

▶ EXAMPLE 9.4

Determine the collector current and emitter current for the transistor with the characteristics of Figures 9.12 and 9.13, when

$V_{BE} = 0.7$ volts and $V_{CB} = 1$ volt. Calculate $\alpha_{d\text{-}c}$ at this point.

(a) First, from the input characteristics the value of I_E is obtained at $V_{BE} = 0.7\text{v}$ using the curve for $V_{CB} = 1\text{v}$. It is $I_E = 0.25$ ma. Now using the output characteristics the value of I_C is obtained at $V_{CB} = 1\text{v}$ using the curve for $I_E = 0.25$ ma. It is $I_C = 0.225$ ma.

(b) The value of $\alpha_{d\text{-}c}$ at this point is $\alpha_{d\text{-}c} = \dfrac{0.225 \text{ ma}}{0.25 \text{ ma}} = 0.9$ ◀

The Com. B output characteristics, often called the *collector characteristics* or *collector family* of curves, do not vary radically from transistor to transistor since $\alpha_{d\text{-}c}$ is very close to *one* for most transistors for values of V_{CB} greater than one volt. This is an important property which will be utilized in certain applications.

The Com. B characteristics of a PNP transistor are essentially the same as those in Figures 9.12 and 9.13 except for the polarities of V_{BE} and V_{CB}; it is understood that I_C flows in the opposite direction. Simply change the polarities on the V_{BE} and V_{CB} values given in these figures and the curves become PNP characteristics.

9.6. Analyzing Common Base Circuits: Load Line Method

In analyzing a transistor Com. B circuit it is necessary to first of all determine input current I_E. Once I_E is known the output current I_C can be determined. Again, two methods of analysis will be presented. The *load-line method* is essentially a graphical technique and is used mainly in the analysis of transistor amplifiers. The *approximate* method is used for quick, easy calculations. Though not as accurate as the load-line method, it is often used in determining the d-c operating point when a great deal of accuracy is not needed.

In either method the value of I_E must be determined first. In determining I_E, the diode-like characteristics of the *E-B* junction are utilized. Consider the circuit of Figure 9.14. The emitter current is supplied by the voltage V_{EE} through the series resistor R_E. We can write the Kirchhoff's voltage equation for the input portion of the circuit. We have

$$V_{EE} = I_E \times R_E + V_{BE} \qquad (9.5)$$

If we rearrange this equation to solve for I_E, it becomes

$$I_E = \frac{V_{EE} - V_{BE}}{R_E} \qquad (9.6)$$

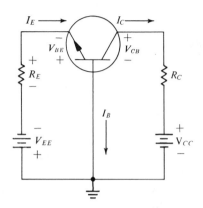

FIG. 9.14.   TYPICAL D-C COMMON-BASE CIRCUIT

The voltage V_{BE} is the voltage drop across the *E-B* junction when it is forward-biased. As with P-N diodes this voltage is typically about 0.7 volt for silicon and 0.3 volt for germanium units. Using this fact in Equation 9.6 makes the value of I_E readily obtainable.

►EXAMPLE 9.5

A silicon transistor is used in the circuit of Figure 9.14 with $V_{EE} = 10.7\text{v}$ and $R_E = 500\Omega$. Determine I_E. Repeat for a germanium transistor.

(a) Using $V_{BE} = 0.7\text{v}$ in Equation 9.6 we have

$$I_E = \frac{10.7\text{v} - 0.7\text{v}}{500\Omega} = 20.0 \text{ ma}$$

(b) Using $V_{BE} = 0.3\text{v}$ in Equation 9.6 we have

$$I_E = \frac{10.7\text{v} - 0.3\text{v}}{500\Omega} = 20.8 \text{ ma}$$ ◄

This procedure for calculating the value of I_E is essentially the same for both the load-line and approximate methods of analysis.

In using the load-line method to find the value of I_C, the procedure is to write the Kirchhoff's voltage equation for the output portion of the circuit and plot this equation (load-line) on the output characteristic curves (I_C and V_C coordinate axes). The intersection of this load-line with the output curve corresponding to the value of I_E previously calculated gives the circuit operating point. Referring to Figure 9.14, the Kirchhoff's voltage equation for the output portion of the circuit is

$$V_{CC} = I_C \times R_C + V_{CB} \qquad (9.7)$$

This equation relates I_C to V_{CB} and is called the load-line equation. Plotting this load-line on the output characteristics is done by choosing two points on the line. The easiest points to choose are $(I_C = 0, V_{CB} = V_{CC})$ and $(I_C = V_{CC}/R_C, V_{CB} = 0)$.

▶ EXAMPLE 9.6

The silicon transistor of Example 9.5 has the output characteristic curves drawn in Figure 9.15. Find I_C and V_{CB} for $I_E = 20$ ma, if $V_{CC} = 40$ volts and $R_C = 1.6$K.
The load-line equation is $40\text{v} = I_C \times 1.6\text{K} + V_{CB}$. Plotting this line on the characteristic curves is shown in the figure.

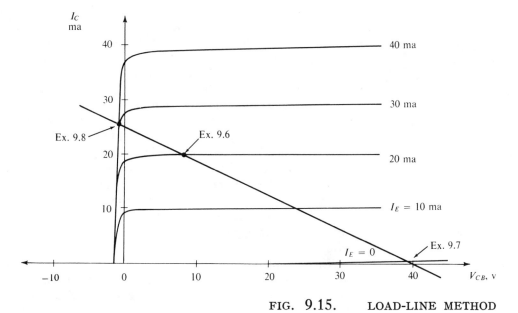

FIG. 9.15.   LOAD-LINE METHOD

The intersection of this load-line and the output curve for $I_E = 20$ ma is the operating point. It is seen to be $I_C = 19.5$ ma and $V_{CB} = 8.8$ volts. The voltage across the 1.6K resistor is (19.5 ma $\times$ 1.6K) = 31.2v. This can be checked by substituting these values into the load-line equation. In this case the operating point lies in the active region of the transistor characteristic. ◀

▶ EXAMPLE 9.7

Repeat the previous example using $I_E = 0$.

The intersection of the load-line and the $I_E = 0$ curve gives the new operating point as $I_C \approx 0$ and $V_{CB} = 40$v. When the transistor is in cutoff all of the supply voltage, V_{CC}, is dropped across the *C-B* junction and none across the resistor.   ◀

▶ EXAMPLE 9.8

Repeat Example 9.6 using $I_E = 30$ ma and $I_E = 40$ ma.

(a) The intersection of the load-line and the $I_E = 30$ ma curve gives the new operating point as $I_C = 25.1$ ma, $V_{CB} = -0.2$v. This operating point lies in the saturation region since V_{CB} is negative.

(b) The operating point when $I_E = 40$ ma is seen to be $I_C = 25.2$ ma, $V_{CB} = -0.3$v. This operating point also lies in the saturation region. The important point to notice is that an increase in I_E from 30 ma to 40 ma results in only a very small increase in I_C. This is because once the emitter current becomes large enough to move the operating point into the saturation region, further increases in I_E do not affect I_C. We say that the transistor output has become *saturated* since I_C can increase no further even if I_E increases. The extra emitter current increases I_B but not I_C. For instance in part (a) I_B is $I_E - I_C = 4.9$ ma while in part (b) I_B is $I_E - I_C = 14.8$ ma.   ◀

In Example 9.8, it may not be clear how saturation can occur since the V_{CC} source acts to reverse-bias the *C-B* junction. As I_E increases, causing a corresponding increase in I_C, the voltage drop across R_C also increases. This resistor voltage is opposed in polarity to the V_{CC} voltage. Thus, a point is reached at which the value of V_{CB} will change the polarity as I_E is increased. At this point, saturation occurs.

The examples above illustrate the use of the load line in finding the currents and voltages in a Com. B transistor circuit. This method will gain importance in later coverage of transistor amplifiers.

9.7.   Analyzing Common Base Circuits: Approximate Method

There are always situations in which analysis using the load-line method is impossible or impractical. In many cases the necessary transistor curves are not immediately available and often the circuit being analyzed contains more than one transistor, which makes load-line analysis, at best, very difficult. At other times the accuracy of the load-line technique may not be required and faster, less accurate methods are more useful. The approximate method we shall discuss here is easier to use than the load-line method since it takes advantage of certain properties common to all transistors and does not utilize the characteristic curves. The Com. B circuit of Figure 9.14 will be analyzed using approximate techniques. Examples 9.6 to 9.8 will be redone using these techniques and the results compared to those of the previous section to see how "approximate" the approximate method really is. The circuit diagram is repeated in Figure 9.16.

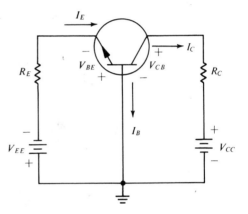

FIG. **9.16.**   D-C COMMON-BASE CIRCUIT

In using the approximate method to analyze a circuit such as this, it is advisable to first determine in what region of its operation the transistor is biased. When the *E-B* junction is reverse-biased or unbiased ($I_E = 0$) the transistor is in *cut-off* and only a small leakage current flows in the collector. In low-power silicon transistors this leakage current may be typically a fraction of 1 μa at room temperature while for corresponding germanium units it may be typically 1 μa. This leakage current can normally be neglected. In this case the voltage drop across R_C is essentially zero. Thus, the entire collector supply voltage, V_{CC}, is dropped across the C_B junction. That is, $V_{CB} = V_{CC}$.

▶ EXAMPLE 9.9

Using $V_{CC} = 40$ volts and $R_C = 1.6$K in the circuit of Figure 9.16 determine I_C and V_{CB} when $I_E = 0$.

With $I_E = 0$ the only collector current flowing will be a small leakage current and $I_C \approx 0$. The voltage drop across the 1.6K resistor is zero. Thus, $V_{CB} = 40v$. Compare these results with those of Example 9.7.   ◀

When the *E-B* junction is forward-biased, emitter current will flow causing a corresponding collector current to flow. The value of I_E is determined in the manner outlined in the last section and used in Example 9.5. When the value of I_E is known, it remains to determine whether the transistor is in the *active* region or *saturated* region of operation. In the *active* region the collector current is approximately equal to $\alpha_{\text{d-c}} \times I_E$. If the value of $\alpha_{\text{d-c}}$ is not known, the collector current may be assumed to be equal to I_E since $\alpha_{\text{d-c}}$ is usually very close to unity. After determining I_C in this manner, its value is used to calculate V_{CB} using Kirchhoff's voltage law (Equation 9.7). If the calculated value of V_{CB} indicates that the *C-B* junction is *reverse-biased*, then the transistor is operating in the *active* region. In this case the previously determined value of I_C is correct and the solution is complete. If, however, V_{CB} turns out to be of the opposite polarity so that the *C-B* junction is forward-biased, then the transistor is not operating in the active region but is in the saturation region. In this case the previously determined value of I_C is incorrect since that value assumed *active* operation. When the transistor is *saturated* the collector current will not equal $\alpha_{\text{d-c}} \times I_E$ but will be essentially limited to that value which causes the *C-B* junction to become forward-biased by a few tenths of a volt (recall Example 9.8). This value of collector current at *saturation* is given the symbol $I_{C(\text{sat})}$ and is approximately determined by assuming a V_{CB} of zero in Equation 9.7 and calculating the collector current. This gives

$$I_{C(\text{sat})} \approx V_{CC}/R_C \qquad (9.8)$$

The actual value of $I_{C(\text{sat})}$ is slightly smaller than that given by Equation 9.8 since V_{CB} is not zero but a few tenths of a volt at saturation. In most calculations, however, Equation 9.8 is sufficient. Equation 9.8 indicates that once the transistor becomes saturated, the collector current is determined by the external circuit (V_{CC} and R_C) rather than the transistor. Once the value of I_E is increased to the value needed to cause I_C to equal $I_{C(\text{sat})}$, further increases in I_E cause I_C to increase only slightly (recall Example 9.8) and the transistor has become saturated.

To summarize the procedure to be followed when calculating I_E, I_C and V_{CB} when the transistor is *not* in cut-off:

(a) Calculate I_E using

$$I_E = \frac{V_{EE} - V_{BE}}{R_E}$$

where $V_{BE} = 0.7v$ for Si and $0.3v$ for Ge.

(b) Assume $I_C = \alpha_{\text{d-c}} \times I_E$ if $\alpha_{\text{d-c}}$ is known; otherwise assume $I_C = I_E$.

(c) Using this value of I_C, calculate V_{CB} using

$$V_{CB} = V_{CC} - I_C \times R_C$$

(d) If V_{CB} indicates the *C-B* junction is reverse-biased then the transistor is operating in the *active* region and the calculated values of I_C and V_{CB} are correct.

(e) If V_{CB} indicates that the *C-B* junction is forward-biased, then the transistor is operating in the *saturation* region and the values of I_C and V_{CB} calculated above are incorrect. The correct collector current is given by

$$I_C = I_{C(\text{sat})} \approx V_{CC}/R_C$$

and V_{CB} is very small.

The following examples illustrate this procedure.

▶ EXAMPLE 9.10

In the circuit of Figure 9.16 find I_C and V_{CB} if $V_{CC} = 40v$, $R_C = 1.6K$ and $I_E = 20$ ma.

Since $\alpha_{\text{d-c}}$ is not given, assume $I_C = 20$ ma. Using this value the voltage drop across the 1.6K resistor is 32v. Thus $V_{CB} = 40 - 32 = 8v$. The *C-B* junction is reverse-biased and the transistor is in the *active* region. Thus, the approximate operating point is $I_C = 20$ ma, $V_{CB} = 8v$. Compare this to the results of Example 9.6.   ◀

▶ EXAMPLE 9.11

Repeat Example 9.10 for $I_E = 30$ ma and $I_E = 40$ ma.

(a) Assume $I_C = I_E = 30$ ma. Calculate $V_{CB} = 40v - 30$ ma $\times 1.6K = -8v$. This indicates forward bias on the *C-B* junction; the transistor is in the *saturation* region. Thus, the value of I_C is not 30 ma but is given by

$$I_{C(\text{sat})} = 40v/1.6K = 25 \text{ ma}$$

and $V_{CB} \approx 0$. Compare this to the solution of Example 9.8(a).

(b) If $I_E = 30$ ma is enough to saturate the transistor, $I_E = 40$ ma will certainly cause saturation. Therefore, the value of I_C is still 25 ma. Compare to Example 9.8(b).   ◀

The results of these examples are not in complete agreement with the corresponding results in the last section. However, this slight inaccuracy is not critical in most circuit calculations. After all, even the resistors and power supply voltage in a circuit have tolerances for inaccuracies, so that any calculation is really only an approximation.

▶ EXAMPLE 9.12

Figure 9.17 shows a silicon PNP transistor in a Com. B circuit. Calculate the value of voltage V_{EE} which just saturates the transistor.

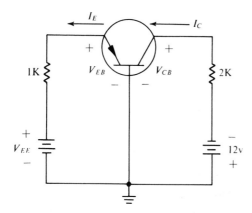

FIG. 9.17.

At saturation the *C-B* junction becomes forward-biased. Since this is a PNP transistor, this means V_{CB} will be slightly positive at saturation. To calculate $I_{C(\text{sat})}$ for this transistor circuit we have

$$I_{C(\text{sat})} \approx 12\text{v}/2\text{K} = 6\text{ ma}$$

Thus the emitter current to just cause saturation is given by

$$I_{E(\text{sat})} = \frac{I_{C(\text{sat})}}{\alpha_{\text{d-c}}} \approx \frac{6\text{ ma}}{1} = 6\text{ ma}$$

To find the value of V_{EE} which will supply an emitter current of 6 ma we have

$$V_{EE} = 6 \text{ ma} \times 1\text{K} + V_{EB}$$
$$= 6\text{v} + 0.7\text{v}$$
$$= 6.7\text{v} \qquad \blacktriangleleft$$

▶ EXAMPLE 9.13

If the 2K resistor is changed to 4K, recalculate the value of V_{EE} to cause saturation.

$$I_{C(\text{sat})} = 12\text{v}/4\text{K} = 3 \text{ ma}$$

thus we have

$$I_{E(\text{sat})} = 3 \text{ ma}$$

and

$$V_{EE} = 3 \text{ ma} \times 1\text{K} + 0.7\text{v} = 3.7\text{v} \qquad \blacktriangleleft$$

These examples illustrate the fact that the value of $I_{C(\text{sat})}$ does not depend on the transistor but on the external circuit components. Changing these components changes the point at which saturation occurs.

9.8. The Common Emitter Configuration

An NPN transistor in the *common emitter* configuration is shown in Figure 9.18 with the bias voltages applied for operation in the *active* region. In the common emitter configuration (abbreviated Com. E) the bias voltages are applied between collector and emitter (V_{CE}) and base and emitter (V_{BE}). The *E-B* junction is forward-biased since the base is made more positive than the emitter by V_{BE}. The collector is more positive than the emitter by V_{CE}. The voltage at the collector with respect to the base is then given by

$$V_{CB} = V_{CE} - V_{BE}$$

To reverse bias the *C-B* junction, V_{CB} must be positive. The value of V_{CE} must then be greater than V_{BE}. When V_{CE} is less than V_{BE}, V_{CB} is negative, the *C-B* junction is forward-biased, and the transistor is in *saturation*.

In the Com. E configuration the *base* terminal is the *input* terminal and the *collector* terminal is the *output* terminal. For a

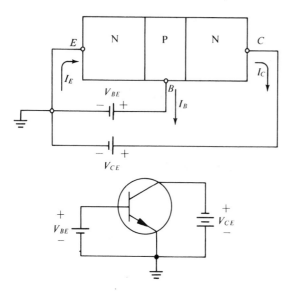

FIG. 9.18.   NPN TRANSISTOR IN THE COMMON EMITTER
CONFIGURATION AND BIASED IN THE AC-
TIVE REGION

particular I_B input there will be a corresponding I_C output. Although the physical operation of the transistor in this configuration
is the same as for Com. B, the basic transistor equations (9.2 and
9.4) have to be rearranged so that I_C and I_E are given in terms of
I_B. Equation 9.4 is repeated below. This equation

$$I_B = (1 - \alpha_{\text{d-c}}) \times I_E - I_{CBO} \qquad (9.4)$$

can be solved for I_E giving

$$I_E = \frac{I_B + I_{CBO}}{(1 - \alpha_{\text{d-c}})}$$

Since $I_E = I_C + I_B$ we can rewrite this as

$$I_C + I_B = \frac{I_B + I_{CBO}}{1 - \alpha_{\text{d-c}}}$$

Rearranging, we have

$$I_C = \frac{\alpha_{\text{d-c}} \times I_B}{1 - \alpha_{\text{d-c}}} + \frac{I_{CBO}}{1 - \alpha_{\text{d-c}}} \qquad (9.11)$$

In this equation I_C is given in terms of I_B. The equations can be
simplified somewhat by defining

$$\beta_{\text{d-c}} = \frac{\alpha_{\text{d-c}}}{1 - \alpha_{\text{d-c}}} \qquad (9.12)$$

and

$$I_{CEO} = \frac{I_{CBO}}{1 - \alpha_{\text{d-c}}} \qquad (9.13)$$

Thus, Equation 9.11 becomes

$$I_C = \beta_{\text{d-c}} \times I_B + I_{CEO} \qquad (9.14)$$

This equation states that I_C is equal to $\beta_{\text{d-c}}$ multiplied by the input I_B, plus a leakage current, I_{CEO}. This leakage current, I_{CEO}, is the current which would flow in the collector if I_B were equal to zero. This is illustrated in Figure 9.19. The value of

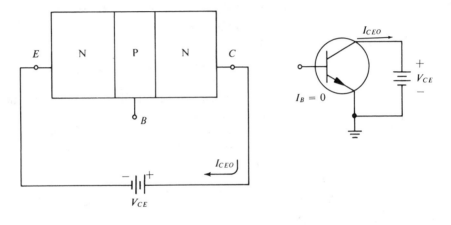

FIG. 9.19.   DEFINITION OF I_{CEO}

I_{CEO} is much larger than I_{CBO} as indicated by Equation 9.13. For example, if $\alpha_{\text{d-c}} = 0.9$, the value of I_{CEO} is ten times that of I_{CBO}.

$\beta_{\text{d-c}}$ is called the *common emitter* d-c *current gain* since it relates the d-c output current I_C to the input current I_B. Equation 9.12 indicates that $\beta_{\text{d-c}}$ can be very large. For example, if $\alpha_{\text{d-c}} = 0.9$, The value of $\beta_{\text{d-c}}$ is

$$\beta_{\text{d-c}} = \frac{0.9}{1 - 0.9} = 9$$

and for $\alpha_{\text{d-c}} = 0.99$ the value of $\beta_{\text{d-c}}$ is 99. Typically $\beta_{\text{d-c}}$ can have values in the range from 10 to 500 although values as high as 1000 are not uncommon.

If we solve Equation 9.14 for $\beta_{\text{d-c}}$ we obtain

$$\beta_{\text{d-c}} = \frac{I_C - I_{CEO}}{I_B} \qquad (9.15)$$

If I_{CEO} is very small compared to I_C this becomes

$$\beta_{\text{d-c}} = I_C/I_B \tag{9.16}$$

Thus, $\beta_{\text{d-c}}$ is the ratio of d-c collector current to d-c base current. It is essentially a measure of how much more of the emitter current becomes collector current than base current. $\beta_{\text{d-c}}$ depends on $\alpha_{\text{d-c}}$ as shown by Equation 9.12. As $\alpha_{\text{d-c}}$ increases, the percentage of emitter current which reaches the collector increases and conversely, the percentage which becomes base current decreases. Thus as $\alpha_{\text{d-c}}$ increases $\beta_{\text{d-c}}$ increases.

Now that we have I_C in terms of I_B as given by Equation 9.14 we can determine I_E in terms of I_B by using the relationship

$$I_E = I_B + I_C$$
$$I_E = I_B + \beta_{\text{d-c}} \times I_B + I_{CEO}$$
$$I_E = (\beta_{\text{d-c}} + 1)I_B + I_{CEO} \tag{9.17}$$

The emitter current is essentially $(\beta_{\text{d-c}} + 1)$ times the base current, plus the leakage current.

A summary of the basic transistor equations for the Com. E configuration is presented in Figure 9.20.

$$I_C = \beta_{\text{d-c}}I_B + I_{CEO}$$
$$I_E = (\beta_{\text{d-c}} + 1)I_B + I_{CEO}$$
$$\beta_{\text{d-c}} = \frac{I_C - I_{CEO}}{I_B} = \frac{\alpha_{\text{d-c}}}{1 - \alpha_{\text{d-c}}}$$
$$I_{CEO} = \frac{I_{CBO}}{1 - \alpha_{\text{d-c}}}$$

FIG. 9.20.   COMMON EMITTER TRANSISTOR EQUATIONS

▶ EXAMPLE 9.14

A transistor has a value of $\alpha_{\text{d-c}} = 0.995$. Calculate $\beta_{\text{d-c}}$ for this transistor. Repeat for $\alpha_{\text{d-c}} = 0.992$.

Using Equation 9.12

$$\beta_{\text{d-c}} = \frac{0.995}{1 - 0.995} = \frac{0.995}{0.005} = 199$$

$$\beta_{\text{d-c}} = \frac{0.992}{1 - 0.992} = \frac{0.992}{0.008} = 124$$

Note that a small change in $\alpha_{\text{d-c}}$ gives a large change in $\beta_{\text{d-c}}$.   ◀

▶ EXAMPLE 9.15

A particular transistor has a $\beta_{\text{d-c}} = 100$ and $I_{CEO} = 10\ \mu\text{a}$. Determine I_C and I_E for $I_B = 0$ and for $I_B = 10\ \mu\text{a}$.

(a) Using Equation 9.14 for I_C we have

$$I_C = 100 \times 0 + 10\ \mu\text{a} = 10\ \mu\text{a}$$

and

$$I_E = I_B + I_C = 0 + 10\ \mu\text{a} = 10\ \mu\text{a}$$

Thus, with $I_B = 0$ the only collector and emitter current flowing is the leakage current I_{CEO}.

(b) Using Equation 9.14 for I_C we have

$$I_C = 100 \times 10\ \mu\text{a} + 10\mu\text{a} = 1010\ \mu\text{a}$$

and

$$I_E = 1010\ \mu\text{a} + 10\ \mu\text{a} = 1020\ \mu\text{a} \qquad ◀$$

▶ EXAMPLE 9.16

Data on a certain transistor is shown in the table below:

I_B	I_C	I_E
0	20 μa	20 μa
100 μa	5.02 ma	5.12 ma

From this data determine (a) I_{CEO} (b) $\beta_{\text{d-c}}$ and (c) I_C when $I_B = 50\ \mu\text{a}$.

(a) From the table when $I_B = 0$, $I_C = 20\ \mu\text{a}$. Thus $I_{CEO} = 20\ \mu\text{a}$.

(b) Using Equation 9.16 for the second set of measurements

$$\beta_{\text{d-c}} = \frac{I_C}{I_B} = \frac{5.02\ \text{ma}}{100\ \mu\text{a}} \approx 50$$

(c) Using these values in Equation 9.14 for $I_B = 50\ \mu\text{a}$

$$I_C = 50 \times 50\ \mu\text{a} + 20\ \mu\text{a} = 2720\ \mu\text{a} = 2.72\ \text{ma} \qquad ◀$$

The equations presented here for the Com. E configuration hold true for both the NPN and PNP junction transistors.

9.9. Common Emitter Characteristic Curves

The equations given in Figure 9.20 do not completely describe the transistor operation in the Com. E configuration. For one thing, $\beta_{\text{d-c}}$ is not constant but varies with I_C and V_{CE}. $\beta_{\text{d-c}}$ *increases as I_C increases* up to a point and then decreases for further increases in I_C. It also increases as V_{CE} increases. Secondly, these equations assume that I_B is known. To find I_B, the variation of I_B with V_{BE} must be available. For these reasons the Com. E characteristic curves are often utilized.

For the NPN transistor in the Com. E configuration, typical input characteristics are shown in Figure 9.21. These are the

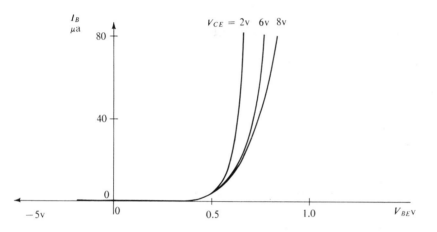

FIG. 9.21. COMMON EMITTER INPUT CHARACTER-
ISTICS FOR NPN TRANSISTOR

common emitter input characteristics and they relate the input current, I_B, to the voltage between emitter and base, V_{BE} for different values of collector to emitter voltage, V_{CE}. The input curves are essentially P-N diode curves, as was the case on the Com. B configuration; however, I_B is not the full forward bias current I_E, but only the recombination current $I_E (1 - \alpha_{\text{d-c}})$.

In Figure 9.21 an increased value of V_{CE} causes the input curves to give a lower value of I_B for a given V_{BE}. This comes about due to the increasing of the space charge region at the *C-B* junction as V_{CE} increases. The base width is effectively narrowed with the result that fewer recombinations take place in the base, and I_B is lowered.

Notice that for negative values of V_{BE} that I_B is very small since the *E-B* junction is reverse-biased. This is the *cut-off* condition.

For the same NPN transistor in the Com. E configuration a set of output characteristics are shown in Figure 9.22. These are the *common emitter output characteristics* and they relate the output current, I_C, to the voltage between collector and emitter, V_{CE}, for various values of input current, I_B.

A study of these output characteristics reveals several interesting points.

(a) For values of V_{CE} above a few tenths of a volt, I_C increases slowly as V_{CE} increases. The slope of these curves is somewhat greater than for the Com. B output characteristics. The increate of I_C with V_{CE} for a constant I_B indicates that $\beta_{d\text{-}c}$ increases wish V_{CE}. This region of the curves is the *active* region.

(b) For values of V_{CE} below a few tenths of a volt, I_C decreases rapidly as V_{CE} decreases. This occurs as V_{CE} drops below the value of V_{BE}, thus causing V_{CB} to become negative $V_{CB} = V_{CE} - V_{BE}$ and forward-biasing the C-B junction. Since the C-B junction is now forward-biased, the transistor is operating in the *saturation* region.

(c) The collector current is not zero when I_B is zero but has a value of I_{CEO}. This is the current which flows when the transistor is *cut-off* ($I_B = 0$).

(d) For a given base current, in the active region, the collector current is $\beta_{d\text{-}c}$ times greater than that base current. Thus, a small input current, I_B, produces a large output current $I_C = \beta_{d\text{-}c} \times I_B$.

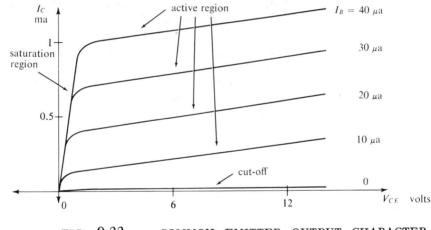

FIG. 9.22.   COMMON EMITTER OUTPUT CHARACTER-
ISTICS FOR NPN TRANSISTOR

▶EXAMPLE 9.17

Determine I_B and I_C for the transistor with the characteristics of Figure 9.21 and 9.22 when $V_{BE} = 0.7$v and $V_{CE} = 6$v. Calculate $\beta_{d\text{-}c}$ at this point.

(a) First, from the input characteristics the value of I_B when $V_{BE} = 0.7$v and $V_{CE} = 6$v is obtained as 40 μa. Now using the output characteristics, the value of I_C is obtained at $V_{CE} = 6$v using the $I_B = 40$ μa curve. It is $I_C = 1$ ma.

(b) The value of $\beta_{\text{d-c}}$ at this point is

$$\beta_{\text{d-c}} = \frac{1 \text{ ma}}{40 \text{ } \mu\text{a}} = 25 \qquad \blacktriangleleft$$

The Com. E output characteristics, unlike the Com. B output characteristics, can vary greatly from transistor to transistor. Whereas values of $\alpha_{\text{d-c}}$ can range from 0.9 to 0.999, values of $\beta_{\text{d-c}}$ usually range from 10 to 1000. Even among transistors of the same type, the values of $\beta_{\text{d-c}}$ can differ by 200 or 300 per cent.

The Com. E output characteristics of a PNP transistor are essentially the same as those in Figures 9.21 and 9.22 except for the polarities of V_{BE} and V_{CE}. Simply change the polarities on the V_{BE} and V_{CE} values given in these figures and the curves become PNP characteristics.

9.10.   Analyzing Common Emitter Circuits: Load Line Method

In analyzing a Com. E circuit the value of input current, I_B, must first be determined. In determining I_B, the diode-like characteristics of the *E-B* junction are again utilized. Consider the Com. E circuit of Figure 9.23. The base current is supplied by the voltage V_{BB} through the series resistor R_B. We can write

$$V_{BB} = I_B \times R_B + V_{BE} \qquad \textbf{(9.18)}$$

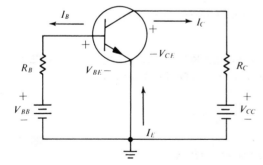

FIG. 9.23.   TYPICAL D-C COMMON EMITTER CIRCUIT

The voltage drop V_{BE} across the E-B junction is typically 0.7v for silicon and 0.3v for germanium units. Using this fact in Equation 9.19 below makes the value of I_B readily obtainable.

$$I_B = \frac{V_{BB} - V_{BE}}{R_B} \qquad (9.19)$$

▶ EXAMPLE 9.18

A silicon transistor is used in the circuit of Figure 9.24 with $V_{BB} = 10.7$v and $R_B = 200$K. Determine I_B. Repeat for a germanium transistor.

(a) Using $V_{BE} = 0.7$v in Equation 9.19 we have

$$I_B = \frac{10.7\text{v} - 0.7\text{v}}{200\text{K}} = 50 \ \mu a$$

(b) Using $V_{BE} = 0.3$v in Equation 9.19 we have

$$I_B = \frac{10.7 - 0.3\text{v}}{200\text{K}} = 52 \ \mu a \qquad ◀$$

This procedure for calculating I_B will be the same for both the load-line and approximate methods of analysis.

The load-line method of analyzing the Com. E circuit essentially parallels what was done in Section 9.6 for the Com. B circuit. The procedure is to write the Kirchhoff's voltage equation for the output portion of the circuit and plot this equation (load-line) on the output characteristic curves ($I_C - V_{CE}$ axes). The intersection of this load-line and the output curve corresponding to the value of I_B which was previously determined gives the circuit operating point. Referring to Figure 9.23 the Kirchhoff's voltage equation is

$$V_{CC} = I_C \times R_C + V_{CE} \qquad (9.20)$$

This equation relates I_C to V_{CE} and is called the load-line equation. To plot this load-line the easiest points to choose are ($I_C = 0$, $V_{CE} = V_{CC}$) and ($I_C = V_{CC}/R_C$, $V_{CE} = 0$).

▶ EXAMPLE 9.19

A transistor has the Com. E output characteristics drawn in Figure 9.24. Find I_C and V_{CE} for $I_B = 50 \ \mu a$, with $V_{CC} = 12$v and $R_C = 1$K. The load-line equation is

$$12\text{v} = I_C \times 1\text{K} + V_{CE}$$

and is plotted as shown in the figure. The intersection of this load-line and the $I_B = 50 \ \mu a$ curve is to be $I_C = 5$ ma and $V_{CE} = 7$v.   ◀

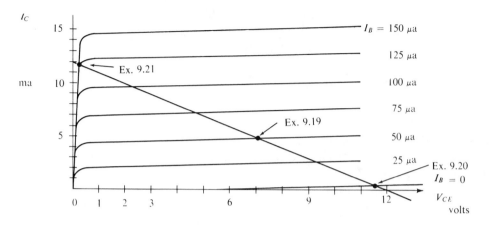

FIG. **9.24.**   LOAD-LINE METHOD

The voltage across the 1K resistor is 5 ma × 1K = 5v. These values can be checked by substituting into the load-line equation. In this case the operating point lies in the *active* region of the transistor characteristics.

► EXAMPLE 9.20

Repeat Example 9.19 using $I_B = 0$.
The intersection of the load-line and the $I_B = 0$ curve gives the new operating as $I_C \approx 0$ and $V_{CE} = 12$v. Since the transistor is in cut-off only a small leakage current flows (I_{CEO}) and the voltage dropped across the series resistor is essentially zero. Thus $V_{CE} = V_{CC}$.   ◄

► EXAMPLE 9.21

Repeat Example 9.19 using $I_B = 125$ μa and $I_B = 150$ μa.
(a) The intersection of the load-line and the $I_B = 125$ μa gives the operating point as $I_C = 11.8$ μa and $V_{CE} = 0.2$v. This operating point lies in the *saturation* region of the characteristics.
(b) The operating point using $I_B = 150$ μa is the same as for $I_B = 125$ μa since the different curves merge in the saturation region. Thus $I_C = 11.8$ ma and $V_{CE} = 0.2$v is still the operating point. In fact, further increases in I_B will still result in the same I_C and V_{CE}. The extra base current does not produce any increase in collector current once the transistor is saturated. Notice that V_{CE} is very small in the saturation region.   ◄

The use of the load-line method for analyzing Com. E circuits will gain importance in our later work on transistor amplifiers.

9.11.   Analyzing Common Emitter Circuits: Approximate Method

In using the approximate method to analyze a Com. E circuit it is necessary to first determine in what region of its operation the transistor is biased. When the *E-B* junction is reverse-biased or unbiased ($I_B = 0$) the transistor is in *cut-off* and only a small leakage current flows in the collector. This current, I_{CEO}, is typically in the low μa range at room temperature and can normally be neglected. In this case the voltage drop across R_C (Figure 9.25)

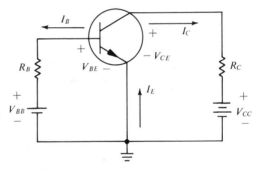

FIG. 9.25.   D-C COMMON EMITTER CIRCUIT

is essentially zero and V_{CE} is equal to the collector supply voltage V_{CC}.

▶ EXAMPLE 9.22

Using $V_{CC} = 12$v and $R_C = 1$K in the circuit of Figure 9.25 determine I_C and V_{CE} when $I_B = 0$.

With $I_B = 0$ the collector current will be essentially zero. The voltage across the 1K resistor will be zero. Thus, $V_{CE} = 12$v. Compare these results with those of Example 9.20.   ◀

When the *E-B* junction is forward-biased, base current will flow causing a corresponding collector current to flow. The value of I_B is determined in the manner outlined in the last section and used in Example 9.18. When the value of I_B is known, it remains to determine whether the transistor is in the *active* or *saturation* region. In the *active* region the collector current is approximately equal to $\beta_{\text{d-c}} \times I_B$. The value of I_C thus obtained is then used to calculate V_{CE}. In the *saturation* region the collector current is approximately given by

$$I_C = I_{C(\text{sat})} \approx \frac{V_{CC}}{R_C} \tag{9.21}$$

since V_{CE} is very small. The procedure for finding the operating point when the *E-B* junction is forward-biased is as follows:

(a) Calculate I_B using

$$I_B = \frac{V_{BB} - V_{BE}}{R_B}$$

where $V_{BE} = 0.7\text{v}$ for silicon and 0.3v for germanium.

(b) Calculate $I_{C(\text{sat})}$ using Equation 9.21.

(c) Calculate $\beta_{\text{d-c}} \times I_B$.

(d) If this value is less than $I_{C(\text{sat})}$, then the transistor *is not* saturated. In this case $I_C = \beta_{\text{d-c}} \times I_B$ and V_{CE} can be calculated from

$$V_{CE} = V_{CC} - I_C \times R_C$$

(e) If the value of $\beta_{\text{d-c}} \times I_B$ is greater than $I_{C(\text{sat})}$, then the transistor *is* saturated. In this case $I_C = I_{C(\text{sat})}$ and $V_{CE} \approx 0$. The following examples illustrate this procedure.

▶ EXAMPLE 9.23

In the circuit of Figure 9.25 find I_C and V_{CE} for $I_B = 50\ \mu\text{a}$ if $V_{CC} = 12\text{v}$ and $R_C = 1\text{K}$. $\beta_{\text{d-c}}$ for this transistor is 100.
Calculate $I_{C(\text{sat})}$:

$$I_{C(\text{sat})} \approx 12\text{v}/1\text{K} = 12\ \text{ma}$$

Now calculate

$$\beta_{\text{d-c}} \times I_B = 100 \times 50\ \mu\text{a} = 5.0\ \text{ma}$$

which is much less than $I_{C(\text{sat})}$. Thus, the transistor is not saturated but is in the active region and $I_C = \beta_{\text{d-c}} \times I_B = 5\ \text{ma}$. The voltage dropped across the 1K resistor is $5\ \text{ma} \times 1\text{K} = 5\text{v}$ and $V_{CE} = 12\text{v} - 5\text{v} = 7.0\text{v}$. Compare this to the results of Example 9.19. ◀

► EXAMPLE 9.24

Repeat Example 9.23 for $I_B = 125$ μa and $I_B = 150$ μa.

(a) $I_{C(sat)}$ as calculated above is 12 ma. $\beta_{d-c} \times I_B = 100 \times 125$ μa $= 12.5$ ma which is greater than $I_{C(sat)}$. Thus, the transistor is saturated and $I_C = I_{C(sat)} = 12$ ma; V_{CE} is approximately zero.

(b) If $I_B = 125$ μa is enough to saturate the transistor, increasing I_B to 150 μa will not cause I_C to increase. Compare these results to Example 9.21.   ◄

The value of base current which exactly causes the transistor to saturate is given the symbol $I_{B(sat)}$ and is obtained using

$$\beta_{d-c} \times I_{B(sat)} = I_{C(sat)}$$

or

$$I_{B(sat)} = \frac{I_{C(sat)}}{\beta_{d-c}} = \frac{V_{CC}}{\beta_{d-c} \times R_C} \qquad (9.22)$$

Any value of base current equal to or greater than this value will produce saturation.

► EXAMPLE 9.25

In the circuit of Examples 9.23 and 9.24, calculate the value of base current just needed to cause saturation and determine the value of V_{BB} which will provide it. Use $R_B = 100K$.

From equation 9.22

$$I_{B(sat)} = \frac{12v}{100 \times 1K} = 120 \ \mu a$$

The value of V_{BB} needed is given by

$$V_{BB} = I_{B(sat)} \times R_B + V_{BE}$$
$$= 120 \ \mu a \times 100K + 0.7v = 12.7v \qquad ◄$$

9.12.   The Common Collector Configuration

The common collector configuration is much like the common emitter configuration except for the fact that the output is taken at the emitter rather than the collector. In either configuration the input is at the base. Figure 9.26 is a typical Com. C circuit using an NPN transistor. Since I_B is the input current in the Com. C configuration it is desirable to relate I_C and I_E in terms of I_B.

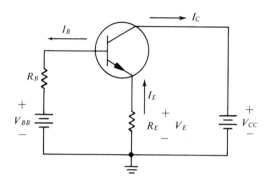

FIG. 9.26.   TYPICAL COMMON COLLECTOR CIRCUIT

These equations, however, are the same as those given in Figure 9.20 for the Com. E configuration. For convenience these equations are repeated in Figure 9.27.

$$I_E = (\beta_{d\text{-}c} + 1)I_B + I_{CEO}$$
$$I_C = \beta_{d\text{-}c}I_B + I_{CEO}$$
$$\beta_{d\text{-}c} = \frac{I_C - I_{CEO}}{I_B} \approx \frac{I_C}{I_B}$$

FIG. 9.27.   COMMON COLLECTOR EQUATIONS

In the Com. C circuit the d-c output emitter current is approximately $(\beta_{d\text{-}c} + 1)$ times the d-c input base current. Thus in this configuration the d-c *current gain* is $\beta_{d\text{-}c} + 1$. This is the highest of all three configurations. Recall that for Com. B the d-c current gain is $\alpha_{d\text{-}c}$ and for Com. E it is $\beta_{d\text{-}c}$.

9.13.   Analyzing Common Collector Circuits

In the circuit of Figure 9.26 the voltage V_{BB} forward-biases the E-B junction and supplies base current. For a given value of I_B the value of I_E will be approximately $(\beta_{d\text{-}c} + 1) \times I_B$. The voltage drop across resistor R_E is then given by

$$V_E = I_E \times R_E = (\beta_{d\text{-}c} + 1)I_B \times R_E \qquad (9.23)$$

The voltage drop across resistor R_B is simply $I_B \times R_B$. If we sum the voltages around the input loop, we have

$$V_{BB} = I_B \times R_B + (\beta_{d\text{-}c} + 1)I_B \times R_E + V_{BE} \qquad (9.24)$$

where V_{BE} is the forward voltage drop across the *E-B* junction. Rearranging Equation 9.24,

$$V_{BB} = I_B[R_B + (\beta_{\text{d-c}} + 1)R_E] + V_{BE} \qquad \textbf{(9.25)}$$

We can solve this equation for I_B resulting in

$$I_B = \frac{V_{BB} - V_{BE}}{R_B + (\beta_{\text{d-c}} + 1)R_E} \qquad \textbf{(9.26)}$$

▶ EXAMPLE 9.26

Calculate I_B, I_E and V_E in the circuit of Figure 9.26 if $V_{BB} = 6v$, $R_B = 10K$, $R_E = 1K$ and $V_{CC} = 12v$ and the transistor has a $\beta_{\text{d-c}}$ of 50 and is silicon.

Since the transistor is silicon, V_{BE} will be approximately 0.7v. Using Equation 9.26 then, we have

$$I_B = \frac{6v - 0.7v}{10K + 51 \times 1K} = \frac{5.3v}{61K} = 0.087 \text{ ma}$$

To calculate I_E we have

$$I_E = 51 \times I_B = 4.44 \text{ ma}$$

The voltage V_E will then be

$$V_E = 4.44 \text{ ma} \times 1K = 4.44v \qquad \blacktriangleleft$$

If we examine Equation 9.26 for the base current in the Com. C circuit we see that as far as the base current is concerned, the resistor R_E *appears* to have a resistance of $(\beta_{\text{d-c}} + 1) \times R_E$. This is due to the current gain of the transistor. The V_{BB} voltage supply is essentially supplying current to a total resistance of $R_B + (\beta_{\text{d-c}} + 1) R_E$. If $\beta_{\text{d-c}}$ is high, this total resistance will be high and the value of I_B which is drawn from V_{BB} will be small. The current in the emitter, on the other hand, will be large due to the transistor current gain. In our study of transistor voltage amplifiers this characteristic of Com. C circuits will be used to great advantage.

9.14. Some Important Transistor Maximum Ratings

Transistor manufacturers supply data sheets which usually contain operating characteristics, parameter values, and maximum ratings that apply to a particular transistor. The information will usually include a description of the device, mechanical data, maximum ratings, electrical characteristics, typical characteristic curves and parameter information.

Before inserting a transistor into a circuit design, it is necessary to avoid using it where its maximum ratings may be exceeded. The manufacturer establishes these ratings which are based on the semiconductor material, the manufacturing process and the physical construction. If these ratings are exceeded, deterioration or destruction of a transistor will occur.

Figure 9.28 lists typical maximum ratings for a junction transistor. The ratings are given at 25C°.

Absolute Maximum Ratings (25°)

BV_{EBO}:	emitter-base voltage: 6v
BV_{CBO}:	collector-base voltage: 25v
BV_{CEO}:	collector-emitter voltage: 20v
$I_{C(max)}$:	collector current: 300 ma
$P_{D(max)}$:	total dissipation: 150 mw
$T_{J(max)}$:	junction temperature: 150°C

FIG. 9.28.   JUNCTION TRANSISTOR RATINGS

The first three ratings are maximum voltage ratings between the various transistor terminals. These ratings are a result of reverse breakdown occurring at the two junctions. BV_{EBO} is usually the lowest of these ratings due to the heavy doping of the emitter. BV_{CBO} is normally higher than BV_{CEO} indicating that a larger collector supply voltage, V_{CC}, can be used in the Com. B connection than in the Com. E connection. $I_{C(max)}$ is the maximum allowable collector current and depends mainly on the physical size of the device. Transistors with collector current ratings up to the high ampere range are presently available. $P_{D(max)}$ is the limitation on the *total* power dissipation across both transistor junctions. In most cases the power dissipated across the *E-B* junction is low so that $P_{D(max)}$ essentially is the limit on *C-B* junction dissipation. This limit is determined by the transistor's maximum junction temperature, $T_{J(max)}$, and its ability to radiate heat away from its junction. This latter ability is characterized by its thermal resistance, θ_{JA}. The discussion in Chapter 5 on this topic is equally applicable here. Power transistors with $P_{D(max)}$ ratings in the hundreds-of-watts range are presently available.

▶EXAMPLE 9.27

Each of the circuits below uses the transistor with the ratings given in Figure 9.28. In each case one of the ratings is exceeded. Determine which one for each circuit.

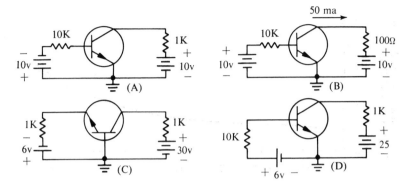

FIG. **9.29.**

(a) In circuit (A) the *E-B* junction is reverse-biased by 10 volts. This is above the maximum BV_{EBO} of 6 volts for this transistor.

(b) In circuit (B) a collector current of 50 ma is flowing. This is well below $I_{C(max)}$. However, the voltage from collector to emitter, V_{CE}, is 5 volts. Thus, the power dissipated by the transistor is $V_{CE} \times I_C = 5v \times 50\,ma = 250\,mw$, which is greater than $P_{D(max)}$.

(c) In circuit (C) the supply voltage between collector and base is 30 volts. This is greater than BV_{CBO} which is 25 volts.

(d) In circuit (D) the supply voltage between emitter and collector is 25 volts. This is greater than BV_{CEO} which is 20 volts. ◄

9.15.   Temperature Effects

The transistor parameters which are most affected by temperature are Com. E d-c current gain β_{d-c}, leakage currents I_{CBO} and I_{CEO}, and base-emitter forward voltage V_{BE}. All vary with temperature and must be accounted for in most circuit designs and especially in amplifiers.

Figure 9.30 shows typical variation of β_{d-c} with temperature using 25°C as the reference temperature. The value of β_{d-c} increases rapidly with temperature above 25°C and decreases less rapidly with decreases in temperature below 25°C. For example, the graph indicates that at 0°C the value of β_{d-c} is down by approximately 15 per cent from its value at 25°C, and at 50°C β_{d-c} is up by 50 per cent. Most germanium and silicon transistors show approximately this variation of β_{d-c} with temperature and the information is usually supplied by the manufacturer. The Com. B d-c current gain α_{d-c} shows much less of a variation with temperature, rarely

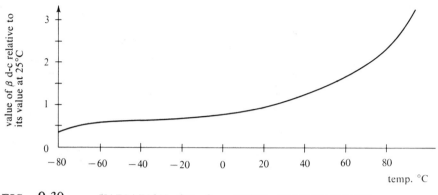

FIG. **9.30.**   VARIATION OF $\beta_{\text{d-c}}$ WITH TEMPERATURE

more than a few percentage points over the useful temperature range.

The transistor leakage currents, I_{CBO} and I_{CEO}, both increase with temperature. The value of I_{CBO} approximately doubles for every 10°C increase in temperature. Since the value of I_{CEO} depends on I_{CBO} according to

$$I_{CEO} = \frac{I_{CBO}}{1 - \alpha_{\text{d-c}}} = (\beta_{\text{d-c}} + 1)I_{CBO} \qquad (9.27)$$

it will more than double every 10°C. This temperature effect is not as critical in silicon units as it is in germanium since the leakages are much smaller to begin with in silicon (I_{CBO} is typically 0.01 μa).

The variation of base-emitter forward voltage V_{BE} is typically 2 mv per °C, with V_{BE} decreasing as temperature increases. For example a silicon transistor with a V_{BE} of 0.7v at 25°C would typically have a V_{BE} of 0.6v at 75°C.

The above effects all serve to increase the output current in transistor circuits. This can be seen in the following example.

▶EXAMPLE 9.28

Calculate I_B and I_C in the circuit of Figure 9.31 at 25°C and at 55°C if the transistor is silicon and has $\beta_{\text{d-c}} = 100$ and $I_{CBO} = 0.1$ μa at 25°C.

(a) At 25°C:

$$I_B = \frac{6v - 0.7v}{1_{\text{meg}}} = 5.3 \ \mu a$$

$$I_C = \beta_{\text{d-c}} \times I_B + I_{CEO}$$
$$= 100 \times 5.3 \ \mu a + 101 \times 0.1 \ \mu a$$
$$= 530 \ \mu a + 10.1 \ \mu a = 540.1 \ \mu a$$

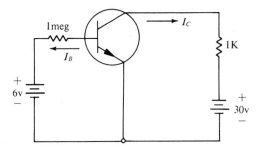

FIG. 9.31.   EXAMPLE 9.28

(b) At 55°C:

$$V_{BE} = 0.7\text{v} - (30) \times (2\text{mv})$$
$$= 0.64\text{v}$$
$$I_{CBO} = 0.1 \ \mu\text{a doubled 3 times}$$
$$= 0.8 \ \mu\text{a}$$
$$\beta_{\text{d-c}} = 1.45 \times 100 = 145 \text{ (from Figure 9.30)}$$

Thus

$$I_B = \frac{6\text{v} - 0.64\text{v}}{1_{\text{meg}}} = 5.36 \ \mu\text{a}$$
$$I_C = 145 \times 5.36 \ \mu\text{a} + 146 \times 0.8 \ \mu\text{a}$$
$$= 777 \ \mu\text{a} + 116.8 \ \mu\text{a} = 893.8 \ \mu\text{a} \qquad \blacktriangleleft$$

This increase in collector current with temperature is very important in the design of transistor amplifiers, especially in the Com. E circuits. We shall see that with proper circuit design procedures the effect of temperature on circuit operation can be minimized.

GLOSSARY

Emitter: the most heavily-doped region of the junction transistor

Collector: region of the junction transistor which is doped with the same impurity type as the emitter

Base: the most lightly-doped region of the transistor. The type of its doping impurity is opposite to that of the emitter and collector.

Emitter-base junction: P-N junction formed by emitter and base regions

Collector-base junction: P-N junction formed by collector and base regions

Active, saturation,
cut-off, inverted: regions of transistor operation determined by biases on the junctions

I_{CBO}: collector leakage current which flows when $I_E = 0$ in the Com. B configuration

α_{d-c}: d-c Com. B current gain

I_{CEO}: collector leakage current which flows when $I_B = 0$ in the Com. E configuration

β_{d-c}: d-c Com. E current gain

$I_{C(sat)}$: the value of collector current at saturation

$I_{B(sat)}$: the value of base current needed to produce $I_{C(sat)}$

$BV_{EBO}, BV_{CBO}, BV_{CEO}$: maximum allowable transistor voltages

Questions

9.1   Sketch the structure of an NPN junction transistor and label the emitter, base and collector regions. Also label the *E-B* and *C-B* junctions.

9.2   Repeat 9.1 for a PNP junction transistor.

9.3   Explain the function of the emitter in the operation of a junction transistor.

9.4   What is done to the base region of a transistor to improve its operation?

9.5   Why is the *C-B* junction of a transistor reverse-biased for active region operation?

9.6   What causes collector current to flow when there is no emitter current? What is this collector current called?

9.7   Why is base current in a transistor usually much smaller than I_C or I_E in active operation?

9.8   Why is collector current in a transistor usually about the same as emitter current in active operation?

9.9   What happens to I_C as the value of reverse bias on the *C-B* junction increases? Explain.

9.10   Indicate in which region (active, saturation or cut-off) the transistors in Figure 9.32 are biased.

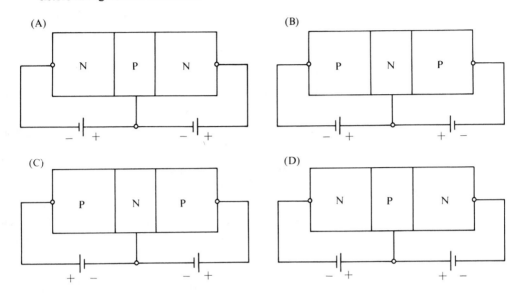

FIG. 9.32.

9.11   Fill in the blanks in the following data table taken for a certain transistor.

I_B (ma)	I_C (ma)	I_E (ma)
1.0	19.0	——
—	18.0	18.95
—	+0.01	0
1.5	——	30

9.12   From the table for Question 9.11, determine I_{CBO} for this transistor. Calculate $\alpha_{d\text{-}c}$ at $I_C = 19$ ma.

9.13   A certain transistor has $\alpha_{d\text{-}c} = 0.99$ and $I_{CBO} = 10$ μa. Calculate I_C and I_B when $I_E = 10$ ma. Repeat for $I_E = 20$ ma. Assume operation in the active region.

9.14   Indicate which of the following statements pertain to NPN transistors and which pertain to PNP transistors.
(a) The emitter injects *holes* into the base region.

(b) When biased in the active region, current flows *into* the emitter terminal.

(c) The collector is biased *positively* relative to the base for active operation.

(d) The principal current carriers are electrons.

(e) The *E-B* junction is forward-biased for active operation.

9.15 What happens to the ability of the collector region to collect injected carriers in the saturated condition?

9.16 How much emitter current flows in the cut-off condition?

9.17 Draw a PNP transistor in the Com. B configuration biased for operation in the *active* region.

9.18 What is considered the input terminal and what is the output terminal in the Com. B configuration?

9.19 Sketch typical Com. B *input* characteristic curves for PNP transistor. Label all variables.

9.20 Sketch typical Com. B *output* characteristic curves for a PNP transistor. Label all variables and indicate active, cut-off and saturation regions.

9.21 Does the value of $\alpha_{\text{d-c}}$ increase or decrease with V_{CB}?

9.22 Using the characteristic curves of Figures 9.12 and 9.13, determine the approximate values of I_C and I_E when $V_{BE} = 0.7\text{v}$ and $V_{CB} = 10\text{v}$.

9.23 Determine I_E in the circuits in Figure 9.33.

(A)

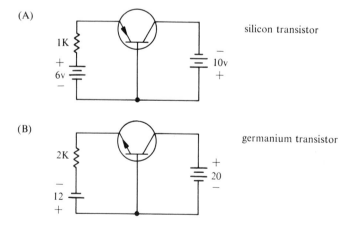

1K

+
6v
−

−
10v
+

silicon transistor

(B)

2K

−
12
+

+
20
−

germanium transistor

FIG. 9.33.

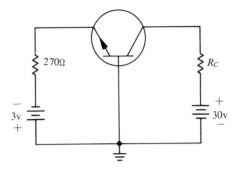

FIG. 9.34.

9.24 The germanium transistor in the circuit in Figure 9.34 has the characteristic curves of Figure 9.15.

(a) Determine I_E, I_C and V_{CB} using the load-line method when $R_C = 1K$.
(b) Determine what value of R_C will exactly cause saturation.

9.25 The circuits in Figure 9.35 use a silicon transistor. Determine I_E, I_C and V_{CB} if $\alpha_{\text{d-c}} = 0.95$ using the approximate method.

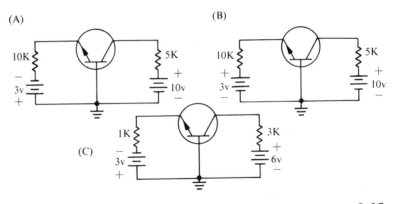

FIG. 9.35.

9.26 In the circuit in Figure 9.36, which uses a germanium transistor, determine what value of V_{EE} will cause saturation.

9.27 A certain transistor circuit has $I_{C(\text{sat})} = 10$ ma. If I_E is increased to 15 ma what will be the values of I_C and I_B?

9.28 Draw a PNP transistor in the Com. E configuration biased for operation in the *active* region.

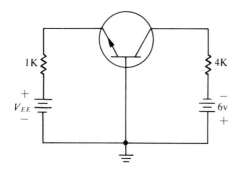

FIG. 9.36.

9.29 What are the input and output terminals in the Com. E configuration?

9.30 Sketch typical Com. E *input* characteristics for a PNP transistor. Label all variables.

9.31 Sketch typical Com. E *output* characteristics for a PNP transistor. Label all variables and indicate active, cut-off and saturation regions.

9.32 Does the value of $\beta_{\text{d-c}}$ increase or decrease with V_{CE}?

9.33 Determine I_B in the circuit in Figure 9.37 which utilizes a silicon transistor.

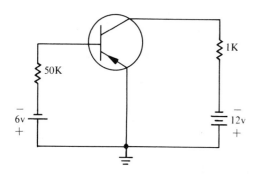

FIG. 9.37.

9.34 The silicon transistor in Figure 9.38 has the characteristic curves of Figure 9.24.

(a) Determine I_B, I_C and V_{CE} using the load-line method when $R_C = 600\Omega$.

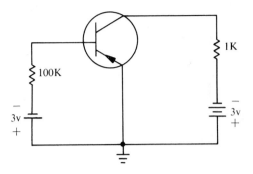

FIG. 9.38.

(b) Determine what value of R_C will cause saturation.

9.35 The circuits in Figure 9.39 use a germanium transistor. Determine I_B, I_C and V_{CE} in each using the approximate method. Use $\beta_{d-c} = 50$.

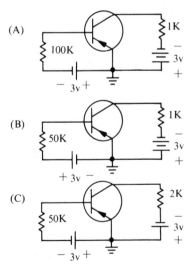

FIG. 9.39.

9.36 In the circuit in Figure 9.40, which uses a silicon transistor, determine what value of V_{BB} will cause saturation.

9.37 In Figure 9.40 if $V_{BB} = 5v$ what value of R_C will just cause saturation?

9.38 Calculate I_B, I_E and V_E in the circuit in Figure 9.41.

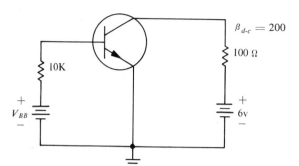

FIG. 9.40.

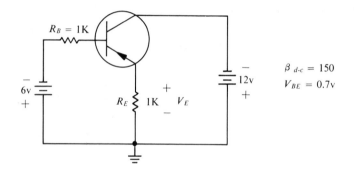

FIG. 9.41.

9.39 In the circuit of Figure 9.41, calculate I_B, I_E and V_E when the 1K base resistor is reduced to zero. The results should bear out the fact that the output current, I_E, and voltage, V_E, do not depend on the base resistor when it is small compared to $\beta_{d-c} \times R_E$. That is, the value of I_B and the voltage across R_B are negligible.

9.40 Using the fact brought out in Question 9.39, find I_E and V_E in Figure 9.42 using the same transistor.

9.41 A certain transistor has the following ratings at 25°C:

BV_{EBO}:	6v
BV_{CBO}:	40v
BV_{CEO}:	30v
$I_C(\text{max})$:	1 amp
$P_D(\text{max})$:	1 watt
$T_J(\text{max})$:	150°C

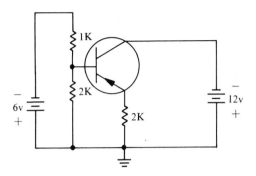

FIG. 9.42.

If the transistor is used in the circuit in Figure 9.43:

(a) What value of V_{CC} is the largest which should be used?

(b) If $V_{CC} = 20v$ is used what is the smallest R_C which could be used if the transistor is to be saturated?

(c) If $I_E = 0.5$ amp what minimum value of R_C is needed to insure that $P_{D(max)}$ is not exceeded? (Use $V_{CC} = 20v$)

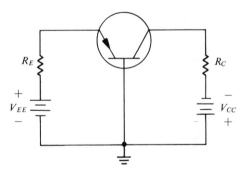

FIG. 9.43.

9.42 A transistor has $P_{D(max)} = 1$ watt at 25°C and $\theta_{JA} = 0.1°C/mw$. Calculate $P_{D(max)}$ at 55°C.

9.43 The transistor in the circuit in Figure 9.44 has the following parameters at 25°C.

$$\beta_{d-c} = 200$$
$$I_{CEO} = 1\ \mu a$$
$$V_{BE} = 0.25v$$

Calculate I_C and V_{CE} at 25°C and 75°C.

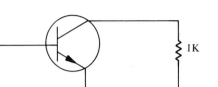
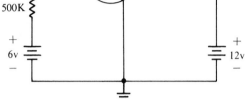

FIG. 9.44.

9.44 In the photocell-relay circuit studied in Chapter Eight the same current flowed through both the photocell and relay. This circuit would be useless for driving high-current relays since photocells are generally low-current devices. If we use a transistor, we can still use a low-current photocell to control a high-current relay. Figure 9.45 is such a circuit.

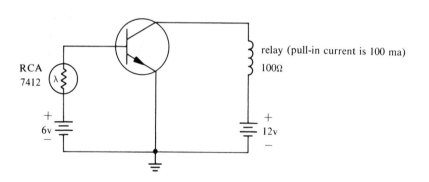

FIG. 9.45.

(a) If the transistor has $\beta_{d-c} = 100$ and is made of germanium, determine the relay current when the cell is in the dark and when it is illuminated with 10 f.c. See Figures 8.3 and 8.6.

(b) Modify the circuit so that the relay pulls in when the cell is in the dark and drops out when it is illuminated.

References

Foster, J. F., *Semiconductors, Diodes and Transistors*, Vol. 3. Beaverton, Oregon: Programmed Instruction Group, Tetronix, Inc., 1964.

Malvino, A. P., *Transistor Circuit Approximations*. New York: McGraw-Hill Book Company, 1968.

Pierce, J. F., *Transistor Circuit Theory and Design*. Columbus, Ohio: Charles E. Merrill Books, Inc., 1963.

Veatch, H. C., *Transistor Circuit Action*. New York: McGraw-Hill Book Company, 1968.

10

Amplifier Principles

10.1.   Introduction

We understand amplifiers when we can predict their performance
by careful analysis of the circuit. As such, we must be prepared to
calculate input and output impedances and amplifier gains. This
chapter introduces many of the fundamental relationships that
characterize amplifier circuits. The material in this chapter is
general, in that no particular amplifying device is mentioned, and
applies to vacuum tube amplifiers as well as the junction transistor
and field effect transistor amplifiers which will be covered in later
chapters.

10.2.   Reproduction and Amplification

Figure 10.1 represents a general amplifier circuit. The input to
the amplifier may be a current or a voltage and can be considered
the *stimulus*. The amplifier output current or output voltage (or
both) can be considered the amplifier's *response* to the input
stimulus. When input voltage or current variations, called the
input signal, are applied to the amplifier, the amplifier circuit acts
on them to produce output current and voltage variations, called
the *output signal*. If the output signal possesses the same variations
as the input signal, the amplifier has duplicated the input variations

213

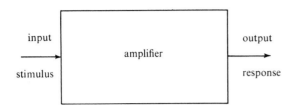

FIG. 10.1.   GENERAL AMPLIFIER

in its output; this is called *reproduction*. If the output signal variations are made larger than the input variations which produced
them, the process is called *amplification*.

Figure 10.2(A) illustrates the process of reproduction, while
10.2(B) illustrates the process of amplification. In part (A) the
output and input signals have exactly the same shape. In part (B)
the output signal is much larger than the input signal. Reproduction is a requirement in applications where the shape of the input
has to be preserved. In many applications faithful reproduction
and amplification are both desired such as in the audio amplifier
stage of radio receivers. Figure 10.2(C) illustrates this. There

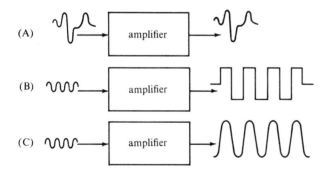

FIG. 10.2.   (A) REPRODUCTION (B) AMPLIFICATION
(C) COMBINED REPRODUCTION AND AM-
PLIFICATION

are a considerable number of applications in which only amplification is required. This is usually the case in photodetection
circuits, for example, where a small signal from a photocell is
amplified to a level necessary to drive control circuitry.

In conclusion, reproduction essentially means duplication,
and amplification means enlargement. It is essential that the

difference between these two processes be clear in the mind of the reader.

10.3.   Voltage Amplification

A circuit which is specifically designed to develop an output voltage signal greater than the input voltage signal, is called a *voltage amplifier*. A voltage amplifier is said to have a *voltage gain* which is defined as the ratio of the change in output voltage to the change in input voltage which produced it. In equation form,

$$A_v = \frac{\Delta e_{\text{out}}}{\Delta e_{\text{in}}} \tag{10.1}$$

where A_v = voltage gain
     Δe_{out} = change in output voltage
     Δe_{in} = change in input voltage

In the remaining chapters of the text lower case letters will be used to denote signal (varying) voltages and currents such as e_{in} and e_{out} while upper case letters will denote d-c (unchanging) voltages and currents.

▶ EXAMPLE 10.1

When the input voltage to a certain amplifier changes from 2v to 3v, its output voltage increases from 10v to 20v. What is the voltage gain of this amplifier?

     Using expression 10.1, we have   ◀

$$A_v = \frac{\Delta e_{\text{out}}}{\Delta e_{\text{in}}} = \frac{20v - 10v}{3v - 2v}$$
$$= 10$$

▶ EXAMPLE 10.2

The output voltage of a certain amplifier changes from 20v to 10v as its input increases from 2v to 3v. What is the voltage gain of this amplifier?

     In this case,

$$A_v = \frac{\Delta e_{\text{out}}}{\Delta e_{\text{in}}} = \frac{10v - 20v}{3v - 2v} = -10$$

Thus, A_v is a negative quantity indicating that an *increase* in e_{in} causes a *decrease* in e_{out}.   ◀

In the examples above the output signal was amplified by a factor of 10. Values of A_v from approximately one on up to hundreds of thousands can be encountered in electronic amplifiers.

10.4.   Current Amplification

A circuit which is specifically designed to develop an output current signal which is greater than the input current signal is called a *current amplifier*. A current amplifier is said to have a *current gain* which is defined as the ratio of the change in output current to the change in input current which produces it. In equation form,

$$A_i = \frac{\Delta i_{out}}{\Delta i_{in}}$$ **(10.2)**

where A_i = current gain
Δi_{out} = change in output current
Δi_{in} = change in input current

Current amplifiers are often called *power amplifiers* since the large output currents result in a substantial output power. Devices to be used in power amplifiers are specially manufactured so that they can withstand large currents.

▶EXAMPLE 10.3

A certain amplifier has its output current increase from 10 ma to 20 ma in response to an input current change from 100 μa to 200 μa. What is the current gain of this amplifier?
Using Equation 10.2, we have

$$A_i = \frac{\Delta i_{out}}{\Delta i_{in}} = \frac{20 \text{ ma} - 10 \text{ ma}}{200 \ \mu\text{a} - 100 \ \mu\text{a}}$$

$$= 100$$ ◀

10.5.   Power Amplification

In amplifiers the ratio of output signal power to input signal power is called *power gain* and is given by

$$A_p = \frac{p_{osig}}{p_{isig}}$$ **(10.3)**

where A_p = power gain

p_{osig} = signal power output

p_{isig} = signal power input

Power gain can also be expressed as the product of voltage gain and current gain. That is,

$$A_p = A_v \times A_i \qquad\qquad \textbf{(10.4)}$$

From Equation 10.4 it is apparent that it is not necessary to have both voltage gain and current gain greater than unity in order to achieve large power gains. In fact, some of the most widely used power amplifier circuits have large current gains and voltage gains less than unity.

It is important to note that power gain as defined in Equations 10.3 and 10.4 is for signal power only. Many amplifiers also have d-c output and input power dissipation which is not included in the expression for power gain.

▶ EXAMPLE 10.4

A certain amplifier has a signal output power dissipation of 10 watts and a signal input power of 10 mw. Find the power gain.

$$A_p = \frac{p_{osig}}{p_{isig}} = \frac{10 \text{ w}}{10 \text{ mw}} = 1000 \qquad ◀$$

▶ EXAMPLE 10.5

The same amplifier has a voltage gain of 10. What is the amplifier's current gain? Since

$$A_p = A_v \times A_i$$

$$A_i = \frac{A_p}{A_v} = \frac{1000}{10} = 100 \qquad ◀$$

Devices which are to be used in high-power amplifiers are usually of special construction so as to permit the large values of power dissipation without being damaged.

10.6.   Impedance Concept

In the circuit analysis of amplifiers the term *impedance* is used to denote the effective a-c resistance. The impedance of a linear resistor is simply equal to its resistance. However, the impedance of a nonlinear device is dependent on operating point (recall zener impedance in Chapter Six). In general, two impedance values are important in amplifier work, *input impedance* and *output impedance*.

The input impedance Z_{in} of an amplifier is the ratio of voltage change to the resulting input current change. In equation form,

$$Z_{in} = \frac{\Delta e_{in}}{\Delta i_{in}} \qquad (10.5)$$

The input impedance is a measure of how much signal current the amplifier draws for a given input signal voltage.

▶ EXAMPLE 10.6

A certain amplifier has its input current increase from 1 ma to 2 ma when its input voltage increases from 0.5v to 0.55v. Determine Z_{in}.

Using Equation 10.5

$$Z_{in} = \frac{\Delta e_{in}}{\Delta i_{in}} = \frac{0.55v - 0.50v}{2 \text{ ma} - 1 \text{ ma}}$$

$$= \frac{0.050v}{0.001a}$$

$$= 50\Omega \qquad \blacktriangleleft$$

The output impedance Z_{out} of an amplifier is the ratio of the change in output voltage to the change in output current. In equation form,

$$Z_{out} = \frac{\Delta e_{out}}{\Delta i_{out}} \qquad (10.6)$$

The output impedance of an amplifier is a measure of its ability to provide the same output signal (voltage or current) to different size loads. An amplifier with a very high output impedance (say 100K) will provide a fairly constant output signal current, while one with a very low output impedance (say 50Ω) will provide a fairly constant output signal voltage.

10.7.   Amplifier Relationships

Figure 10.3(A) represents a voltage amplifier. The input signal voltage is applied between terminals 1 and 2 and the output terminals are 3 and 4. Most often, terminals 2 and 4 will be one and the same, but to preserve generality they will be treated separately. Included in the representation are the amplifier input impedance Z_{in}, output impedance Z_{out} and voltage gain A_v. Since Z_{in}, Z_{out} and A_v are all a-c parameters this representation is useful for a-c signal voltages only.

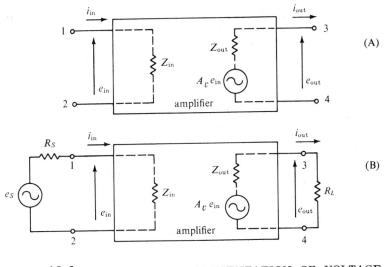

FIG. 10.3.   GENERAL REPRESENTATION OF VOLTAGE AMPLIFIER (A) AMPLIFIER ALONE (B) LOADED AMPLIFIER DRIVEN BY A SIGNAL SOURCE

The input to the amplifier is represented by its input impedance Z_{in}. Application of an input signal voltage results in a signal current flowing into the amplifier equal to e_{in}/Z_{in}. The output of the amplifier is represented by a signal generator equal to $A_v e_{in}$ in series with the output impedance Z_{out}. Usually some type of load is connected across the amplifier output terminals. In Figure 10.3(B) the amplifier is shown with its input being driven from a signal source e_S and its output connected to a load resistor R_L. The source resistance (output impedance) of the signal source is represented by R_S. Generally speaking the value of e_{in} will be some fraction of e_S depending on the relative values of Z_{in} and R_S, and the value of e_{out} will be some fraction of $A_v e_{in}$ depending on the relative values of Z_{out} and R_L. The value of e_{in} is given by

$$e_{in} = \frac{Z_{in} e_S}{Z_{in} + R_S} \qquad (10.7)$$

and the value of e_{out} is given by

$$e_{out} = \frac{(A_v e_{in}) R_L}{R_L + Z_{out}} \qquad (10.8)$$

The overall circuit voltage gain G_v is the ratio of e_{out} to e_S and is given by

$$G_v = \frac{e_{out}}{e_S} = \frac{A_v(R_L)(Z_{in})}{(R_L + Z_{out})(Z_{in} + R_S)} \qquad (10.9)$$

Some interesting points can be derived from Equations 10.7 to 10.9. It is apparent that the overall voltage gain, G_v, is always less than the amplifier voltage gain, A_v. This is due to the attenuation at the input (Equation 10.7) and at the output (Equation 10.8). In an ideal voltage amplifier Z_{in} is infinite and Z_{out} is zero, both impractical conditions. In the ideal case, then, e_{in} is equal to e_S and e_{out} is equal to $A_v e_{in}$ giving an overall gain of $G_v = A_v$. Thus, only for an ideal amplifier will the circuit of 10.3(B) have a gain of A_v. Practical amplifiers would yield a somewhat lower gain. A high value of Z_{in} and low value of Z_{out} will give an overall gain close to A_v.

It is well, then, to think of A_v as the ideal or theoretical voltage gain. Actually, it is the amplifier's voltage gain when it is driven from an ideal signal source ($R_S = 0$), and its output is unloaded ($R_L = \infty$). In general, these conditions are never met. As such, the amplifier voltage gain is reduced to G_v which takes into account the effects of the non-zero source resistance and the load on the output. The following examples should illustrate these effects.

► EXAMPLE 10.7

An amplifier circuit with parameters

$$Z_{in} = 10K$$
$$Z_{out} = 1K$$
$$A_v = 10$$

is driven by a 1 volt peak-peak (hereafter abbreviated p-p) input signal with a source resistance R_S of 1K. Calculate e_{out} and overall gain when $R_L = 1K$.

Using Equation 10.7 the value of e_{in} to the amplifier is

$$e_{in} = \frac{10K \times e_S}{10K + 1K} = 0.91 \, e_S$$
$$= 0.91 \text{ volts p-p}$$

Using Equation 10.8 the value of e_{out} is

$$e_{out} = \frac{(10e_{in})1K}{1K + 1K} = 5e_{in}$$
$$= 4.55 \text{ volts p-p}$$

Overall gain is

$$G_v = e_{out}/e_S = \frac{4.55}{1} = 4.55 \quad \blacktriangleleft$$

▶ EXAMPLE 10.8

For the same amplifier calculate overall gain when $R_S = 10\Omega$. Following the same procedure

$$e_{in} = \frac{10K}{10K + 10\Omega} \times e_S = 0.99 \text{ volts p-p}$$

$$e_{out} = \frac{(10e_{in})1K}{1K + 1K} = 5e_{in} = 4.995 \text{ volts p-p}$$

$$G_v = 4.995$$

Thus, overall gain can be increased by using a lower resistance source. ◄

▶ EXAMPLE 10.9

Now increase R_L to 10K and calculate overall gain. From the previous example

$$e_{in} = 0.999 \text{ volts p-p}$$

Now using $R_L = 10K$ we have

$$e_{out} = \frac{(10e_{in})(10K)}{10K + 1K} = 9.1e_{in}$$

$$= 9.1 \text{ volts p-p}$$

$$G_v = 9.1 \quad \blacktriangleleft$$

Thus, overall gain can be increased by using a larger load resistance. In fact using $R_S = 0$ and $R_L = \infty$ will give an overall gain of A_v. These conditions are never met in practice.

For the amplifier of Figure 10.3B we can also write the expression for overall current gain G_i. The input signal current i_{in} is given by

$$i_{in} = \frac{e_S}{R_S + Z_{in}} \tag{10.10}$$

The output signal current is given by

$$i_{out} = \frac{e_{out}}{R_L} \tag{10.11}$$

Thus G_i becomes

$$G_i = \frac{i_{out}}{i_{in}} = \frac{e_{out}}{e_S} \frac{R_S + Z_{in}}{R_L} \tag{10.12}$$

which can be written as

$$G_i = G_v \frac{R_S + Z_{in}}{R_L} \qquad (10.13)$$

or conversely

$$G_v = \frac{G_i(R_L)}{R_S + Z_{in}} \qquad (10.14)$$

Thus, when G_v is known G_i may be calculated using Equation 10.13. Otherwise, G_i may be obtained from the expression below which results from substituting Equation 10.9 for G_v in Equation 10.13.

$$G_i = \frac{A_v Z_{in}}{(R_L + Z_{out})} \qquad (10.15)$$

Referring to Equation 10.15, it can be seen that as the load resistor is made smaller the current gain will increase. In fact, when $R_L = 0$ the current gain becomes

$$G_i = A_i = \frac{A_v Z_{in}}{Z_{out}} \qquad (10.16)$$

where A_i is the amplifier's short-circuit current gain. This is the maximum current gain possible.

The overall power gain G_p of the general amplifier is of course given by

$$G_p = G_i \cdot G_v \qquad (10.17)$$

▶ EXAMPLE 10.10

Calculate G_i for the amplifier of Example 10.7. From the results of Example 10.7

$$G_v = 4.55$$

Using Equation 10.13, we have

$$G_i = \frac{4.55(11\text{K})}{1\text{K}} = 50 \qquad ◀$$

▶ EXAMPLE 10.11

Calculate G_i when R_L is increased to 10K as in Example 10.9. Also calculate power gain G_p.

Using Equation 10.13 with $G_v = 9.1$ as calculated in Example 10.9

$$G_i = \frac{9.1(11\text{K})}{(10\text{K})} = 10$$

The resultant power gain is

$$G_p = 9.1 \times 10 = 91 \qquad \blacktriangleleft$$

10.8.   Impedance Matching in Amplifiers

The *maximum power transfer principle* states that the power transferred from a source to a load is at a maximum when the load impedance is equal to the source impedance. Applying this principle to the general amplifier of Figure 10.3(B), it can be seen that for maximum power transfer from the signal source, e_s, to the amplifier input, the input impedance Z_{in} must match the source resistance R_s. Similarly, for maximum power transfer from the amplifier output to the load R_L, the value of R_L must match Z_{out}.

     Thus, for maximum power transfer from the signal source to the amplifier load, Z_{in} must equal R_S, and R_L must equal Z_{out}. In practice these conditions are not often met. For example, transistor audio amplifiers have output impedances typically around $1 - 10K$ and must frequently drive a low impedance (typically 8Ω) load. To provide impedance matching at the input and output of an amplifier, *impedance matching transformers* or *impedance matching circuits* are normally inserted as illustrated in Figure 10.4. The impedance matching circuit on the input

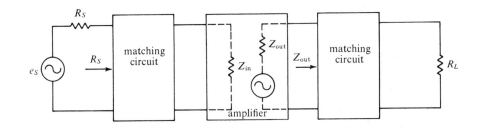

FIG. **10.4.**   IMPEDANCE MATCHING

serves to transform the amplifier's input impedance to a value equal to R_S so that the signal source is essentially driving a load impedance equal to its source impedance, allowing maximum power transfer from the source. A similar function is performed by the output matching circuit.

Often, the output of an amplifier is fed into the input of another amplifier. In this case the input impedance of the second amplifier serves as the load for the first amplifier. Here again, impedance matching is used to match Z_{in} of the second amplifier to the Z_{out} of the first amplifier.

GLOSSARY

Input signal: variations in input voltage or current (a-c portion of input)

Output signal: variations in output voltage or current (a-c portion of output)

Reproduction: duplication of input signal by an amplifier

Amplification: enlargement of input signal by an amplifier

Voltage (current, power) amplifier: circuit specifically designed to develop an output signal voltage (current, power) greater than the input signal voltage (current, power)

Impedance: effective a-c resistance

Input (output) impedance: impedance seen looking into the input (out-put) terminals of a circuit

Impedance matching: matching of source and load impedances for maximum power transfer

Questions

10.1 Will the circuit in Figure 10.5 perform reproduction and/or amplification of the input signal?

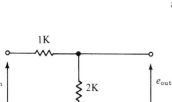

e_{in} 1K   2K e_{out}

FIG. 10.5.

10.2   What is the voltage gain A_v in each of the amplifiers in Figure 10.6?

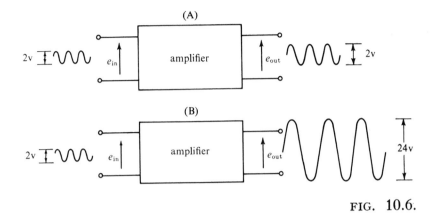

FIG. 10.6.

10.3   Does reproduction take place in both amplifiers of Figure 10.6?

10.4   The amplifier in part (A) of Figure 10.6 has an input current signal of 1 ma p-p causing an output signal current of 10 ma p-p. What is the amplifier's current gain A_i and power gain A_p?

10.5   The input and output curves of a certain amplifier are shown in Fig. 10.7. From these curves calculate Z_{in} and Z_{out} around the points indicated.

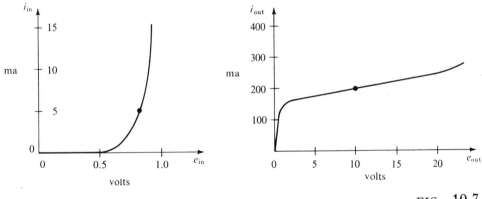

FIG. 10.7.

10.6   Consider the amplifier in Figure 10.8. The amplifier parameters are $Z_{in} = 100K$, $A_v = 1000$, $Z_{out} = 100\Omega$.
(a) If the signal source is 1 mv p-p with a source resistance of 1K, determine e_{out} when $R_L = 10K$. Calculate G_v.
(b) Repeat for $R_L = 1K$ and $R_L = 100\Omega$.
(c) Repeat part (a) with a source resistance of 10K.

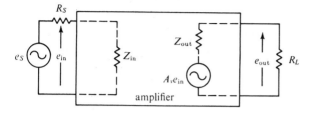

FIG. 10.8.

(d) Calculate G_i for a source resistance of 1K and $R_L = 1$K. Calculate overall power gain $G_p = G_v \times G_i$

(e) What value of R_L is needed to provide maximum output power? Calculate G_v and G_i for this value of R_L (use 1K source resistance). Calculate G_p and compare to part (d).

11

Transistor Amplifiers

11.1.   Introduction

Thus far, all of our work on junction transistors has dealt with d-c currents and voltages. In this chapter we shall investigate the operation of transistors when driven by a-c voltages and currents. In particular, the concentration will be on the transistor's ability to amplify an input signal. The application of the transistor as an *amplifier* is of such importance that devoting a whole chapter to this subject is warranted even in a text concerned primarily with devices. The same can be said for *transistor switches* which are covered in Chapter 12.

In the treatment of transistor amplifiers the major differences among Com. B, Com. E and Com. C amplifier configurations will be brought out. The emphasis will be on fundamental concepts rather than on exact circuit relationships.

Introduction of biasing methods, small signal equivalent circuits and high frequency effects should give the student sufficient background to pursue more thorough coverage of transistor amplifier circuits in later courses.

11.2.   How a Transistor Amplifies

The *E-B* junction is the controlling circuit of the transistor in the same way that the control grid is the controlling element of the

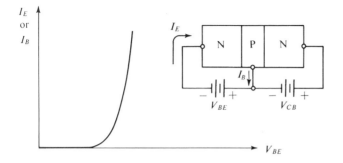

FIG. 11.1.   NONLINEAR RELATIONSHIP BETWEEN I_E
(OR I_B) AND V_{BE}

vacuum tube. The voltage-versus-current curve for the *E-B* junction is shown in Figure 11.1. The current and voltage in the *E-B* junction have a *nonlinear* relationship in that the emitter current will not change linearly as the voltage from the base to emitter changes. Since a certain portion of the current crossing the *E-B* junction becomes base current, the base current versus base-emitter voltage curve has the same shape as that in Figure 11.1.

Amplification with a transistor is accomplished by varying the *E-B* junction forward bias V_{BE} which in turn causes a variation in the emitter (or base) current. This will be accompanied by a change in the collector current flowing across the reverse-biased *C-B* junction. Since the *E-B* junction is a forward-biased junction, it has a relatively low impedance and small changes in V_{BE} will cause large changes in current. The same or a greater current variation occurring across the reverse-biased *C-B* junction, which has a high impedance, can result in voltage amplification.

In other words, if the *emitter* current is changed by some amount through a small change in V_{BE} we can expect the *collector* current to also change but by a slightly smaller amount. Recall that the current gain from emitter to collector is always less than *one* since a small portion of emitter current flows through the base lead. It is possible to place a large load resistor in the collector circuit; across this load resistor, the change in collector current will develop a large change in voltage. This results in voltage amplification since the load signal voltage will be much greater than the small change in V_{BE} which produced it.

The amount by which the *collector* current will change in response to a change in *emitter* current is indicated by the transistor parameter α (alpha) which is the *a-c common base current gain* and is given by

$$\alpha = \frac{\Delta I_C}{\Delta I_E}\bigg|\, V_{CB} = \text{constant} \qquad \textbf{(11.1)}$$

This formula states that α is obtained by taking the ratio of the collector current change to the emitter current change while holding the collector-base voltage constant since the value of V_{CB} does have a small effect on collector current. α is the a-c counterpart of $\alpha_{\text{d-c}}$ and pertains only to changing (a-c) currents. Like $\alpha_{\text{d-c}}$, the value of α is also very close to unity. Figure 11.2 illustrates

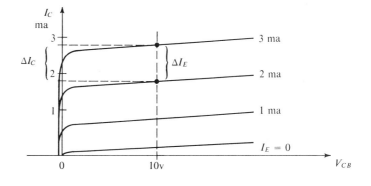

FIG. **11.2.**   CALCULATION OF α

how the value of α is obtained from the Com. B output curves. In general, the value of α will vary slightly depending on where in the active region it is measured. It is usually in the range of 0.95 to 0.999.

▶ EXAMPLE 11.1

From the data table below determine α.

I_E	I_C	V_{CB}
10 ma	9.9 ma	10v
20 ma	19.75 ma	10v

Using Equation 11.1

$$\alpha = \frac{\Delta I_C}{\Delta I_E}\bigg|\, V_{CB} = 10v = \frac{19.75 - 9.9}{20 - 10} = 0.985 \qquad ◀$$

The magnitude of *emitter* current change for a given change in V_{BE} is indicated by the parameter r_{ib} which is the a-c resistance of the *E-B* junction when I_E is the input current (as in Com. B). It is given by the formula

$$r_{ib} = \frac{\Delta V_{BE}}{\Delta I_E}\bigg|_{V_{CB}} = \text{constant} \qquad (11.2)$$

This parameter, also called the *Com. B input impedance* (*a-c resistance*), is a measure of how much the emitter current changes for a small change in V_{BE}. Figure 11.3 illustrates how it may be obtained from the Com. B input curve.

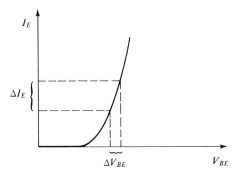

FIG. **11.3.**   CALCULATION OF r_{ib}

The value of r_{ib} is normally in the range from 10 to 300 ohms. However, it depends on where on the input curve it is measured. As can be seen from Figure 11.3, r_{ib} gets smaller as I_E increases and the curve becomes steeper.

▶ EXAMPLE 11.2

A particular transistor has an r_{ib} of 20 ohms. For a decrease in V_{BE} of 1 mv what will be the resultant decrease in I_E?
Since

$$r_{ib} = \frac{\Delta V_{BE}}{\Delta I_E}$$

then

$$\Delta I_E = \frac{\Delta V_{BE}}{r_{ib}}$$

$$\Delta I_E = \frac{-1 \text{ mv}}{20} = -50\ \mu\text{a} \qquad ◀$$

▶ EXAMPLE 11.3

If the same transistor has $\alpha = 0.98$, calculate the resultant change in I_C and then calculate the change in voltage across a collector resistor, R_C of 10K.

Since

$$\alpha = \frac{\Delta I_C}{\Delta I_E}$$

then

$$\Delta I_C = \alpha \Delta I_E$$
$$= 0.98(-50 \ \mu a) = -49 \ \mu a$$

The voltage change across R_C is given by

$$\Delta V_{RC} = \Delta I_C \times R_C$$
$$= -49 \ \mu a \times 10K$$
$$= -490 \ mv$$

Recall from Example 11.2 that the original change in V_{BE} was -1 mv. Thus a 490 mv decrease in the output resulted from a 1 mv decrease in the input—a voltage gain of 490.   ◀

By the same approach, if the *base* current is changed by some amount through a small change in V_{BE} we can expect the *collector* current to also change but by a much greater amount. Recall that the current gain from base to collector is always much greater than one. Here again the change in voltage developed across a load resistor in the collector circuit will be much greater than the small change in V_{BE}, resulting in voltage amplification.

The amount by which the *collector* current will change in response to a change in *base* current is indicated by the transistor parameter β which is the *a-c common emitter gain* and is given by

$$\beta = \frac{\Delta I_C}{\Delta I_B}\bigg|_{V_{CE} \text{ constant}} \qquad \qquad \textbf{(11.3)}$$

This formula states that β is obtained by taking the ratio of the collector current change to the base current change while holding the collector-emitter voltage constant. β is the a-c counterpart of $\beta_{\text{d-c}}$ and pertains only to changing (a-c) currents. The value of β can be determined from the Com. E output curves as shown in Figure 11.4 and will vary depending on where in the active region it is measured. Typically, it is in the range of 30-300 and can reach 1000. β is normally slightly below the value of $\beta_{\text{d-c}}$ at the same point on the characteristics.

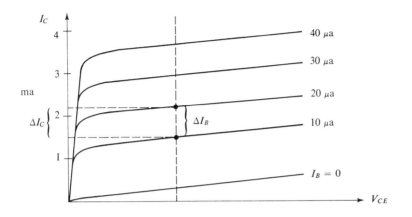

FIG. 11.4.   CALCULATION OF β

▶ EXAMPLE 11.4

Calculate β from the data table below.

I_B	I_C	V_{CE}
100 μa	6 ma	10v
125 μa	7 ma	10v

Using Equation 11.3

$$\beta = \frac{\Delta I_C}{\Delta I_B}\bigg| V_{CE} = 10\text{v} = \frac{7\text{ ma} - 6\text{ ma}}{125\ \mu\text{a} - 100\ \mu\text{a}} = 40 \qquad \blacktriangleleft$$

The magnitude of *base* current change for a given change in V_{BE} is indicated by the parameter r_{ie} which is the a-c resistance of the *E-B* junction when I_B is the input current (as in Com. E and Com. C). It is given by the formula

$$r_{ie} = \frac{\Delta V_{BE}}{\Delta I_B}\bigg| V_{CE} = \text{constant} \qquad \textbf{(11.4)}$$

This parameter, also called the *Com. E input impedance*, is a measure of how much the base current changes for a small change in V_{BE}. Figure 11.5 illustrates how it may be determined from the Com. E input curve.

The value of r_{ie} is normally in the range from 500Ω to 5K and depends on where on the curve it is measured. Its value decreases as I_B increases.

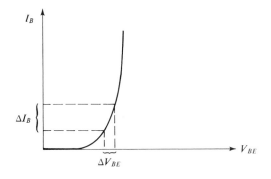

FIG. **11.5.**　　　CALCULATION OF r_{ie}

▶ EXAMPLE 11.5

A certain transistor has an r_{ie} of 1000Ω. For an increase in V_{BE} of 1 mv what will be the resultant increase in I_B?
Since

$$r_{ie} = \Delta V_{BE}/\Delta I_B$$

then

$$\Delta I_B = \Delta V_{BE}/r_{ie}$$
$$\Delta I_B = 1\ mv/1000 = 1\ \mu a$$

▶ EXAMPLE 11.6

If the same transistor has a β of 100, calculate the resultant increase in I_C and I_E.
Since

$$\beta = \frac{\Delta I_C}{\Delta I_B}$$

then

$$\Delta I_C = \beta \Delta I_B$$
$$= 100 \times 1\ \mu a = 100\ \mu a$$

and

$$\Delta I_E = \Delta I_C + \Delta I_B$$
$$= (\beta + 1)\, \Delta I_B$$
$$= (101)\,(1\ \mu a) = 101\ \mu a$$ ◀

We are now prepared to pursue the study of transistor amplification in more detail, keeping in mind the main points of this section:

(a) The base-emitter forward bias V_{BE} is the controlling variable in the transistor amplifier.

(b) A small change in V_{BE} causes a large change in emitter current which produces a corresponding change in collector current.

(c) The change in collector current, if allowed to flow through a load resistor in the collector circuit, can develop a relatively large signal voltage.

(d) The signal voltage across the load resistor will be much greater than the V_{BE} signal which produced it. This action is voltage amplification.

11.3.   Common Base Amplifiers: Basic Circuit

The basic Com. B amplifier circuit is shown in Figure 11.6. Except for the input signal and coupling capacitor the circuit is identical

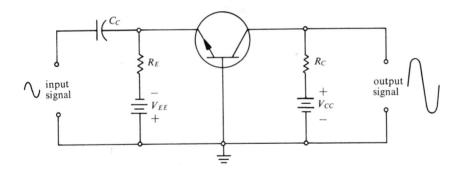

FIG. 11.6.   COM. B AMPLIFIER CIRCUIT

to the Com. B circuit studied in Chapter 9. The input signal is applied to the transistor emitter through the coupling capacitor which serves to block any d-c current from flowing from the emitter supply V_{EE} back through the signal source. As far as the d-c currents and voltages in this circuit are concerned, the methods for determining their values are exactly those outlined in Chapter 9. The d-c values of I_E, I_C and V_{CB} are called the *bias values* or *quiescent values* and they represent a certain point on the transistor characteristic curves. This point is called the *bias point* or *quiescent point* (Q-point) and in most cases is in the *active* region. The transistor operates at this point when no signal is applied. The Q-point, which depends only on the d-c voltage sources and resistors R_E and R_C and is in no way dependent on the input signal, places the transistor in the *active* region of its operation.

The input signal, as we shall see, will cause the transistor curcuit values to change around the Q-point yet still remain in the active region. As a result of the input signal the transistor currents and voltages will have signal or a-c portions as well as their d-c values. In all the work to follow upper case symbols such as I_E will be used to represent d-c (Q-point) values and lower case symbols such as i_E will represent a-c (signal) values. The complete representation of any circuit value will be the superposition of its d-c value and its a-c value. This is exemplified in Figure 11.7 where typical emitter current values are illustrated.

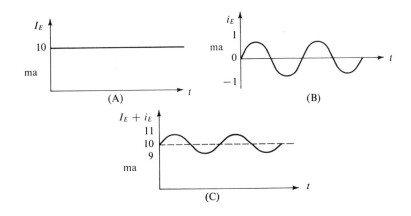

FIG. 11.7.   (A) D-C EMITTER CURRENT (B) A-C EMITTER CURRENT (C) TOTAL EMITTER CURRENT

11.4.   Common Base Amplifiers: Current Gain

In the Com. B amplifier the emitter current is the input current and the collector current is the output current. In order to analyze the a-c current gain from emitter to collector we can disregard the d-c circuit values for the moment and concentrate on the a-c values only. In Figure 11.8 only a-c values are shown. The signal source e_S supplies a signal current i_S. Although a portion of this signal current will flow down through R_E as i_X, in properly designed amplifiers this portion will be very small so that the value

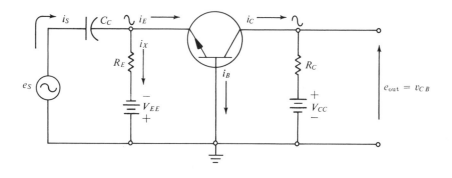

FIG. 11.8.   A-C CURRENTS IN COM. B AMPLIFIER

of i_E can be assumed to be equal to i_S. The majority of this input i_E will become i_C in the collector circuit with the remainder flowing in the base as i_B. Because the signal current output i_C is *less* than the signal current input i_E the current gain of a Com. B amplifier is always *less than one*. We know from the previous discussion in Section 11.2 that this current gain is α which in this case is given by

$$\alpha = \frac{\Delta I_C}{\Delta I_E}\bigg|_{V_{CB}} = \frac{i_C}{i_E} < 1 \qquad (11.5)$$

In the usual sense there is no "gain" in current since α is less than one, yet the term "gain" is still employed.

▶EXAMPLE 11.6

In the circuit of Figure 11.8 the transistor has an α of 0.98. If the input signal current i_S is 100 μa p-p determine the value of i_E, i_C and i_B.
Assume

$$i_E = i_S = 100 \ \mu\text{a p-p}$$

Then

$$i_C = \alpha i_E = 98 \ \mu\text{a p-p}$$

and

$$i_B = i_E - i_C = 2 \ \mu\text{a p-p} \qquad \blacktriangleleft$$

Strictly speaking the overall current gain, A_i, from signal source to output will be slightly less than α due to some loss of current through R_E and to the finite transistor output impedance. However, in most cases the value of A_i is very close to α.

11.5.   Common Base Amplifiers: Voltage Gain

The logical question now arises: If the output signal current is less than the input signal current in the Com. B amplifier, how is *voltage gain* possible?

In the Com. B amplifier the input signal voltage is supplied between emitter and base and the output signal voltage is taken from collector to base as in Figure 11.8. Note that the collector signal current flows in the collector resistor R_C. This will result in a signal voltage across R_C and, since the d-c collector supply V_{CC} cannot have an a-c voltage drop across its terminals, the output signal voltage will equal the a-c voltage across R_C. Voltage amplification occurs when this voltage is greater than e_S, the input signal voltage.

Let us examine the signal currents and voltages of the Com. B amplifier without concerning ourselves with the d-c bias point. That is, we can ignore V_{BB} and V_{CC} if our only interest lies in a-c currents and voltages and if we assume that V_{BB} and V_{CC} have *biased* the transistor in the *active* region. In considering a-c values we can also ignore the effect of the coupling capacitor if its impedance is made very small at the a-c frequency of interest. This can always be accomplished if the value of C_C is made large enough since the magnitude of its impedance is given by

$$|Z_C| = X_C = \frac{1}{2\pi f C_C} \qquad (11.6)$$

The Com. B amplifier of Figure 11.8 can now be replaced with that of Figure 11.9 for purposes of a-c analysis. The d-c supplies

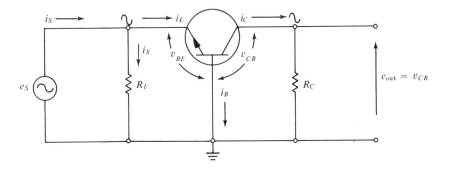

FIG. **11.9.**   THE COM. B AMPLIFIER WITH D-C SUPPLIES AND COUPLING CAPACITOR REPLACED BY SHORT CIRCUITS FOR A-C ANALYSIS

and the coupling capacitor have been replaced by short circuits since their a-c voltage drops can be considered negligible.

Examination of the input portion of the circuit reveals that the input signal e_S appears directly across the E-B junction such that the value of the a-c base to emitter voltage v_{BE} is given by

$$v_{BE} = -e_S \qquad (11.7)$$

The negative sign simply indicates that v_{BE} is 180° out of phase with e_S. That is, as e_S increases the emitter becomes more positive than the base or equivalently the base becomes more negative than the emitter. Thus, base to emitter voltage v_{BE} decreases as e_S increases and increases as e_S decreases. This is illustrated in Figure 11.10.

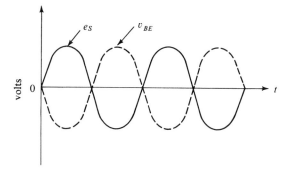

FIG. 11.10.   RELATIONSHIP BETWEEN e_S AND v_{BE} ILLUSTRATING 180° PHASE DIFFERENCE

Keeping in mind the fact that the E-B junction has a d-c bias across it (V_{BE}), it is apparent that the signal voltage v_{BE} will alternately *subtract from* and *add to* this bias. It is this changing forward bias across the E-B junction which will produce a change in the emitter current flowing across the junction. The d-c bias, for example, might be 0.7v for a typical silicon transistor. An input signal e_S of 0.1v p-p would then result in the base to emitter voltage varying from 0.65v to 0.75v. This is illustrated in Figure 11.11.

The a-c portion of emitter current i_E which flows in response to the changing base-emitter voltage can be determined by utilizing the *a-c Com. B input impedance* r_{ib} which was introduced in Section 11.2. Repeating its definition here we have

$$r_{ib} = \frac{\Delta V_{BE}}{\Delta I_E}\bigg|_{V_{CB} = \text{constant}}$$

In the amplifier circuit ΔV_{BE} is simply the a-c base emitter voltage v_{BE} and ΔI_E is the a-c emitter current i_E. Thus we have

$$r_{ib} = \frac{v_{BE}}{i_E}$$

or

$$i_E = \frac{v_{BE}}{r_{ib}} = \frac{-e_S}{r_{ib}} \qquad\qquad \textbf{(11.8)}$$

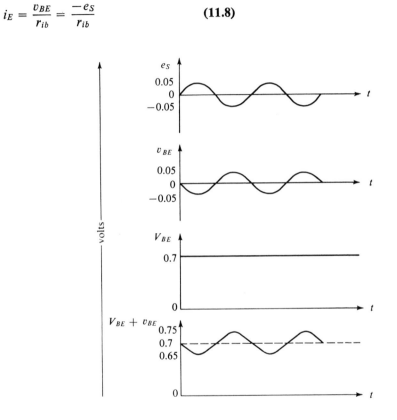

FIG. **11.11.**   (A) INPUT SIGNAL (B) A-C BASE-EMITTER VOLTAGE (C) D-C BASE-EMITTER VOLTAGE (D) TOTAL BASE-EMITTER VOLTAGE

In other words, the a-c impedance seen between emitter and base is r_{ib}. This is emphasized in Figure 11.12 where the input to the transistor has been replaced by its input impedance. Strictly speaking the transistor input impedance will be slightly greater than r_{ib}. However, the difference is normally unimportant. In any case the exact value of transistor input impedance is not important in our discussion of amplification action. For our

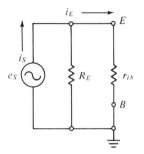

FIG. 11.12.   REPLACING E-B JUNCTION BY ITS A-C
IMPEDANCE r_{ib} TO CALCULATE i_E

0.1v p-p input signal and assuming an r_{ib} of 20Ω the a-c emitter
current would be (from Equation 11.8)

$$i_E = \frac{0.1\text{v p-p}}{20\Omega} = 5 \text{ ma p-p}$$

This emitter signal current would also "ride" on a d-c level (I_E).
This is illustrated in Figure 11.13 corresponding to the signals
of Figure 11.11.

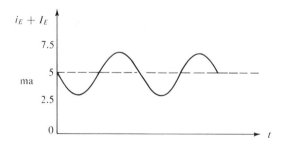

FIG. 11.13.   TOTAL EMITTER CURRENT $i_E + I_E$ IN
RESPONSE TO INPUT SIGNAL SHOWN IN
FIGURE 11.11

The a-c collector current which will flow as a result of i_E is
given by

$$i_C = \alpha i_E$$

This collector signal current will develop an a-c voltage across R_C which produces an a-c collector-base voltage v_{CB} which is also the output signal e_{out}. That is,

$$e_{out} = v_{CB} = i_C \times R_C = \alpha i_E \times R_C \qquad (11.9)$$

Here is the key to Com. B voltage amplification. Since the *C-B* junction is reverse-biased it has a very high internal resistance. This high resistance permits a large value of R_C to be used in the collector circuit without affecting the output current. Thus, e_{out} can become very large by making R_C large. For example, with our 5 ma p-p emitter current and an α of 0.98, a value of $R_C = 10K$ will produce (using 11.9)

$$e_{out} = 0.98 \times 5 \text{ ma p-p} \times 10K = 49v \text{ p-p}$$

This output signal voltage is $49/0.1 = 490$ times greater than e_S indicating a voltage gain of 490. Even though the collector signal current is slightly less than i_E (4.9 ma in this case), the fact that it flows through a relatively large resistance (R_C) while i_E flows through a small resistance (r_{ib}) permits voltage amplification to occur. In common-base amplifiers the voltage gain can be very large and is typically in the range 250-2500.

An approximate formula for voltage gain can be derived from the previous discussion. Starting with e_{out} and working back to the input we have

$$e_{out} = i_C R_C \approx \alpha i_E R_C$$

$$= \frac{\alpha v_{BE}}{r_{ib}} R_C$$

$$e_{out} \approx \frac{\alpha e_S R_C}{r_{ib}} \qquad (11.10)$$

From Equation 11.10 the voltage gain A_v is seen to be

$$A_v = \frac{e_{out}}{e_S} \approx \frac{\alpha R_C}{r_{ib}} \qquad (11.11)$$

To be exact, the value of A_v will be less than that given by 11.11 because of the assumptions made concerning α and r_{ib}. However, the discrepancy is seldom large enough to warrant a more exact expression for gain. In fact, in many cases it may be simplified even further by assuming $\alpha = 1$. This becomes

$$A_v \approx \frac{R_C}{r_{ib}} \qquad (11.12)$$

It may be well to study a few examples to further clarify the Com. B amplifier action.

▶ EXAMPLE 11.7

The transistor used in the Com. B amplifier of Figure 11.14 is biased at the following Q-point:

$$I_E = 1 \text{ ma}$$
$$V_{BE} = 0.7\text{v}$$
$$I_C = 0.99 \text{ ma}$$
$$V_{CB} = 15.15\text{v}$$

(This should be verified by the student). At this Q-point the transistor has an $\alpha = 0.985$ and an $r_{ib} = 35\Omega$. Calculate the values of i_E, i_C, v_{CB} and A_v for an input signal of 10 mv p-p.

The emitter signal current is determined using Expression 11.8.

$$i_E = \frac{10 \text{ mv p-p}}{35\Omega} = 0.286 \text{ ma p-p}$$

This produces

$$i_C = \alpha i_E = 0.985 \times 0.286$$
$$= 0.281 \text{ ma p-p}$$

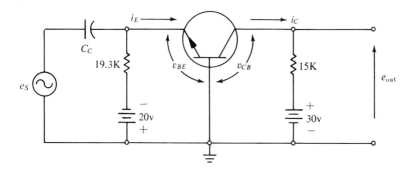

FIG. 11.14.   EXAMPLE 11.7

The output signal will be

$$e_{\text{out}} = v_{CB} = 0.281 \text{ ma} \times 15\text{K} = 4.22\text{v p-p}$$

This gives a voltage gain of

$$A_v = \frac{e_{\text{out}}}{e_S} = \frac{4.22\text{v p-p}}{10 \text{ mv p-p}} = 422$$ ◀

▶ EXAMPLE 11.8

In the circuit of the previous example calculate the new value of A_v when R_C is decreased to 10K.
From the results of Example 11.7

$$i_C = 0.281 \text{ ma p-p}$$

giving an output signal

$$e_{\text{out}} = 0.281 \text{ ma} \times 10K = 2.81\text{v p-p}$$

producing a voltage gain

$$A_v = \frac{2.81\text{v p-p}}{10 \text{ mv p-p}} = 281 \qquad ◀$$

The voltage gain A_v varies in proportion to the value of R_C as the examples above illustrate. However, voltage gain cannot be increased indefinitely by making R_C larger. This is due to the transistor's finite output impedance which will be discussed later.

11.6.   Common Base Amplifier: Power Gain

Because it can develop very high voltage gain, the Com. B amplifier is also capable of substantial power gain. Power gain is the ratio of output signal power to input signal power. It is also the product of current gain and voltage gain. That is, the power gain can be expressed as

$$A_p = A_i \times A_v \qquad \textbf{(11.13)}$$

For the Com. B amplifier the current gain is approximately α and the voltage gain is given by Equation 11.11. This results in

$$A_p \approx \frac{\alpha^2 R_C}{r_{ib}} \qquad \textbf{(11.14)}$$

Since A_i is slightly less than one, the power gain will always be slightly less than the voltage gain.

▶ EXAMPLE 11.9

Calculate the power gain for the amplifier of Example 11.7.
From the results of Example 11.7

$$A_i = 0.985 \text{ and } A_v = 422$$

Using Equation 11.13 the power gain becomes

$$A_p = 0.985 \times 422 \approx 416 \qquad ◀$$

▶ EXAMPLE 11.10

Verify the result of the previous example by calculating the input signal power and output signal power from Example 11.7.

In order to calculate power we must first convert the signal voltages from p-p values to *rms* values. This can be accomplished using the relationship

$$e_{rms} = \frac{e_{\text{p-p}}}{2\sqrt{2}} \approx 0.3535 e_{\text{p-p}}$$

Referring to Example 11.7 the input signal voltage was 10 mv p-p which becomes 3.54 mv *rms*. This input signal produces power in the input resistance r_{ib}. For this circuit the input power becomes

$$P_{isig} = \frac{(3.54 \text{ mv } rms)^2}{35\Omega} = 0.357 \times 10^{-6} \text{ watts}$$

The output signal voltage was calculated as 4.26v p-p which becomes 1.5v *rms*. The output signal produces power in the collector resistance R_C. For this circuit the output power becomes

$$P_{osig} = \frac{(1.5v \text{ } rms)^2}{15K} = 1.5 \times 10^{-4} \text{ watts}$$

Now calculating power gain we have

$$A_p = \frac{P_{osig}}{P_{isig}} = \frac{1.5 \times 10^{-4} \text{ watts}}{0.357 \times 10^{-6} \text{ watts}} \approx 420$$

This result agrees with the previous example.   ◀

The power gain (420) of the examples above is typical for Com. B amplifiers. The value of A_p usually ranges from 250 to 2500 and like A_v it increases with increases in R_C.

11.7.   Common Base Amplifier: Input and Output Impedance

When discussing input and output impedances we must distinguish between the transistor and the entire amplifier circuit. In previous discussions the *transistor* input impedance in the Com. B configuration was found to be r_{ib} which is typically very small (10Ω-300Ω). As can be seen in Figure 11.9 the transistor input is in parallel with the emitter resistor R_E. This places the transistor input impedance r_{ib} in parallel with R_E as shown in Figure 11.12.

This parallel combination is what the signal source sees and hence it is the *amplifier* input impedance. Denoting the Com. B *amplifier input impedance* by the symbol Z_{ib} we have

$$Z_{ib} = R_E \| r_{ib}$$
$$= \frac{R_E \times r_{ib}}{R_E + r_{ib}} \tag{11.15}$$

Normally the value of R_E is much larger than r_{ib} (as in Examples 7 and 8, Figure 11.14) and Z_{ib} is essentially equal to r_{ib}.

▶ EXAMPLE 11.11

Calculate the input impedance for the amplifier in Example 7.
In the amplifier of Figure 11.14 $R_E = 19.3\text{K}$ and $r_{ib} = 35\Omega$. Thus, Z_{ib} is given by

$$Z_{ib} = \frac{19,300\Omega \times 35\Omega}{19,300\Omega + 35\Omega} \approx 35\Omega \qquad ◀$$

It is apparent that the input impedance of a Com. B amplifier is very low. This characteristic makes it difficult to drive a Com. B amplifier from moderate or high impedance signal sources without some sort of impedance matching network (Chapter 10.) On the other hand, the low input impedance makes it ideal for amplifying signals from low impedance sources such as magnetic phonograph pickups.

The transistor's Com. B *output impedance* is a measure of the effect of the collector-base voltage V_{CB} on the collector current. It is given the symbol r_{ob} and is essentially the a-c resistance of the reverse-biased *C-B* junction. Its value is given by the formula

$$r_{ob} = \frac{\Delta V_{CB}}{\Delta I_C}\bigg|_{I_E} = \text{constant} \tag{11.16}$$

Figure 11.15 illustrates how it may be obtained from the Com. B output characteristics. It is obvious from the figure that the value of r_{ob} can be very high since large changes in V_{CB} produce only very small changes in collector current in the active region. In practice, values ranging from 250K to greater than 1 meg are common for r_{ob}.

In the Com. B amplifier circuit, the transistor output impedance, which is essentially the a-c resistance of the *C-B* junction, is in parallel with the collector resistor R_C. Thus, the amplifier output impedance will be the parallel combination of R_C and

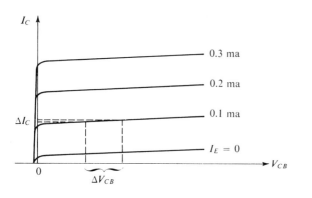

FIG.   **11.15.**   CALCULATION OF r_{ob}

r_{ob}. Denoting the Com. B *amplifier output impedance* by the symbol Z_{ob} we have

$$Z_{ob} = R_C \| r_{ob}$$

$$= \frac{R_C \times r_{ob}}{R_C + r_{ob}} \qquad (11.17)$$

The value of R_C is usually made fairly high for high voltage gain. Therefore, the value of Z_{ob} can be relatively high.

▶ EXAMPLE 11.12

Calculate the output impedance of a Com. B transistor amplifier which has $R_C = 50K$ and a transistor with $r_{ob} = 1$ megohm.
From 11.17 we have

$$Z_{ob} = \frac{50K \times 1 \text{ megohm}}{50K + 1 \text{ megohm}} = 47.6K \qquad ◀$$

If the R_C used has a value of less than one tenth of r_{ob}, it is usually accurate enough to assume that Z_{ob} equals R_C.

The high output impedance of the Com. B amplifier makes it unsuitable for driving low impedance loads unless some impedance matching circuit is used. However, it can work directly into high impedance loads such as the input to vacuum tube amplifiers.

11.8.   Common Base Amplifiers: General Representation

Now that approximate expressions for input impedance, output impedance, current gain and voltage gain have been developed for the Com. B amplifier, the general amplifier relationships developed in Section 10.7 may be employed. In this way the effects of signal source impedance and load impedance may be determined.

Let us consider the Com. B amplifier circuit in Figure 11.16 and let us further assume that the transistor has the following parameters at the Q-point:

$$\alpha = 0.99$$
$$r_{ib} = 50\Omega$$
$$r_{ob} = 1 \text{ megohm}$$

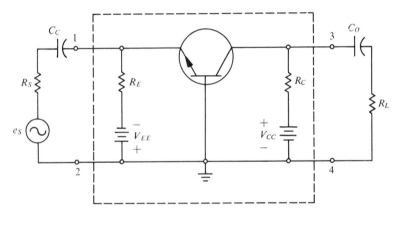

FIG. 11.16.   COM. B AMPLIFIER CIRCUIT

The circuit values are:

$$R_E = 10\text{K}$$
$$V_{EE} = 6\text{v}$$
$$R_C = 10\text{K}$$
$$V_{CC} = 12\text{v}$$

The portion of the circuit enclosed by the dotted line is the amplifier proper which was analyzed in the previous sections. Feeding the input terminals (1-2) of the amplifier is the signal source e_S which is coupled to the amplifier input through C_C. Also included is the source resistance R_S which until now has been neglected. The amplifier output terminals (3-4) are connected to a load resistance R_L through an output coupling capacitor C_O. The coupling capacitor prevents d-c current from flowing to the load allowing only a-c voltage to appear across R_L.

We can replace the amplifier proper by the general amplifier circuit discussed in Section 10.7 and shown in Figure 10.3. It is redrawn in Figure 11.17 for convenience. Since we are going to be

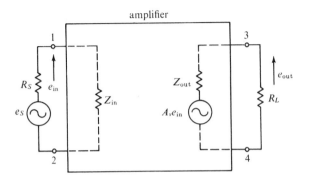

FIG. **11.17.** EQUIVALENT REPRESENTATION OF AM-
PLIFIER IN FIGURE **11.16**

interested in a-c currents and voltages only, the coupling capacitors have been replaced by short circuits. In order for the circuit of Figure 11.17 to be equivalent to the amplifier in Figure 11.16 the appropriate values of Z_{in}, Z_{out}, and A_v must be used. These values may be calculated using Equations 11.15, 11.17, and 11.11 respectively, along with the transistor and circuit values given. The calculations are shown below:

$$Z_{in} = Z_{ib} = R_E \| r_{ib}$$
$$\approx 50\Omega$$
$$Z_{out} = Z_{ob} = R_C \| r_{ob}$$
$$= \frac{10^4 \times 10^6}{10^4 + 10^6}$$
$$\approx 9.9\text{K}$$
$$A_v = \frac{\alpha R_C}{r_{ib}} = \frac{0.99 \times 10\text{K}}{50\Omega} = 198$$

With these values inserted in Figure 11.17 the two circuits are essentially equivalent (for a-c calculations only, of course).

We can now calculate the overall circuit voltage gain $G_v = e_{out}/e_S$ using Equation 10.9 which is repeated below using the Com. B amplifier parameters.

$$G_v = \frac{A_v R_L(Z_{ib})}{(Z_{ib} + R_S)(Z_{ob} + R_L)} \tag{11.18}$$

Recall from Chapter 10 that G_v is always less than A_v due to the signal voltage lost across the source resistance and the output impedance.

▶ EXAMPLE 11.13

For the circuit under consideration calculate the overall voltage gain if $R_S = 10\Omega$ and $R_L = 20K$.
Using Equation 10.18

$$G_v = \frac{198 \times 20K \times 50\Omega}{(50\Omega + 10\Omega)(9.9K + 20K)} \approx 110 \qquad ◀$$

▶ EXAMPLE 11.14

Repeat for $R_S = 1000\Omega$ and $R_L = 20K$.

$$G_v = \frac{198 \times 20K \times 50\Omega}{(1050\Omega)(29.9K)} \approx 6.3 \qquad ◀$$

▶ EXAMPLE 11.15

Repeat for $R_S = 10\Omega$ and $R_L = 1K$

$$G_v = \frac{198 \times 1K \times 50}{(60)(11K)} = 15 \qquad ◀$$

The results of these examples point out that overall voltage gain decreases as the source resistance increases (Examples 11.13 and 11.14) and as the load resistance decreases (Examples 11.13 and 11.15). The overall gain G_v will approach A_v when $R_L \gg Z_{out}$ and $R_S \ll Z_{in}$.

Some very useful approximations to Equation 11.18 can be made under certain conditions. In many cases the value of r_{ob} is much greater than R_C in which case Z_{ob} is approximately equal to R_C. In this situation we can write

$$G_v = \frac{A_v Z_{ib} R_L}{(Z_{ib} + R_S)(R_L + R_C)} \qquad \text{(11.18A)}$$

Often the source resistance R_S is much larger than Z_{ib} and we can neglect the effect of Z_{ib} in the denominator of Equation 11.18. Using this fact and recalling that $A_v = \alpha R_C / r_{ib}$, we have

$$G_v \approx \frac{\alpha R_C R_L}{R_S(R_C + R_L)} \qquad \text{(11.18B)}$$

If we further approximate α by calling it *one* and denote $R_C \| R_L$ by the symbol R' we have

$$G_v \approx \frac{R'}{R_S} \qquad\qquad (11.18C)$$

which is a very simple formula indeed. It should be used only when $R_S \gg r_{ib}$ and $r_{ob} \gg R_C$, say by a factor of ten or more. Its usefulness lies in the fact that the gain is given as a ratio of resistances R' and R_S which are external to the transistor implying that the transistor parameters have little effect on gain under the conditions stated. This characteristic can be very useful since it indicates that voltage gain will not change as r_{ib} changes. The value of r_{ib} will change as the emitter current changes due to the non-linearity of the Com. B input curve (Figure 11.3). This would normally result in some distortion of the output signal. If $R_S \gg r_{ib}$, however, this effect is "swamped" out by the large R_S in series with r_{ib}. The price paid for this improvement is the obviously lower gain which accompanies a large value of R_S.

A look at the following example should demonstrate the usefulness of the approximate formula given by Equation 11.18C.

▶ EXAMPLE 11.16

Repeat Example 11.14 using the approximations cited above.
From Example 11.14, $R_S = 1000\Omega$ and $R_L = 20K$. Since R_S is $\gg r_{ib}$ (50Ω) and since r_{ob} (1 meg) is $\gg R_C$ (10K) we can use the approximate formula. Thus,

$$G_v \approx \frac{R'}{R_S} = \frac{R_C \| R_L}{1K} = \frac{6.7K}{1K}$$
$$= 6.7$$

which agrees to within 5 per cent of the more accurate result of Example 11.14.   ◀

The less accurate formula is very easy to use since it requires knowing only the values of R_C, R_L and R_S and none of the transistor parameters. It should be used wherever possible.

It should be re-emphasized that none of the equations developed in this chapter are exact due to certain, often slight, effects which have been neglected. It is not the intent of this text to derive the exact design equations of transistor amplifiers since, after all, exact parameters of a transistor are rarely known. Its purpose is rather to give the student an understanding of transistor amplification and a feeling for the effects of certain components and transistor parameters on amplifier operation.

11.9.   Common Base Amplifiers: Graphical Analysis of Amplifier Waveforms

Further insight into the Com. B amplifier may be obtained using the familiar load-line technique. In particular, amplifier waveforms may be analyzed more closely using the graphical approach and the effects of the Q-point and input signal amplitude on the output waveform can be determined.

Let us consider the amplifier circuit in Figure 11.18. The circuit values are as shown:

$$e_S = 25 \text{ mv p-p}$$
$$R_E = 4.7\text{K}$$
$$V_{EE} = 5\text{v}$$
$$R_C = 10\text{K}$$
$$V_{CC} = 20\text{v}$$
$$R_L = 10\text{K}$$

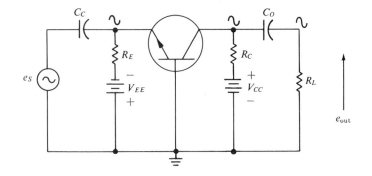

FIG. 11.18.   COM. B AMPLIFIER

The transistor is germanium and has a value of $r_{ib} = 25\Omega$ at $I_E = 1$ ma. Its Com. B output curves are shown in Figure 11.19.

The procedure will be to first determine the Q-point (d-c operating point). Since only d-c values are to be considered in finding the Q-point, the signal source e_S and the load resistor R_L do not affect its determination because of the d-c isolation provided by the coupling capacitors. The load-line to be used to find the Q-point will be called the "d-c load-line." It is determined by V_{CC} and R_C as outlined in Chapter 9. The load-line for $V_{CC} = 20$v and $R_C = 10$K is superimposed on the curves of Figure 11.19. The Q-point will reside at the intersection of the d-c load-

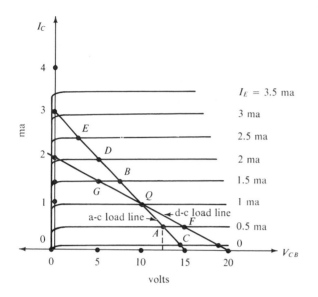

ma

FIG. 11.19.   OUTPUT CURVES FOR TRANSISTOR IN
FIGURE 11.18

line and the transistor curve corresponding to the d-c value of emitter current. The latter quantity is easily calculated as

$$I_E = \frac{V_{EE} - V_{BE}}{R_E}$$

$$= \frac{5v - 0.3v}{4.7K} = 1 \text{ ma}$$

The resulting Q-point is at $I_C = 0.99$ ma and $V_{CB} = 10.1$v.

The a-c operation can now be determined. In doing so we must now include the effect of R_L. In the collector circuit there is essentially a total resistance of R_C in parallel with R_L for a-c current, assuming C_o is a short circuit to a-c. Thus, for the a-c analysis, our load-line will be determined by

$$R' = \frac{R_C \times R_L}{R_C + R_L}$$

This load-line, called the "a-c load-line," will pass through the Q-point and will have a slope of $-1/R'$. For the circuit under consideration R' is 5K and the resulting a-c load-line has been constructed in Figure 11.19. The a-c load-line is steeper than the d-c load-line since R' is less than R_C. This is usually the case unless a-c and d-c load-lines coincide and are thus one and the same.

It remains to determine the variation in input emitter current produced by the signal source. This can be calculated as in Equation 11.8. Using $e_S = 25$ mv p-p we have

$$i_E = \frac{e_S}{r_{ib}} = \frac{25 \text{ mv p-p}}{25} = 1 \text{ ma p-p}$$

This tells us that the emitter current variation is 0.5 ma on either side of the d-c emitter current (1 ma in this case). That is, the emitter current will vary from 0.5 ma to 1.5 ma as the signal voltage is applied. This is illustrated in Figure 11.20. As a result

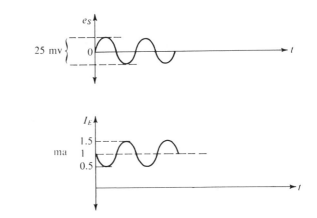

FIG. 11.20.   VARIATION IN EMITTER CURRENT DUE TO INPUT SIGNAL

of this variation in emitter current the operating point will move up and down the a-c load-line. At the lower limit of emitter current, 0.5 ma, the operating point moves down to point A in Figure 11.19 while at the upper limit of emitter current (1.5 ma) the operating point moves up to point B. The current and voltage values at these points are recorded in Table 11.1 below. From the table it is seen that as the emitter current makes a complete excursion from 0.5 ma to 1.5 ma the collector-base voltage makes a corresponding excursion from 12.6v to 7.6v. Figure 11.21 shows the various waveforms. The waveform of collector-base voltage contains both a d-c level (10.1v) and an a-c component (5v p-p). Only the a-c component appears across R_L becoming e_{out}. Thus e_{out} is 5v p-p and the overall amplifier gain is

$$G_v = \frac{e_{out}}{e_S} = \frac{5 \text{v p-p}}{25 \text{ mv p-p}} = 200$$

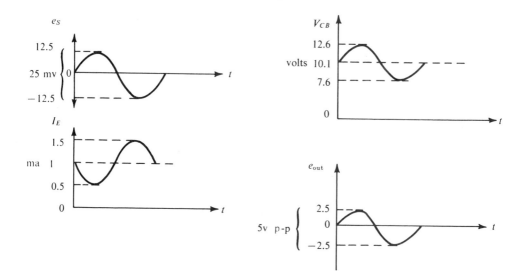

FIG. 11.21.   AMPLIFIER WAVEFORMS

TABLE 11.1

Point	I_E	I_C	V_{CB}	e_S
B	1.5 ma	1.48 ma	7.6v	−12.5 mv
Q	1 ma	0.99 ma	10.1v	0
A	0.5 ma	≈0.5 ma	12.6v	+12.5 mv

From Figure 11.21 an important characteristic of Com. B amplifiers is observed: the output signal is *in phase* with the input signal. This is always the case at medium frequencies of operation for Com. B amplifiers with a resistive load.

In all the discussions up to this point the input signal has been restricted to values small enough to keep the transistor operating in the active region. It is not unusual to have the input signal voltage become large enough to cause the transistor to become cut-off or saturated during a portion of the input swing. For example, referring to Figure 11.19, if the input signal were increased so that the emitter current variation became 2 ma p-p around the Q-point, the circuit operating point would move between the extremes of points C and D. This gives an output voltage swing of approximately 10 volts. The point C is right at cut-off at which point $V_{CB} = 15v*$ and $I_C = 0$. Further increase in the input signal may cause the upper excursion of emitter current to increase, say to 2.5 ma, but it will not affect the lower excursion since I_E cannot go below zero. This would cause the V_{CB} waveform to stay at 15v during the interval in which $I_E = 0$. This may be more easily understood with the help of Figure 11.22 in which

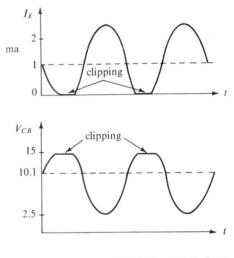

FIG. 11.22.   WAVEFORMS   ILLUSTRATING   CUT-OFF
CLIPPING

the e_S, I_E and V_{CB} waveforms are shown for this case. The V_{CB} waveform is seen to be "clipped" at the 15 volt level during the interval when the transistor is driven into cut-off by the input signal.

A similar result occurs when the input signal causes the transistor to become saturated. In this case the V_{CB} waveform will be clipped at $V_{CB} = 0v$ during the interval in which the transistor is saturated. Referring to Figure 11.18, this would occur when the input signal is large enough to cause the emitter current to reach approximately 3.0 ma and greater, causing saturation. Both types of clipping are normally undesirable since the output waveform becomes highly distorted. To minimize the possibility that clipping will occur, the Q-point should be chosen about

---

*For interested students, $V_{CB} \neq V_{CC} = 20v$ at cut-off because of the charged capacitor C_0 which acts like a d-c source of 10v (V_{CB} at Q-point).

halfway between saturation and cut-off along the a-c load-line at point B. It is obvious that in the circuit under consideration the maximum output voltage swing is 15v p-p, between $V_{CB} = 15v$ at cut-off and $V_{CB} \approx 0$ at saturation. An increase in R_L or in V_{CC} will increase the possible output voltage swing.

▶EXAMPLE 11.17

For the circuit of Figure 11.18 and the transistor curves of Figure 11.19, determine the voltage gain using the circuit values given previously, except let $R_L = \infty$.

In this case the a-c load-line is the same as the d-c load-line determined by V_{CC} and R_C in Figure 11.19. Using this load-line and the $I_E = 1.5$ ma curve to locate point G and the $I_E = 0.5$ ma curve to locate point F, the swing in V_{CB} is from 5 volts to 15 volts. In other words the output signal is 10v p-p giving a voltage gain of

$$G_v = \frac{10v}{25 \text{ mv}} = 400 \qquad \blacktriangleleft$$

▶EXAMPLE 11.18

For the conditions of Example 11.17 determine the maximum possible output voltage swing.

Referring to the d-c load-line in Figure 11.19 it is apparent that V_{CB} can range from 20v to approximately 0v giving a possible 20v swing. ◀

11.10.   Common Base Amplifiers: Summary

A brief summary of the Com. B transistor amplifier is presented in Table 11.2 listing its major characteristics with an eye toward comparing it to the Com. E and Com. C amplifiers in subsequent sections.

TABLE 11.2

COMMON BASE AMPLIFIER

Current gain A_i:	approximately 1
Voltage gain A_v:	very high; 500 is typical
Power gain A_p:	high; 500 is typical
Input impedance Z_{ib}:	very low; 50Ω is typical
Output impedance Z_{ob}:	very high; 50K is typical
Phase shift (input to output):	0°

11.11.　　Common Emitter Amplifiers: Basic Circuit

The basic Com. E amplifier circuit is shown in Figure 11.23.
The circuit is identical to the one studied in Chapter 9 except for

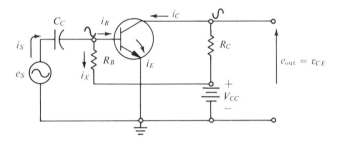

FIG. 11.23.　　COM. E AMPLIFIER CIRCUIT

the addition of the input signal and coupling capacitor. The
Q-point values, which depend only on the d-c voltage sources and
resistors R_B and R_C and not on the input signal, are calculated in
the manner outlined in Chapter 9. As in the Com. B amplifier, the
input signal will cause the circuit operating point to vary around
the Q-point producing a-c components of voltage and current.
As such, the complete representation of any circuit value will be
the superposition of its quiescent value and its a-c value.

11.12.　　Common Emitter Amplifiers: Current Gain

In the Com. E amplifier the base current is the input current and
the collector current is the output current. If we consider the a-c
currents in Figure 11.23 the signal source supplies a signal current
i_S. Although a portion of this signal current will flow through the
branch containing R_B, in properly designed amplifiers this portion
will be very small so that we can assume that most of i_S is supplied
to the transistor base as i_b. That is, $i_b \approx i_S$. As a result of the
base signal current i_b a large signal current i_c will flow in the
collector circuit because of the large a-c current gain from base
to collector. We know from previous discussion in Section 11.2
that this current gain is β which is given by

$$\beta = \frac{\Delta I_C}{\Delta I_B}\bigg|V_{CE} = \frac{i_c}{i_b} \qquad (11.19)$$

▶EXAMPLE 11.19

In the circuit of Figure 11.23 the transistor has a β of 60. If the input signal current i_s is 10 μa p-p determine the value of i_B, i_C and i_E.

Assume

$$i_B = i_S = 10 \text{ μa p-p}$$

Then

$$i_C = \beta i_B = 60 \times 10 \text{ μa p-p}$$
$$= 600 \text{ μa p-p}$$

and

$$i_E = i_C + i_B = 610 \text{ μa p-p} \qquad ◀$$

Strictly speaking, the overall current gain, A_i, from signal source to output will be less than β due to some loss of current through R_B and to the finite transistor output impedance. However, in most cases the value of A_i may be assumed to be equal to β.

11.13. Common Emitter Amplifiers: Voltage Gain

We can analyze the voltage amplification of the Com. E amplifier in the same manner employed in Section 11.5 for the Com. B circuit. Proceeding along those lines we can represent the amplifier of Figure 11.23 by its a-c equivalent as shown in Figure 11.23A

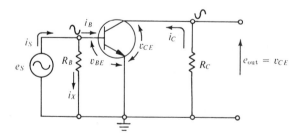

FIG. **11.23**A. THE COM. E AMPLIFIER SIMPLIFIED FOR A-C ANALYSIS

where for purposes of a-c analysis the d-c supply voltages and coupling capacitor have been replaced by short circuits.

Examination of the input portion of the circuit reveals that the input signal e_S appears directly across the E-B junction such that the value of the a-c base to emitter voltage v_{BE} is equal to e_S. This signal portion of base to emitter voltage will alternately *subtract from* and *add to* the d-c bias V_{BE}. It is this changing forward bias across the E-B junction which will produce a changing base current. The relationship between i_B and v_{BE} is given by the a-c *Com. E input impedance* r_{ie} which was introduced in Section 11.2. Repeating its definition here we have

$$r_{ie} = \frac{\Delta V_{BE}}{\Delta I_B}\bigg|V_{CE} = \frac{v_{BE}}{i_B} \qquad (11.20)$$

or equivalently

$$i_B = v_{BE}/r_{ie}$$

In other words, the a-c impedance seen between base and emitter is r_{ie}. This is emphasized in Figure 11.24 where the input to the

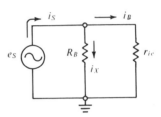

FIG. 11.24.   REPLACING E-B JUNCTION BY ITS A-C IMPEDANCE r_{ie}

transistor has been replaced by its input impedance. If we assume a 10 mv p-p input signal and an r_{ie} of 1K the a-c base current would be

$$i_B = \frac{10 \text{ mv p-p}}{1K} = 10 \ \mu a \text{ p-p}$$

The a-c collector current which will flow as a result of i_B is given by

$$i_C = \beta i_B$$

This a-c collector current will flow through R_C and will develop a large output voltage e_{out}. That is

$$e_{\text{out}} = v_{CE} = i_c \times R_C \approx \beta i_B R_C \qquad (11.21)$$

As in the Com. B amplifier, a high value of R_C may be used in the collector circuit, resulting in an output voltage which can be many times greater than e_S. For example, with our 10 μa p-p base current and a β of 100, a value of $R_C = 5K$ will produce (using Equation 11.21)

$$e_{\text{out}} = 100 \times 10\ \mu\text{a p-p} \times 5K$$
$$= 5\text{v p-p}$$

This output signal voltage is $5/0.01 = 500$ times greater than e_s indicating a voltage gain of 500. This value is typical of Com. E amplifiers in which voltage gain may range from 100 to 2000.

An approximate formula for voltage gain can be derived from the previous equations as follows:

$$e_{\text{out}} = i_c R_C = \beta i_B R_C$$
$$= \frac{\beta v_{BE} R_C}{r_{ie}}$$
$$e_{\text{out}} = \frac{\beta e_s R_C}{r_{ie}} \tag{11.22}$$

Thus

$$A_v = \frac{e_{\text{out}}}{e_s} = \frac{\beta R_C}{r_{ie}} \tag{11.23}$$

It may appear on the surface that the Com. E voltage gain given by Equation 11.23 is quite different from that given by Equation 11.11 for the Com. B. However, this is not so. It can be shown that the Com. E input impedance r_{ie}, is related to the Com. B input impedance r_{ib} by

$$r_{ie} = (\beta + 1)r_{ib} \tag{11.24}$$

This relationship should be intuitively clear since the Com. B input current (i_E) is $\beta + 1$ times the Com. E input current (i_B) for the same value of v_{BE}. Using this fact in Equation 11.23 we have

$$A_v = \frac{\beta R_C}{(\beta + 1)r_{ib}} = \frac{\alpha R_C}{r_{ib}} \tag{11.25}$$

since $\alpha = \beta/\beta + 1$ (obtained from $\beta = \alpha/1 - \alpha$). This result is identical to the Com. B voltage gain.

▶ EXAMPLE 11.20

The transistor used in the Com. E amplifier of Figure 11.25 is biased at the following Q-point:

$$V_{BE} = 0.7\text{v}$$
$$I_B = 113\ \mu\text{a}$$
$$I_C = 9\ \text{ma}$$
$$V_{CE} = 3\text{v}$$

At this Q-point the transistor has a $\beta = 75$ and an $r_{ie} = 500\Omega$. Calculate the values of i_B, i_c, v_{CE} and A_v when e_s is 5.0 mv p-p.

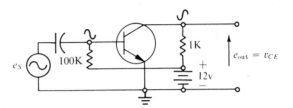

FIG. 11.25.   EXAMPLE 11.20

The base signal current is determined using Expression 11.20

$$i_B = \frac{5.0\ \text{mv p-p}}{500\Omega} = 10.0\ \mu\text{a p-p}$$

This produces

$$i_c = \beta i_B = 75 \times 10.0\ \mu\text{a p-p}$$
$$= 0.75\ \text{ma p-p}$$

The output signal will be

$$e_{\text{out}} = v_{CE} = 0.75\ \text{ma} \times 1\text{K}$$
$$= 0.75\text{v p-p}$$

This gives a voltage gain of

$$A_v = \frac{e_{\text{out}}}{e_S} = \frac{0.75\text{v p-p}}{5.0\ \text{mv p-p}} = 150 \qquad \blacktriangleleft$$

▶ EXAMPLE 11.21

For the amplifier of Example 11.20 sketch the waveform of the total collector current.

The d-c collector current is $I_C = 9$ ma while the a-c collector current is $i_c = 0.75$ ma p-p. The collector current waveform is shown below in Figure 11.26.   ◀

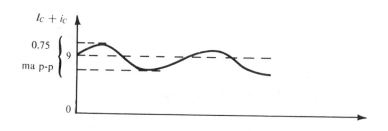

FIG. 11.26.   EXAMPLE 11.21

▶EXAMPLE 11.22

For the same circuit calculate $I_{C(\text{sat})}$ and determine what value of e_s would just cause the transistor to go into saturation.

$$I_{C(\text{sat})} = V_{CC}/R_C = 12\text{v}/1\text{K} = 12 \text{ ma}$$

Since $I_C = 9$ ma, the value of i_c would have to go to 6 ma p-p in order for the total collector current to reach 12 ma. Thus

$$i_B = \frac{i_c}{\beta} = \frac{6 \text{ ma p-p}}{75}$$

$$= 80 \ \mu\text{a p-p}$$

To produce this value of i_B the value of e_s needed is

$$e_S = v_{BE} = i_B \times r_{ie}$$

$$= 80 \ \mu\text{a p-p} \times 500\Omega$$

$$e_S = 40 \text{ mv p-p} \qquad \blacktriangleleft$$

11.14.   Common Emitter Amplifier: Power Gain

In Com. E amplifiers the current gain, which is approximately equal to β, and the voltage gain, which is given by Equation 11.23, are both much greater than one. Consequently very large power gains can be provided. The power gain is given by

$$A_p = A_i \times A_v$$

$$= \beta \times \frac{\beta R_C}{r_{ie}}$$

$$= \frac{\beta^2 R_C}{r_{ie}} \qquad\qquad \textbf{(11.26)}$$

Since A_i is much greater than one, the power gain will always be larger than the voltage gain.

▶ EXAMPLE 11.23

Calculate the power gain for the amplifier of Example 11.20. From the results of Example 11.20

$$A_i = 75$$
and
$$A_v = 150$$
giving
$$A_p = 75 \times 150$$
$$= 11,250$$ ◀

▶ EXAMPLE 11.24

Verify the result above by calculating the input signal power and output signal power from Example 11.20.

Referring to Example 11.20 the input signal voltage was 5.0 mv p-p which converts to 1.77 mv *rms*. This input signal produces power in the input resistance r_{ie}. Thus

$$P_{isig} = \frac{(1.77 \text{ mv } rms)^2}{500\Omega} = 0.006 \text{ uw}$$

The output signal voltage was calculated to be 0.75v p-p which becomes 0.265v *rms*. This output signal produces power in the collector resistor R_C. Thus

$$P_{osig} = \frac{(0.265\text{v } rms)^2}{1\text{K}} = 0.07 \text{ mw}$$

Calculating power gain we have

$$A_v = \frac{P_{osig}}{P_{isig}} = \frac{0.07 \text{ mw}}{0.006 \text{ uw}} = 11,600$$

This result agrees with the previous example within the accuracy of our calculations.   ◀

The power gain of the examples above is typical for Com. E amplifiers. Because of the large current gain the Com. E amplifier has a much greater power gain than the Com. B amplifier.

11.15.   Common Emitter Amplifiers: Input and Output Impedance

The *transistor* input impedance in the Com. E configuration is r_{ie} which is typically moderately low ($500\Omega - 5\text{K}$). As can be seen in Figure 11.24 the transistor input impedance is in parallel with R_B. This parallel combination is what the signal source sees and hence it is the *amplifier* input impedance. Denoting the Com. E *amplifier input impedance* by the symbol Z_{ie} we have

$$Z_{ie} = \frac{R_B \times r_{ie}}{R_B + r_{ie}} \tag{11.27}$$

▶ EXAMPLE 11.25

Calculate the input impedance of the amplifier in Example 11.20. In the amplifier of Example 11.20, $R_B = 100K$ and $r_{ie} = 2K$. Thus

$$Z_{ie} = \frac{100K \times 2K}{102K} = 1.96K \qquad ◀$$

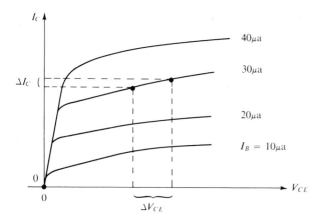

FIG. 11.27.   CALCULATION OF r_{oe}

The Com. E input impedance is somewhat higher than the Com. B input impedance making it more readily driven by moderate impedance signal sources. In fact an important feature of the Com. E amplifier is its ability to drive other Com. E amplifier stages without special impedance matching methods as a result of its comparable input and output impedances.

The transistor's Com. E *output impedance* is a measure of the effect of the collector-emitter voltage V_{CE} on the collector current. It is given the symbol r_{oe} and is given by the formula

$$r_{oe} = \frac{\Delta V_{CE}}{\Delta I_C}\bigg|_{I_B} \tag{11.28}$$

Figure 11.27 illustrates how it may be obtained from the Com. E output characteristics. As can be seen from the figure the value of r_{oe} can be fairly high since large changes in V_{CE} produce small changes in collector current. Typically, values of r_{oe} are in the range of 10K to 100K which makes it somewhat lower than r_{ob} for Com. B.

In the Com. E amplifier circuit, the transistor output impedance is in parallel with the collector resistor R_C. Thus, the Com. E *amplifier output impedance*, which we will denote as Z_{oe}, is given by

$$Z_{oe} = \frac{r_{oe}R_C}{r_{oe} + R_C} \qquad \textbf{(11.29)}$$

The value of R_C is usually made fairly large to increase voltage gain. This results in a moderate value of output impedance.

▶ EXAMPLE 11.26

Calculate the output impedance of a Com. E transistor amplifier which has R_C = 5K and uses a transistor with r_{oe} = 30K. From 11.29 we have

$$Z_{oe} = \frac{30\text{K} \times 5\text{K}}{35\text{K}} = 4.28\text{K} \qquad ◀$$

In contrast to the Com. B amplifier, the Com. E amplifier's input and output impedances are typically of the same order of magnitude. As mentioned previously, this allows cascading Com. E amplifiers without a need for impedance matching.

11.16. Common Emitter Amplifiers: General Representation

We can now utilize the general amplifier representation of Figure 11.17 for the Com. E amplifier as was done for Com. B. Consider the Com. E circuit in Figure 11.28. The transistor has the following parameters at the Q-point:

$$\beta = 100$$
$$r_{ie} = 1.2\text{K}$$
$$r_{oe} = 25\text{K}$$

Again, the portion of the circuit enclosed by the dotted lines is the amplifier proper. The values of Z_{in}, Z_{out} and A_v for the amplifier proper can be calculated for subsequent use in the general

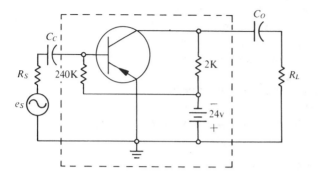

FIG. 11.28.   COM. E AMPLIFIER

amplifier relationships. Using the transistor values given above together with the circuit values we have:

$$Z_{in} = Z_{ie} = 240K \| 1.2K$$
$$\approx 1.2K$$
$$Z_{out} = Z_{oe} = 25K \| 2K$$
$$= 1.85K$$
$$A_v = \frac{\beta R_C}{r_{ie}} = \frac{100(2K)}{1.2K} = 167$$

For this amplifier the general representation becomes that shown in Figure 11.29. Here again, Figures 11.28 and 11.29 are equivalent for a-c signals only as indicated by the absence of coupling capac-

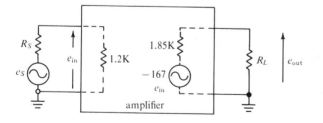

FIG. 11.29.   EQUIVALENT REPRESENTATION OF THE CIRCUIT IN FIGURE 11.28

itors and d-c supplies. The negative sign in front of the voltage gain in Figure 11.29 is to indicate the 180° phase shift from input to output in Com. E amplifiers. (This will be discussed in the next section.)

▶ EXAMPLE 11.27

Calculate the overall voltage gain of the circuit in Figure 11.28 if $R_S = 1.5K$ and $R_L = 2K$.

Using Equation 11.18 with the Com. E parameters we have

$$G_v = \frac{167 \times 2K \times 1.2K}{(2.7K) \times (3.85K)}$$

$$= 38.5 \qquad \blacktriangleleft$$

▶ EXAMPLE 11.28

Calculate the overall current gain G_i for the same circuit. Using Equation 10.13 we have

$$G_i = \frac{G_v(R_S + Z_{ie})}{R_L}$$

$$= \frac{(38.5)(2.7K)}{2K}$$

$$= 52 \qquad \blacktriangleleft$$

Note that the overall current gain G_i is less than β. This is because the output current to the load R_L is only a portion of the entire collector signal current. The collector signal current actually divides between R_C and R_L.

▶ EXAMPLE 11.29

Calculate the overall power gain G_p.

$$G_p = G_v \times G_i$$

$$= 38.5 \times 52$$

$$\approx 2000 \qquad \blacktriangleleft$$

The power gain of 2000 is the largest which can be obtained from this amplifier (with R_S fixed at 1.5K) since R_L is approximately matched with Z_{oe}. This can be verified by using values of R_L above and below 2K and recalculating G_p. This is left as an exercise for the student.

As in the Com. B amplifier under certain conditions the voltage gain expression can be greatly simplified. For the Com. E amplifier, if $R_S \gg r_{ie}$ and $r_{oe} \gg R_C$, the expression for overall voltage gain becomes

$$G_v \approx \frac{\beta R'}{R_S} \qquad (11.30)$$

where R' is the parallel combination of R_C and R_L.

11.17.   Common Emitter Amplifiers: Graphical Analysis of Amplifier Waveforms

Graphical analysis of the Com. E amplifier is performed in much the same way as for the Com. B. Let us consider the Com. E circuit in Figure 11.30.

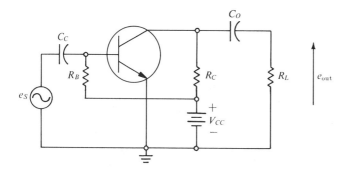

FIG. 11.30.   COM. E AMPLIFIER

The circuit values are as follows:

$$e_S = 30 \text{ mv p-p}; R_S \text{ negligible}$$
$$R_B = 1 \text{ meg}$$
$$V_{CC} = 10\text{v}$$
$$R_C = 10\text{K}$$
$$R_L = 10\text{K}$$

The transistor is germanium and has an input impedance $r_{ie} = 3\text{K}$ at $I_B = 10 \ \mu\text{a}$. Its Com. E output curves are presented in Figure 11.31. Once again the Q-point is found by constructing the d-c load-line which in this case is determined by $V_{CC} = 10\text{v}$ and $R_C = 10\text{K}$. The resulting d-c load-line is shown in the figure.

The d-c value of base current is easily calculated as

$$I_B = \frac{V_{CC} - V_{BE}}{R_B}$$

$$= \frac{10v - 0.3v}{1 \text{ meg}} = 9.7 \; \mu a \approx 10 \; \mu a$$

The resulting Q-point is at $I_C = 0.5$ ma and $V_{CE} = 5v$.

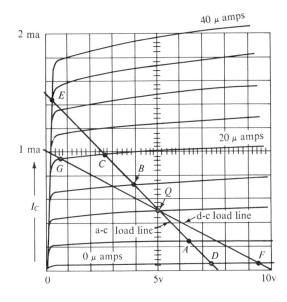

FIG. **11.31.**   OUTPUT CURVES FOR TRANSISTOR OF FIGURE **11.30**

To determine the output signal voltage the a-c load-line must be constructed. It passes through the Q-point and has a slope of $-1/R'$ (recall that R' equals $R_C \| R_L$). In this case $R' = 5K$ producing the a-c load-line shown in the figure.

The circuit operating point will move up and down the a-c load-line as the signal voltage is applied. The limits depend on the a-c base current which is given by

$$i_B = \frac{e_S}{r_{ie}} = \frac{30 \text{ mv p-p}}{3K} = 10 \; \mu a \text{ p-p}$$

which indicates that the base current will vary 5 μa on either side of its Q-point value of 10 μa. That is, the base current will swing from 5 μa to 15 μa in response to the input signal. This is illustrated in

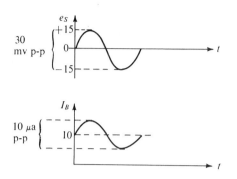

FIG. 11.32.   VARIATION IN BASE CURRENT DUE TO INPUT SIGNAL

Figure 11.32. Note that the base current waveform is *in phase* with the e_S waveform since, as e_S increases, the base to emitter voltage becomes more positive, which for an NPN transistor means an increase in base current. This variation in base current moves the operating point between A and B along the a-c load-line. The collector current and voltage values at these points are recorded in Table 11.3 below. Notice that as the base current

TABLE 11.3

Point	I_B	I_C	V_{CE}	e_S
B	15 μa	0.72 ma	3.9v	+15 mv
Q	10 μa	0.5 ma	5v	0
A	5 μa	0.25 ma	6.25v	−15 mv

makes a complete excursion from 5 μa to 15 μa the collector-emitter voltage V_{CE} makes a corresponding excursion from 6.25v to 3.9v. Figure 11.33 shows the various waveforms. The wave-form of collector-emitter voltage contains a d-c level (5v) and an a-c component (2.35v p-p). Only the a-c component appears across R_L producing $e_{out} = 2.35$v p-p. Thus, the overall amplifier gain is

$$G_v = \frac{e_{out}}{e_S} = \frac{2.35\text{v p-p}}{30\text{ mv p-p}} = 78.3$$

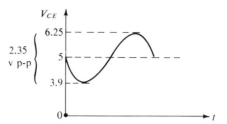

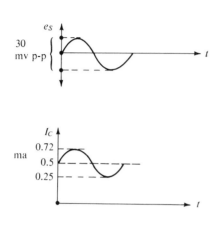

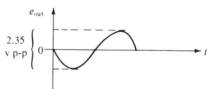

FIG. **11.33.**   AMPLIFIER WAVEFORMS

From Figure 11.33 an important characteristic of Com. E amplifiers is observed: the output signal is 180° *out of phase* with the input signal. This is always the case at medium frequencies of operation with a resistive load. At low frequencies the coupling capacitors introduce phase shift while at high frequencies the transistor junction capacitances have the same effect.

Waveform clipping will also occur in the Com. E amplifier as the input signal is increased. It should be apparent from Figure 11.31 that any input signals which would produce a base current variation of more than 20 μa p-p would result in cut-off clipping while any input signal which would increase the base-current to 35 μa or more would result in saturation clipping. For an undistorted (unclipped) output the maximum base current variation is 20 μa p-p. This gives an output swing from 2.7v (point *C*) to 7.2v (point *D*) or 4.5v p-p.

▶ EXAMPLE 11.30

As the input signal is gradually increased, what type of clipping would occur first if the circuit Q-point were at point *C* in Figure 11.31?

The base current at point C is 20 μa. An increase of over slightly 10 μa will cause saturation (point E) while a decrease of 20 μa is needed to reach cut-off. Thus, saturation clipping will occur first. ◀

▶ EXAMPLE 11.31

What is the maximum unclipped output signal which can be obtained from the amplifier under consideration when $R_L = \infty$?

In this case the a-c load-line is the same as the d-c load-line in Figure 11.31. Along this load-line the base current can swing 20 μa p-p before cut-off occurs. This gives a V_{CE} swing from 1v (point G) to 9.2v (point F) producing $e_{\text{out}} = 8.2$v p-p. ◀

11.18.   Common Emitter Amplifiers: Q-Point Stability

The first consideration in designing transistor amplifiers is the choosing of the quiescent operating point. The d-c collector current and voltage must be chosen so that the a-c variations caused by the input signal will remain within the linear region of the transistor output characteristics, thus avoiding distortion or clipping of the output waveform. For many applications the best choice of Q-point lies midway along the a-c load-line in order to allow the maximum undistorted output signal. Any change in the Q-point will result in distortion at a lower level of output signal.

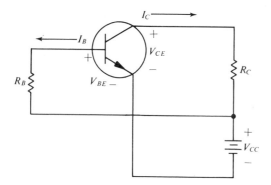

FIG. 11.34.   BASE CURRENT BIAS

Two principal factors can contribute to a change in Q-point once it has been set: one is the effect of temperature on the transistor parameters; the other is the change in transistor characteristics which occurs with transistor replacement. Of the three transistor amplifier configurations, the Com. E is the only one which suffers considerably from shifts in the Q-point. Thus, our concentration will be centered on the Q-point stability of the Com. E amplifier for various types of biasing circuits.

The simplest method of setting the Q-point in the Com. E amplifier is to arrange to have a d-c base current flow so that when this base current is multiplied by β_{d-c} the required value of collector current is obtained. This type of bias is illustrated in Figure 11.34 and is the type which has been used in all of the Com. E amplifiers we have looked at so far. Since the base current is determined by V_{CC} and R_B and is essentially independent of the transistor parameters, this type of amplifier bias is called *base current bias*. In this circuit the base current is given by

$$I_B = \frac{V_{CC} - V_{BE}}{R_B} \qquad (11.31)$$

and the collector current then becomes

$$I_C = \beta_{d-c} I_B + I_{CEO} \qquad (11.32)$$

This produces a collector-emitter voltage

$$V_{CE} = V_{CC} - I_C R_C \qquad (11.33)$$

Examination of Equation 11.32 reveals the limitations of this simple method of setting the amplifier Q-point. First, with any given type of transistor, the variation of current gain β_{d-c} between different transistors is usually between two and three to one. This means that if I_B is chosen to give the desired value of I_C for one transistor, changing the transistor may result in a much different I_C, and the Q-point will have shifted from the desired point. Secondly, as we have seen in Chapter 9, the leakage current I_{CEO} and current gain β_{d-c} both increase rapidly with temperature. For this reason the value of collector current is very temperature-dependent (see Example 9.28). Thus, if the circuit Q-point is set at 25°C, at higher temperature it will have shifted to a new point. As far as the transistor is concerned, junction temperature increases may be due to a rise in ambient temperature or to heat generated as a result of junction power dissipation, or both.

The shifting of circuit operating point can be demonstrated graphically as in Figure 11.35 for a typical set of Com. E output curves. The solid curves are for a temperature of 25°C. If we

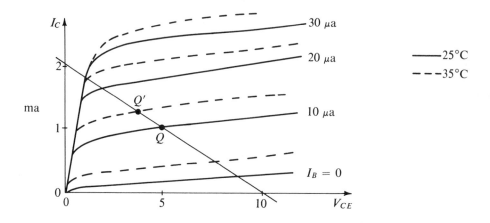

FIG. 11.35.   EFFECT OF TEMPERATURE ON Q-POINT

assume $I_B = 10$ μa, the load-line intersects the 10 μa curve at the
Q-point, $I_C = 1$ ma and $V_{CE} = 5$v. A rise in temperature to 35°C
causes the output curves to move upward due to the increase in
I_{CEO} and β_{d-c} as indicated by the dotted curves. The result is that
the Q-point has moved up to point Q' where $I_C = 1.2$ ma and
$V_{CE} = 4$v. Further increases in temperature would cause the
Q-point to move even further up the load-line, closer to saturation.
This shift in the Q-point will cause distortion in the output signal
to occur at a lower value of input signal thus decreasing the possible
undistorted output voltage swing.

From these considerations it can be seen that for stable operation of a Com. E transistor amplifier some alternative to the base
current bias method must be found. This subject is usually referred to as *bias or Q-point stabilization*. The problem of Q-point
instability does not arise in the Com. B circuit since changes in
α_{d-c} are small and the only leakage current flowing is I_{CBO}. Although this increases with temperature it is small enough to be
negligible.

The most widely-used method of bias stabilization is called,
among other names, *base voltage bias* and is illustrated in Figure
11.36. In this configuration a fixed voltage V_B rather than a fixed
base current is applied to the base. This voltage is determined
mainly by the voltage divider ratio of R_{B2} and R_{B1} and the supply
voltage V_{CC}. This is not entirely true since some small amount of
current must be supplied from the voltage divider to the transistor
base. This effect will become negligible by making R_E large

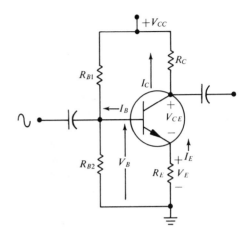

FIG. 11.36.   BASE VOLTAGE BIAS

enough. Recall from our discussion of the Com. C circuit in Chapter 9 that the resistor R_E when viewed from the base appears to have a resistance of $(\beta_{d-c} + 1)R_E$. If we disregard the small base-emitter voltage drop for the moment, this value of resistance is essentially the d-c input resistance of the transistor and is in parallel with R_{B2}. If $(\beta_{d-c} + 1)R_E$ is much greater than R_{B2}, say by a factor of 10 or more, we can assume that it does not affect the voltage V_B. Thus, we can approximate V_B by

$$V_B \approx \left(\frac{R_{B2}}{R_{B1} + R_{B2}}\right) \times V_{CC} \qquad \textbf{(11.34)}$$

▶ EXAMPLE 11.32

Determine the value of V_B if $R_{B1} = R_{B2} = 10K$, $R_E = 2K$, $V_{CC} = 12v$ and $\beta_{d-c} = 100$.

Since $(\beta_{d-c} + 1)R_E = 202K$ which is much greater than R_{B2} we can use Equation 11.34. Thus

$$V_B = \frac{10K}{10K + 10K} \times 12v = 6v \qquad ◀$$

Once V_B is determined, then the value of V_E, the voltage from emitter to ground, is given by

$$V_E = V_B - V_{BE} \qquad \textbf{(11.35)}$$

This gives an emitter current

$$I_E = V_E/R_E \qquad \textbf{(11.36)}$$

Thus, we can write the value of collector current as

$$I_C = \alpha_{\text{d-c}} I_E + I_{CBO} \qquad (11.37)$$

The value of V_{CE} is then

$$V_{CE} = V_{CC} - I_C \times R_C - V_E \qquad (11.38)$$

Equations 11.34 through 11.38 essentially determine the Q-point values of I_C and V_{CE}. Examination of these expressions reveals an important fact: the values of I_C and V_{CE} do not depend on the values of $\beta_{\text{d-c}}$ and I_{CEO}, the two very temperature-dependent parameters, but rather on $\alpha_{\text{d-c}}$ and I_{CBO}. This is a result of the base voltage bias which essentially fixes the voltage across R_E and thus I_E. In fact, we could call this fixed emitter current bias if we desired. As a result of the Q-point's independence of variations in $\beta_{\text{d-c}}$ and I_{CEO} this type of bias is very stable with temperature changes and transistor replacement.

The value of R_E is very important in determining just how stable the Q-point will be. The larger the value of R_E, the more insensitive the Q-point will be to transistor variations. However, R_E cannot be made too large since it determines the Q-point value of I_E and I_C. An excessive value for R_E would result in a low value of I_C and thus lower voltage gain.*

▶ EXAMPLE 11.33

The circuit of Figure 11.36 has the values indicated in example 11.32 as well as $R_C = 1\text{K}$. Determine I_E, I_C and V_{CE}. Assume $V_{BE} = 0.7\text{v}$.

From the results of Example 11.32 the value of V_B is 6 volts. This gives $V_E = 6 - 0.7 = 5.3$ volts resulting in $I_E = 5.3/2\text{K} = 2.65$ ma. The value of I_C is approximately 2.65 ma also. Thus V_{CE} becomes (using 11.38)

$$V_{CE} = 12\text{v} - 2.65 \text{ ma} \times 1\text{K} - 5.3\text{v}$$
$$= 4.05\text{v} \qquad \blacktriangleleft$$

In most applications the resistor R_E is shunted with a capacitor C_E as illustrated in Figure 11.37. The purpose of the capacitor is to provide a very low impedance from emitter to ground for a-c conditions. If this were not done the input signal would not appear directly across the E-B junction but would divide between the E-B junction (impedance of r_{ie}) and the resistor R_E. This results in a lower amplifier voltage gain since a smaller signal across r_{ie} means

---

*As I_c decreases, β decreases and r_{ie} increases, reducing A_v

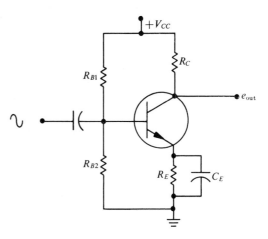

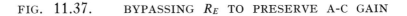

FIG. 11.37. BYPASSING R_E TO PRESERVE A-C GAIN

a smaller i_b and i_c and thus e_{out}. This capacitor, called the *emitter bypass capacitor*, must have a value large enough to present a low a-c impedance at the lowest frequency to be amplified.

The a-c analysis of the base voltage biased amplifier follows the same procedure as in Section 11.13 as long as R_E is bypassed with C_E. Everything discussed in Section 11.13 pertains to this circuit also and does not need to be repeated here.

11.19.   Common Emitter Amplifier: Summary

The important characteristics of the Com. E transistor amplifier are summarized in Table 11.4 below:

TABLE 11.4

COMMON EMITTER AMPLIFIER

Current gain A_i: much greater than 1 (β)
Voltage gain A_v: very high; 500 is typical
Power gain A_p: extremely high; 20,000 is typical
Input impedance Z_{ie}:   moderately low; 1K is typical
Output impedance Z_{oe}:   moderately high; 2K is typical
Phase shift: 180°

11.20.   Common Collector Amplifiers: Basic Circuit

The basic Com. C amplifier circuit is shown in Figure 11.38. Except for the absence of a collector resistor R_C and emitter bypass capacitor C_E, the circuit is identical to the Com. E circuit with base voltage bias shown in Figure 11.37. The Com. C amplifier also utilizes base voltage bias. However, the output signal is taken from the emitter instead of the collector.

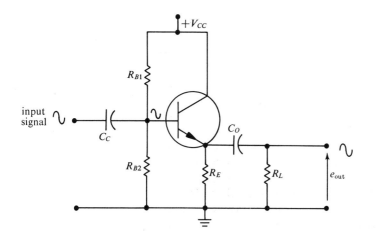

FIG. 11.38.   COMMON COLLECTOR AMPLIFIER

   Typical circuit action is as follows. The input signal is coupled through the capacitor into the base of the transistor. This produces a changing base current and consequently a changing emitter current. This changing emitter current produces a signal voltage across R_E as shown, which is then coupled to the load resistor R_L. We shall find that this output signal will always be slightly less in amplitude than the input signal e_S, resulting in a voltage gain of less than one. A natural question to ask is: Of what use is this circuit if its voltage gain is less than unity? The answer is that this circuit has the advantage of a very high input impedance while at the same time possessing a low output impedance. This characteristic makes it useful as an impedance matching circuit between a high impedance signal source and a low impedance load. For readers who are familiar with vacuum tube amplifiers, the Com. C amplifier is analogous to the Common Plate (cathode follower) amplifier.

11.21.   Common Collector Amplifiers: Gain and Impedance Relationships

To analyze the a-c operation of the Com. C amplifier we will again replace the circuit by its a-c equivalent circuit with the d-c supply and the coupling capacitors shorted out as in Figure 11.39A. Notice in the a-c circuit that the collector terminal is grounded since it is tied to $+V_{CC}$. Thus, R_{B1} and R_{B2} essentially appear in parallel for a-c as shown in the figure. As such, we will refer to this parallel combination as R_B during the rest of this discussion. That is

$$R_B = \frac{R_{B1} R_{B2}}{R_{B1} + R_{B2}} \qquad (11.39)$$

The emitter resistor R_E and load resistor R_L are also in parallel as far as a-c is concerned (assuming C_o is large enough). This parallel combination will be referred to as $(R_L)'$, the effective load. Thus

$$(R_L)' = \frac{R_E R_L}{R_E + R_L} \qquad (11.40)$$

The symbols R_B and $(R_L)'$ are used in Figure 11.39B.

The signal source e_s supplies a current i_s to the amplifier. A certain portion of i_s will flow through R_B to ground (i_x) with the remainder becoming base current for the transistor. In most practical circuits the value of i_x will be of the same or greater order of magnitude than i_B and so *cannot* be neglected. In order to find the values of i_x and i_B we must first determine the impedance seen looking into the base of the transistor since it is in parallel with R_B. Let us call this impedance Z_B. Thus, we can write

$$Z_B = \frac{v_B}{i_B} \qquad (11.41)$$

where v_B is the a-c voltage from base to ground. Note that v_B is not the same as v_{BE} since the emitter is not at ground potential. As the first step in determining Z_B we can write using Kirchhoff's voltage law

$$v_B = v_{BE} + v_E \qquad (11.42)$$

This states that the voltage signal at the base will distribute itself such that a portion (v_{BE}) will be dropped across the E-B junction and the rest (v_E) across the effective load $(R_L)'$. If we replace v_E by $i_E(R_L)'$ in Equation 11.42 and then divide both sides of the equation by i_b the result is

$$Z_B = \frac{v_B}{i_B} = \frac{v_{BE}}{i_B} + \frac{i_E(R_L)'}{i_B} \qquad (11.43)$$

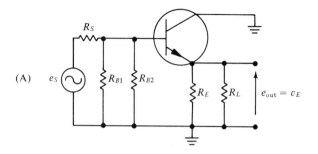

(A)

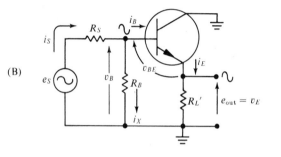

(B)

FIG. 11.39.   COMMON COLLECTOR CIRCUIT FOR A-C
ANALYSIS

The first term on the right side of this equation should be recognized as r_{ie}, the transistor Com. E input impedance. The second term can be simplified by noting that i_E/i_B is equal to $\beta + 1$. Making these simplifications we have

$$Z_B = r_{ie} + (\beta + 1)(R_L)' \qquad (11.44)$$

This expression reveals the fundamental characteristic of the Com. C amplifier. The impedance looking into the transistor is equal to the impedance across the E-B junction, r_{ie}, plus the effective load $(R_L)'$ multiplied by $\beta + 1$. This is illustrated in Figure 11.40 when the transistor is replaced by its input impedance, r_{ie} from base to emitter in series with $(\beta + 1) (R_L)'$ from emitter to ground. The fact that $(R_L)'$ appears to be a much greater resistor when viewed from the base indicates that Z_B can become large even for relatively small values of $(R_L)'$.

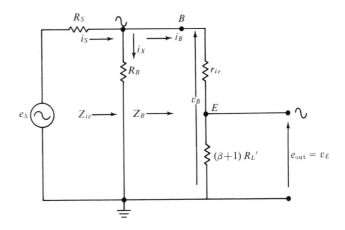

FIG. **11.40.** REPLACING THE TRANSISTOR BY ITS INPUT IMPEDANCE Z_B

▶ EXAMPLE 11.34

If a certain transistor has $\beta = 75$ and $r_{ie} = 2K$, determine Z_B for $(R_L)' = 100\Omega$ and then for $(R_L)' = 1K$.

Using Equation 11.44 for $(R_L)' = 100\Omega$

$$Z_B = 2K + (76) \times 100 = 9.6K$$

Repeating for $(R_L)' = 1K$

$$Z_B = 2K + (76) \times 1K = 78K \qquad ◀$$

It is apparent that the value of load resistor has a marked effect on Z_B and consequently on the total amplifier input impedance which is simply $R_B \| Z_B$. The effect of load impedance on input impedance is relatively slight for the Com. B and Com. E circuits and, in fact, was neglected in our previous analysis of these amplifiers.

The amplifier input impedance which is seen by the signal source is given by the parallel combination of R_B and Z_B. Denoting the *Com. C amplifier input impedance* by the symbol Z_{ic} we have

$$Z_{ic} = \frac{R_B Z_B}{R_B + Z_B} \qquad (11.45)$$

We are now in a position to determine the base signal voltage v_B. Referring to Figure 11.40, the portion of the input signal voltage e_S which becomes v_B is obtained using the voltage divider ratio between the amplifier input impedance Z_{ic} and the source resistance R_S. The result is

$$v_B = \left(\frac{Z_{ic}}{Z_{ic} + R_S}\right) \times e_S \qquad (11.46)$$

▶ EXAMPLE 11.35

For the transistor of the previous example calculate Z_{ic} if $R_{B1} = 100K$, $R_{B2} = 100K$ and $(R_L)' = 2K$.

First we must calculate Z_B using 11.44.

$$Z_B = 2K + 76(2K) = 154K$$

The value of R_B is

$$R_B = 100K \| 100K = 50K$$

Thus

$$Z_{ic} = 154K \| 50K = 37.7K \qquad ◀$$

▶ EXAMPLE 11.36

If a 1v p-p source with a resistance of 1K is used in the amplifier of the previous example, calculate the resultant v_B.

$$v_B = \frac{37.7K}{37.7K + 1K} \times 1\text{v p-p}$$

$$= 0.974\text{v p-p} \qquad ◀$$

We can see from these last two examples that the amplifier input impedance can be fairly high and, as such, will not load down the signal source appreciably. This allows most of the signal voltage to reach the base. The values of Z_{ic} may typically be as high as 50 to 200K. The next step will be to determine the overall voltage gain e_{out}/e_S.

The value of e_{out} can be obtained once v_B is known. Referring to Figure 11.40 it is obvious that e_{out} is given by

$$e_{\text{out}} = \left[\frac{(\beta + 1)(R_L)'}{(\beta + 1)(R_L)' + r_{ie}}\right] v_B \qquad (11.47)$$

and using the previously developed expression for v_B, we have

$$G_v = \frac{e_{\text{out}}}{e_S} = \left[\frac{(\beta + 1)(R_L')}{(\beta + 1)(R_L)' + r_{ie}}\right]\left[\frac{Z_{ic}}{Z_{ic} + R_S}\right] \qquad (11.48)$$

It is obvious from this expression that the Com. C voltage gain is always less than one since both factors on the right side of the equation are fractions. This should not be surprising. If we again refer to Figure 11.40, it can be seen that of the applied signal e_S only a fraction (the second factor in Equation 11.48) becomes v_B and only a fraction (the first factor in Equation 11.48) of v_B becomes e_{out}. Typically both factors are very close to one and the voltage gain will necessarily be nearly unity.

▶ EXAMPLE 11.37

Consider the transistor Com. C amplifier shown in Figure 11.41. If the transistor parameters are $r_{ie} = 1K$ and $\beta = 100$ calculate the voltage gain G_v.

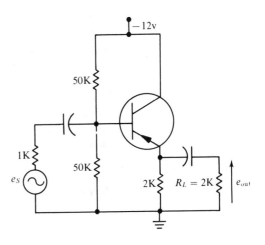

FIG. 11.41. EXAMPLE 11.37

To calculate gain we must determine the amplifier input impedance Z_{ic} which depends on the transistor input impedance Z_B. Using Equation 11.44

$$Z_B = 1K + 101(1K) = 102K$$

where $(R_L') = 1K$. The value of R_B is

$$R_B = 50K \| 50K = 25K$$

Thus we have, using Equation 11.45,

$$Z_{ic} = \frac{102K \times 25K}{127K} \approx 20K$$

Now using Equation 11.48 the voltage gain becomes

$$G_v = \left(\frac{101\text{K}}{101\text{K} + 1\text{K}}\right)\left(\frac{20\text{K}}{20\text{K} + 1\text{K}}\right)$$
$$= 0.943 \qquad \blacktriangleleft$$

It should be clear at this point that the output signal of the Com. C amplifier is *in phase* with the input signal. Referring to Figure 11.40 it can be seen that e_{out} is some fraction (usually close to one) of e_S and in phase with e_S. We can essentially say that the output variations follow almost exactly the input signal variations. For this reason, the Com. C amplifier is often referred to as an *emitter follower*.

Let us now consider the output impedance of the Com. C amplifier. The amplifier's output impedance is what the load resistor sees looking back into the amplifier. Referring to Figure 11.39A, the load resistor R_L looking back into the emitter sees three parallel paths to ground. One of these is the emitter resistor R_E. Another path is back through the emitter and out of the collector; the third path is back through the emitter and out of the base. This last path is usually the most significant because it has the least resistance. Any resistance in the base lead appears, when viewed from the emitter, to be *less* than its actual value by the factor $\beta + 1$. The output impedance will essentially be the impedance seen looking back from the emitter into the base. Denoting the *Com. C amplifier output impedance* by the symbol Z_{oc} we have

$$Z_{oc} = \left[r_{ib} + \frac{R_B \| R_S}{(\beta + 1)}\right]\| R_E \qquad (11.49)$$

Where r_{ib} is the *E-B* junction resistance looking from the emitter and the second term is the total resistance in the base circuit $(R_B \| R_S)$ reduced by the $\beta + 1$ factor. The value of Z_{oc} is normally very low and usually is in the range of 20 to 100 ohms.

▶ EXAMPLE 11.38

For the amplifier of Example 11.37 determine the value of output impedance Z_{oc}. Use $r_{ib} = 20\Omega$.

For the transistor $\beta = 100$ as stipulated in Example 11.37. Using Equation 11.49 we have

$$Z_{oc} = \left(20\Omega + \frac{25\text{K} \| 1\text{K}}{101}\right)\| 2\text{K}$$
$$= (20\Omega + 9.5\Omega)\| 2\text{K}$$
$$= 29.0\Omega \qquad \blacktriangleleft$$

Now that the expressions for Com. C input and output impedance have been developed, two interesting observations can be made. Referring to Equations 11.44 and 11.45 it should be obvious that the amplifier input impedance value depends on the value of load resistance. Input impedance becomes higher as R_L becomes larger. In our study of the Com. B and Com. E amplifiers the effect of load resistance on input impedance was neglected since it is normally slight. In the Com. C, however, it cannot be neglected.

Referring to Equation 11.49 it can be seen that the Com. C output impedance depends on the resistance of the signal source. The larger the source impedance the higher the output impedance. Again, the effect was neglected in the Com. B and Com. E analyses but must be considered in the Com. C amplifier.

A word should be said here about current and power gain. Referring to Figure 11.39B it can be seen that only a portion of the signal current input i_S reaches the base. This base current i_B is amplified by the transistor by the factor $\beta + 1$ to become the emitter current i_E. Now, only a portion of i_E will flow through the actual load R_L; the rest flows through R_E. Overall, there will be some current gain greater than one but it will never reach the value $\beta + 1$ unless the value of R_L is made very small. This may become clearer if we can develop the expression for current gain G_i. Utilizing the general relationship between G_i and G_v given by Equation 11.13

$$G_i = G_v\left(\frac{R_S + Z_{\text{in}}}{R_L}\right) \tag{11.13}$$

and assuming $G_v \approx 1$ as is normally the case, we have

$$G_i \approx \frac{R_S + Z_{ic}}{R_L} \tag{11.50}$$

Normally Z_{ic} is much greater than R_L and G_i is necessarily greater than one.

▶ EXAMPLE 11.39

Calculate current gain G_i for the amplifier of Example 11.37. Using Equation 11.50

$$G_i = \frac{1K + 20K}{2K} = 10.5 \qquad \blacktriangleleft$$

The power gain G_p of a Com. C amplifier will be greater than one since G_v is nearly one and G_i is larger than one. The available power gain is not as great as for the Com. E or Com. B amplifiers. From our previously determined value of G_i we can write

$$G_p = G_i G_v \approx G_i$$
$$= \frac{R_S + Z_{ic}}{R_L} \qquad \textbf{(11.51)}$$

since G_v is usually near one. Typical values of power gain for the Com. C amplifier range between 10 and 100.

It was mentioned previously that the high input impedance and low output impedance of a Com. C amplifier make it suitable for matching a high impedance source to a low impedance load. A practical application would be in preamplifiers that are operated from a high impedance signal source, such as microphones or phonograph pickups. A typical example of such a circuit is shown in Figure 11.42. In this circuit a fairly high input impedance is

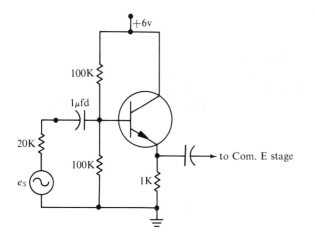

FIG. 11.42.   COMMON COLLECTOR PREAMPLIFIER

provided to the signal source, while the low output impedance of the amplifier can be used to drive a Com. E amplifier to give the required voltage gain.

A second common application utilizes the very low output impedance of the Com. C amplifier to drive the base of a Com. E power amplifier which is normally the last stage of amplification (the output stage). The power amplifier requires a large amount of input current in order to deliver maximum power to the load. Such an arrangement is shown in Figure 11.43 for driving a speaker.

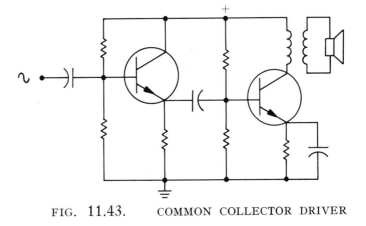

FIG. 11.43.   COMMON COLLECTOR DRIVER

11.22.   Common Collector Amplifiers: Summary

Table 11.5 summarizes some of the Com. C characteristics which
we have discussed.

TABLE 11.5

COMMON COLLECTOR AMPLIFIER

Current gain A_i: greater than 1 (as high as $\beta + 1$)
Voltage gain A_v: less than 1
Power gain A_p: moderately high; 50 is typical
Input impedance Z_{ic}:   high; 50K is typical
Output impedance Z_{oc}:   very low; 50Ω is typical
Phase shift: 0°

11.23.   Transistor Equivalent Circuits: T-Equivalent

The previous discussion of transistor amplifiers was a deliberately
simplified one in which many approximations and assumptions
were made in order to avoid overcomplicating the explanation of
transistor amplification. This does not mean that the gain and
impedance expressions derived in the previous sections are of no
practical use. On the contrary, they provide a quick method of
determining amplifier parameters and in many cases provide
suitable accuracy.

There often exists, however, a need to more accurately evaluate
a circuit. Thus, in transistor circuit design and analysis it is help-

ful to represent the transistor by an *equivalent circuit* consisting of ordinary passive components, resistors and capacitors, together with current generators, voltage generators, or both, which simulate the amplifying properties of the transistor. Such equivalent circuits are useful in two ways: they enable the circuit designer to use basic linear circuit analysis tools such as Kirchhoff's and Ohm's Laws in evaluating different circuit arrangements, and they enable the transistor manufacturer to supply data on his devices in a manner that will be useful to the circuit designer and analyst. Equivalent circuits are mathematical tools and should be treated as such. There are many possible transistor equivalent circuits; some of these equivalent circuits are based on the transistor's physical properties, while others are based on the transistor's terminal electrical characteristics. Two of the most widely used a-c equivalent circuits will be presented here. The a-c equivalent circuits are only used in analyzing the a-c currents and voltages in the transistor. As such, all the parameters which make up the a-c equivalent circuits are a-c parameters.

One of the earliest equivalent circuits that was developed was the *T-equivalent circuit*. It is based on the physical structure of the device which is shown in Figure 11.44A. Also represented in

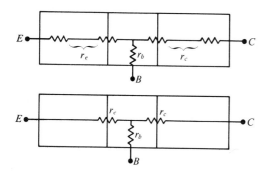

FIG. 11.44.   (A) REPRESENTATION OF TRANSISTOR PHYSICAL STRUCTURE AND INTERNAL RESISTANCES (B) SIMPLIFIED REPRESENTATION

the figure is the transistor internal resistance. Considering the emitter region first, the emitter current, in flowing from the emitter terminal through the *E-B* junction, encounters a resistance r_e which consists of two components, the ohmic resistance of the emitter region and the a-c resistance of the *E-B* junction. Normally, the former is very low due to the high level of emitter doping. Similarly, the collector current in flowing through the *C-B* junction to the collector terminal encounters a resistance r_c which consists of the high resistance across the reverse-biased *C-B* junction and the ohmic resistance of the collector region. The latter resistance can also be neglected. The base current in flowing toward the base terminal encounters a resistance r_b which is the ohmic resistance of the base region which is normally not negligible since the base is doped very lightly and consequently has a high resistivity. Figure 11.44B shows the simplified representation which neglects the emitter and collector region resistances.

All that remains to complete the T-equivalent circuit is to represent the transistor's current gain. This is accomplished by including a current generator in the collector circuit equal to αi_e, the emitter current multiplied by the Com. B current gain, which represents the collector current flowing due to the emitter current i_e. This results in the final T-equivalent circuit shown in Figure 11.45.

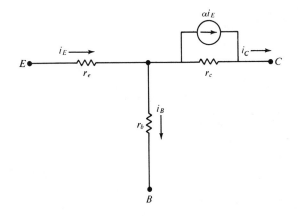

FIG. **11.45.**   T-EQUIVALENT CIRCUIT

A few things should be said concerning the T-equivalent, or any a-c equivalent circuit for that matter. First, the parameters will vary with the Q-point (d-c operating point) and for this reason the values to be used must be those measured at or near the Q-point of the circuit being considered. Secondly, and for the same reason, the equivalent circuit will be an exact equivalent only when the signal currents and voltages in the circuit remain small enough to assure that the parameters do not change appreciably. The accuracy of the equivalent circuit approach, then, will decrease as the signals in the circuit increase. However, even under large signal conditions the equivalent circuit can be a useful method for determining approximate circuit operation. Besides, the exact values of the equivalent circuit parameters are rarely known, so that even the small signal analysis is only approximate.

Referring again to the T-equivalent circuit, the resistor r_e, which is called the *E-B junction a-c resistance*, has a value which is greatly dependent on the value of d-c emitter current I_E. The value of r_e decreases as I_E increases. The relationship between r_e and I_E can be approximated at room temperature by

$$r_e \approx \frac{K_E}{I_E} \tag{11.52}$$

where K_E is a constant normally around 25 mv for most transistors.

▶ EXAMPLE 11.40

Calculate the value of r_e for a d-c emitter current of 1 ma. Assume $K_E = 25$ mv. Repeat for $I_E = 5$ ma.

Using Equation 11.52 with $I_E = 1$ ma

$$r_e = \frac{25 \text{ mv}}{1 \text{ ma}} = 25\Omega$$

Repeating for $I_E = 5$ ma

$$r_e = \frac{25 \text{ mv}}{5 \text{ ma}} = 5\Omega \qquad ◀$$

The value of r_b, which is called the *base bulk resistance*, depends mainly on the base region doping and geometry and is relatively independent of the Q-point. The magnitude of r_b can vary from 10Ω for high-power transistors to 3K for some low-performance types. For typical high-performance transistors r_b ranges from 100 to 1000Ω.

The *C-B junction a-c resistance*, r_c, has a large value typically between 500K and 1 meg and *decreases* when the collector current *increases*. Its value at $I_C = 1$ ma could be 1 meg while its value at 2 ma might be 750K. It also *decreases* slightly with *decreases* in V_{CB}. The resistance r_c is essentially the same as the transistor's Com. B output impedance r_{ob} which was introduced in Section 11.7 and illustrated in Figure 11.15.

The T-equivalent circuit of Figure 11.45 can be used to represent the transistor in any of its three configurations. If we consider the basic Com. B amplifier circuit shown in Figure 11.46A, the transistor may be replaced by its T-equivalent when considering

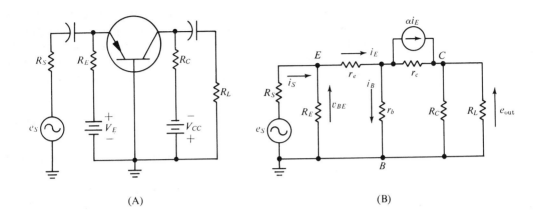

FIG. 11.46.   (A) COM. B AMPLIFIER (B) A-C EQUIV-
ALENT CIRCUIT USING T-EQUIVALENT
FOR THE TRANSISTOR

the a-c operation of the amplifier. This is done in part B of the
figure. This a-c equivalent circuit may now be analyzed using
linear circuit techniques to obtain values of gains and impedances.
The procedure is lengthy and beyond the scope of this text. However, the results are as follows:

Transistor Com. B input resistance (using $(R_L)' = R_C \| R_L$):

$$r_{ib} = \frac{v_{BE}}{i_E} = r_e + r_b - \frac{r_b(\alpha r_c + r_b)}{(R_L)' + r_c + r_b} \qquad (11.53)$$

Amplifier Com. B input impedance:

$$Z_{ib} = \frac{v_{BE}}{i_s} = r_{ib} \| R_E \qquad (11.54)$$

Transistor Com. B output impedance:

$$r_{ob} = r_c + r_b - \frac{r_b(\alpha r_c + r_b)}{R_s + r_b + r_e} \qquad (11.55)$$

Amplifier Com. B output impedance:

$$Z_{ob} = r_{ob} \| R_c \qquad (11.56)$$

Overall circuit voltage gain:

$$G_v = \frac{e_{out}}{e_s} = \frac{(R_L)'(\alpha r_c + r_b)}{[(R_L)' + r_c + r_b](R_s + r_e + r_b) - r_b(\alpha r_c + r_b)} \qquad (11.57)$$

Overall circuit current gain:

$$G_i = \frac{i_{out}}{i_s} = \frac{R_C(\alpha r_c + r_b)}{(R_L + R_c)(R_C + r_c + r_b)} \qquad (11.58)$$

It should be made clear that these exact formulas are not often used in day-to-day circuit calculations. The approximate formulas developed previously (Sections 11.4 to 11.8) are used most. In these approximate formulas the values of r_{ib} and r_{ob} were assumed. From Equation 11.53 the approximate value of r_{ib} in terms of the T-equivalent parameters is given by

$$r_{ib} \approx r_e + r_b(1 - \alpha) = r_e + \frac{r_b}{\beta + 1} \qquad (11.59)$$

This states that the input resistance of the transistor in the Com. B configuration is made up of the a-c junction resistance r_e in series with a small fraction $1/\beta + 1$ of the base bulk resistance r_b. This is illustrated in Figure 11.47. The importance of Equation 11.59

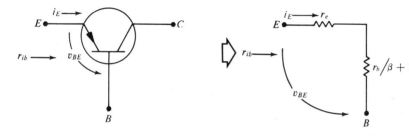

FIG. **11.47.**   APPROXIMATE REPRESENTATION OF r_{ib}

lies in the fact that the effect of r_b is diminished by the factor $1/\beta + 1$ and may sometimes be neglected.

▶EXAMPLE 11.41

A certain transistor has $r_b = 200\Omega$, $\beta = 100$ and $K_E = 25$ mv. Determine r_{ib} at a Q-point of $I_E = 1$ ma. Repeat for $I_E = 10$ ma. At $I_E = 1$ ma the value of r_e is

$$r_e \approx \frac{25 \text{ mv}}{1 \text{ ma}} = 25\Omega$$

Thus

$$r_{ib} \approx 25 + \frac{200}{100} = 27\Omega$$

At $I_E = 10$ ma the value of r_e is

$$r_e \approx 2.5\Omega$$

resulting in

$$r_{ib} \approx 2.5 + 2 = 4.5\Omega$$

In this example the effect of r_b could have been neglected at $I_E = 1$ ma to yield $r_{ib} \approx r_e = 25\Omega$. However, at $I_E = 10$ ma, r_e became very small and the effect of r_b was of the same order of magnitude and could not be neglected. ◀

The approximate value of r_{ob} may be obtained from 11.55 to be

$$r_{ob} \approx r_c \qquad \textbf{(11.60)}$$

which was pointed out previously. These approximate values of r_{ib} and r_{ob} can be used in the approximate gain and impedance formulas developed previously.

A similar approach may be taken for the Com. E and Com. C amplifiers. The results will not be presented here but are given in Appendix III. All that concerns us here are the approximate expressions for the transistor's Com. E input resistance r_{ie} and output resistance r_{oe}.

$$r_{ie} \approx \beta r_e + r_b \qquad \textbf{(11.61)}$$

$$r_{oe} \approx \frac{r_c}{\beta}$$

These expressions can be used in the approximate gain and impedance formulas of Sections 11.12 to 11.16.

▶ EXAMPLE 11.42

Determine r_{ie} for the transistor and conditions of Example 11.41.

At $I_E = 1$ ma, $r_e = 25\Omega$. Thus

$$r_{ie} = 100 \times 25\Omega + 200\Omega$$
$$= 2700\Omega$$

At $I_E = 10$ ma, $r_e = 2.5\Omega$ and

$$r_{ie} = 100 \times 2.5\Omega + 200\Omega$$
$$= 450\Omega \qquad ◀$$

The T-equivalent circuit as described above is useful in representing the transistor. It gives insight into the device's physical makeup. However, difficulties are usually encountered in measuring the values of the T parameters, and it has now become customary in the semiconductor industry to employ a different equivalent circuit representation called the hybrid equivalent circuit.

11.24. Transistor Equivalent Circuits: Hybrid Equivalent

The T-equivalent circuit is based on the internal workings of the transistor. The hybrid equivalent circuit which we will now discuss is based on how the transistor reacts when placed in a certain configuration. It is formulated by making measurements on the transistor's terminal voltages and currents under certain conditions. Taking, for example, the Com. E arrangement, the hybrid equivalent circuit is shown in Figure 11.48. The *h-parameters* which make up the equivalent circuit are defined as:

h_{ie}: a-c *i*nput resistance, common *e*mitter with output a-c short-circuited ($v_{CE} = 0$)

h_{fe}: *f*orward current gain, common *e*mitter with output a-c short-circuited ($v_{CE} = 0$)

h_{re}: *r*everse voltage feedback ratio, common *e*mitter, input a-c open-circuited ($i_B = 0$)

h_{oe}: *o*utput admittance (reciprocal of impedance) common *e*mitter, input a-c open-circuited ($i_B = 0$)

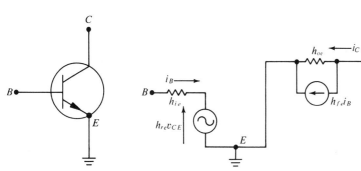

FIG. 11.48. COMMON EMITTER HYBRID EQUIVALENT CIRCUIT

It can be seen that this set of parameters consists of one resistance (h_{ie}), one admittance (h_{oe}), one voltage ratio (h_{re}) and one current ratio (h_{fe}); hence the name hybrid.

The values of the h-parameters are obtained by biasing the transistor at a particular Q-point, varying the appropriate current or voltage and then measuring the resultant change in current and voltage at other points. For example, the formula for h_{ie} is

$$h_{ie} = \frac{\Delta V_{BE}}{\Delta I_B} \bigg|_{\Delta V_{CE} = 0} \qquad (11.62)$$

To obtain the value of h_{ie} at a given Q-point, then, the base-emitter voltage must be varied and the resultant variation in base current measured while V_{CE} is held constant. One method of doing this is illustrated in Figure 11.49. The transistor is biased

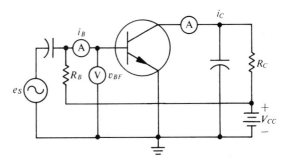

FIG. 11.49.   CIRCUIT FOR OBTAINING h_{ie} AND h_{fe}

at a particular Q-point and a signal is applied at the input to vary the base-emitter voltage. This variation is measured by the a-c voltmeter shown and the resultant variation in base current is measured by the a-c current meter. A large capacitor is placed between collector and emitter to maintain a constant V_{CE} under the signal condition. The ratio of the voltage to current readings will give the value of h_{ie}. It is very important that the signal variations be kept small since h_{ie}, and in fact all the h-parameters, will change over the range of transistor operating points.

The input resistance h_{ie} may be recognized as being the same as r_{ie} which was introduced in Section 11.2. One value of h_{ie} is often listed on manufacturers' data sheets under the symbol h_{ie} rather than r_{ie}. From our previous discussion of r_{ie} we can expect h_{ie} values to fall typically in the range of 500 to 5000Ω.

The formula for h_{fe}, the forward current gain, is

$$h_{fe} = \frac{\Delta I_C}{\Delta I_B} \bigg|_{\Delta V_{CE} = 0} \qquad (11.63)$$

Its value may be obtained using the circuit in Figure 11.49 using the measured values of a-c collector and base currents with V_{CE} constant. h_{fe} should be recognized as being the same as β which was introduced in Section 11.2. The symbol h_{fe} has gained common usage and is the one most often used on manufacturers' spec sheets. In fact, the d-c current gain $\beta_{\text{d-c}}$ is often replaced with the symbol h_{FE} (the upper case subscripts indicate d-c) which appears on most spec sheets. The student should be familiar with both representations β and h_{fe} (also $\beta_{\text{d-c}}$ and h_{FE}) since they both appear in electronics literature.

The formula for h_{re}, the reverse voltage ratio, is

$$h_{re} = \frac{\Delta V_{BE}}{\Delta V_{CE}}\bigg|_{\Delta I_B = 0} \qquad\qquad (11.64)$$

To obtain the value h_{re} at a given Q-point, the collector-to-emitter voltage is varied and the resultant change in base-to-emitter forward voltage is measured while the base current is held constant. One method of doing this is illustrated in Figure 11.50.

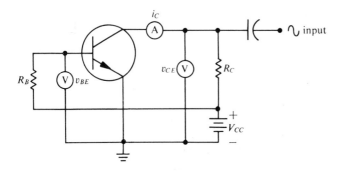

FIG. **11.50.**   CIRCUIT FOR OBTAINING h_{re} AND h_{oe}

A signal is applied at the collector in order to vary V_{CE}. The resultant change in V_{BE} is then measured and h_{re} calculated using Equation 11.64. The value of h_{re} is typically very small, in the range of 10^{-3} to 10^{-5}, and this value is a measure of how much the output voltage affects the transistor input characteristics. In our approximate analysis of Com. E amplifiers this effect was assumed to be zero.

Finally, the formula for h_{oe} is

$$h_{oe} = \frac{\Delta I_C}{\Delta V_{CE}}\bigg|_{\Delta I_B = 0} \qquad\qquad (11.65)$$

and its value may be determined using the circuit in Figure 11.50 by measuring the variation in I_C as the signal is applied. The units of h_{oe}, the output admittance, are *mhos*, the reciprocal of ohms. The output admittance h_{oe} should be recognized as the reciprocal of r_{oe} which was introduced in Section 11.15. That is

$$r_{oe} = 1/h_{oe} \qquad \textbf{(11.66)}$$

where r_{oe} was called the transistor output impedance. From our discussion of r_{oe} the values of h_{oe} will be seen to be in the range of 0.01 to 0.1 millimhos.

The same procedure may be followed to obtain the Com. B and Com. C hybrid equivalent circuits. The Com. B hybrid equivalent is shown in Figure 11.51.

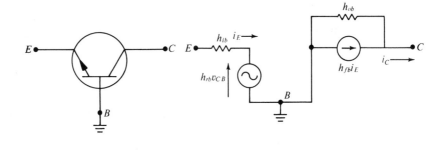

FIG. **11.51.**   COMMON BASE HYBRID EQUIVALENT CIRCUIT

The Com. B h-parameters are defined as:

h_{ib}: a-c input resistance (same as r_{ib} introduced in Section 11.2). Typical values range from $10 - 300\Omega$.

h_{fb}: a-c current gain (same as α)

h_{rb}: a-c reverse voltage ratio. Typical values range from 10^{-3} to 10^{-6}.

h_{ob}: a-c output admittance. Typical values range from 10^{-6} to 10^{-5}mho.

The Com. C hybrid equivalent is shown in Figure 11.52. Its parameters are defined as:

h_{ic}: a-c input impedance (equal to h_{ie})

h_{fc}: a-c current gain (equivalent to $\beta + 1$)

h_{rc}: a-c reverse voltage ratio—typically near one.

h_{oc}: a-c output admittance (equal to h_{oe})

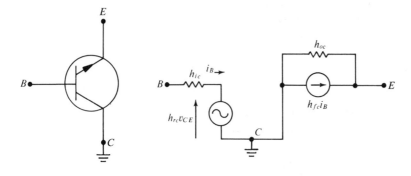

FIG. 11.52.   COMMON COLLECTOR HYBRID EQUIVA-
LENT CIRCUIT

These hybrid equivalent circuits can be used to replace a transistor in an amplifier circuit. Then, gain and impedance formulas can be derived using Kirchhoff's equations. However, as was the case for the T-equivalent circuits, these formulas are rather cumbersome and do not lend themselves to day-to-day usage. The exact formulas are presented in Appendix III. The approximate formulas developed earlier are more valuable for quick calculations. This should not imply that the h-parameters are useless. On the contrary, since transistor data sheets usually contain a number of h-parameters, their values can be used in the approximate formulas. Unfortunately, most transistor data sheets do not list all of the h-parameters. In cases where the desired parameter is not listed it may be obtained using the conversion formulas listed in Table 11.6. The following examples illustrate its use.

▶ EXAMPLE 11.43

A certain transistor's data sheet lists the following h-parameter values at $V_{CB} = 20$v and $I_E = 1$ ma:

$$h_{fe} = 50$$
$$h_{ib} = 40\Omega$$
$$h_{ob} = 10^{-6} \text{ mhos}$$
$$h_{rb} = 2 \times 10^{-4}$$

Determine input impedance r_{ie} and output impedance r_{oe} for use in the Com. E formulas derived earlier.

TABLE 11.6

PARAMETER CONVERSION FORMULAS

---

1. $h_{fe} = \beta = \dfrac{\alpha}{1 - \alpha}$; $h_{FE} = \beta_{\text{d-c}}$

2. $h_{fb} = \alpha = \beta/\beta + 1$; $h_{FB} = \alpha_{\text{d-c}}$

3. $h_{ib} = r_e + \dfrac{r_b}{\beta + 1}$

4. $h_{ie} = r_b + r_e(\beta + 1) = h_{ib}(\beta + 1)$

5. $h_{ob} \approx 1/r_c$

6. $h_{oe} \approx \beta/r_c = \beta h_{ob}$

7. $h_{rb} \approx r_b/r_c$

8. $h_{re} \approx \dfrac{\beta r_e}{r_c} \approx h_{ie} h_{ob}$

9. $h_{rc} \approx 1$

10. $h_{oc} = h_{oe}$

11. $h_{ic} = h_{ie}$

12. $h_{fc} = \beta + 1$

13. $r_{ib} \approx h_{ib}$

14. $r_{ie} \approx h_{ie}$

15. $r_{ob} \approx 1/h_{ob}$

16. $r_{oe} \approx 1/h_{oe}$

From Table 11.6 r_{ie} is equal to h_{ie} and h_{ie} can be obtained from Formula 4 since h_{ib} is given and β is equal to h_{fe}. Thus

$$r_{ie} = h_{ie} = 40\Omega(50 + 1) = 2040\Omega$$

The value of r_{oe} is obtained using Formulas 16 and 6.

$$r_{oe} = \frac{1}{h_{oe}} = \frac{1}{\beta h_{ob}} = \frac{1}{50 \times 10^{-6} \text{ mhos}}$$

$$= 20\text{K} \qquad \blacktriangleleft$$

▶ EXAMPLE 11.44

For the same transistor determine α, r_{ib} and r_{ob} for use in the Com. B formulas.

Using Formulas 2, 13 and 15 we have

$$\alpha = \frac{\beta}{\beta + 1} = \frac{50}{51} = 0.98$$

$$r_{ib} = h_{ib} = 40\Omega$$

$$r_{ob} = \frac{1}{h_{ob}} = \frac{1}{10^{-6} \text{ mhos}} = 1 \text{ meg} \qquad \blacktriangleleft$$

It should be re-emphasized that all equivalent circuit parameter values will be dependent on the d-c operating point. Thus, for any reasonable degree of accuracy in our calculations, the values used should be measured at or near the Q-point of the circuit under analysis. Again, all of the equations presented in this chapter, with few exceptions, are approximate and should be treated as such. In most circuit work these formulas will be adequate for evaluating the behavior of transistor amplifiers.

11.25.   Effects of Frequency on Amplifier Operation

In the previous discussions on transistor amplifiers it was tacitly assumed that the signal frequency was neither low enough nor high enough to affect amplifier operation. In practice, signals of very low or very high frequency are encountered and one must understand how the amplifier responds to these different signals. A typical amplifier will suffer from a loss of gain (current, voltage and power) as the signal frequency increases or decreases beyond certain limits. Figure 11.53 illustrates this in a gain-versus-

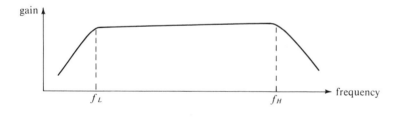

FIG. 11.53.   TYPICAL   AMPLIFIER   GAIN-VS.-FRE-QUENCY PLOT

frequency plot for such an amplifier. It can be seen that over a range of frequencies (sometimes referred to as the *mid-band*) the amplifier gain is fairly constant but drops off at frequencies below f_L and above f_H. The following discussion deals with the causes of this gain dropoff in a rather qualitative manner. The numerous formulas which usually accompany such a discussion are beyond the scope of this text and so are not included.

If we consider the low frequency effects first, it can generally be stated that any loss of gain can be attributed to the coupling and bypass capacitors in the circuit. As an example consider the

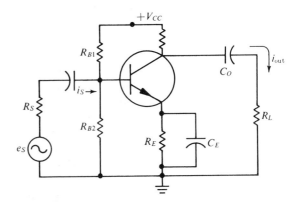

FIG. 11.54.   COMMON EMITTER AMPLIFIER

Com. E amplifier shown in Figure 11.54 which contains two coupling capacitors and one bypass capacitor. At mid-band frequencies or greater these capacitors will have a very small impedance if chosen correctly. This allows us to assume ideal coupling and bypassing at such frequencies. However, at low frequencies the impedance of these capacitors will eventually increase (recall $X_c = 1/2\pi fC$) to the point where these assumptions are no longer valid. For example, the impedance of C_c will increase to the point where a portion of the input signal e_S will be dropped across it. It follows, then, that a smaller portion of the signal will reach the base of the transistor and become amplified. Similarly, at low frequencies a portion of the output signal will be lost across C_o resulting in a smaller e_{out}. The function of C_E, as discussed in Section 11.18, is to provide a low-impedance bypass across R_E so that all of the input signal would appear across the E-B junction and none would be lost across R_E. Obviously, the bypassing of C_E at low frequencies becomes less and less effective. All these effects contribute to a smaller output signal and thus lower gain. The individual effects will generally occur at different frequencies. For example, loss of gain due to C_c may begin at 100HZ, due to C_o at 50HZ, and due to C_E at 10HZ. In this case, the most critical effect will be that of C_c because it occurs at the highest frequency. It may be reasoned that elimination of these capacitors entirely would eliminate their affect on low frequency gain. In certain types of amplifiers this is actually done, usually at the expense of lower mid-band gain and problems in biasing and stability. These amplifiers, called *DC (Direct Coupled) amplifiers*, are very important in electronics and should be encountered in later courses. Although the Com. E amplifier was used in our example, similar low frequency effects occur in the Com. B and Com. C amplifiers.

The loss of gain at high frequencies can be attributed to two major factors, one of which is the decrease in transistor current gain α. The decrease in α is related to the transit time of the current carriers as they move from the emitter to the collector. The carriers injected from the emitter into the base will either recombine or diffuse the entire width of the base region to reach the collector. As the signal frequency increases a frequency will be reached at which the time involved in the transit of the carriers across the base will be longer than the signal period. When this occurs, the change in collector current will not be able to follow exactly the change in emitter current caused by the applied signal across the *E-B* junction. As a result, a build-up of carriers will take place in the base region, thus increasing the amount of recombinations and decreasing α. Of course, the greater the transit time, the lower the frequency at which the decrease in α occurs. The transit time depends on the width of the base region and the diffusion speed of the carriers which in turn depends on the semiconductor material and carrier polarity. In general, for the same base thickness, germanium will have a shorter transit time than silicon and NPNs will have a shorter transit time than PNPs.

The variation of α with frequency is shown in Figure 11.55. Manufacturers usually specify the frequency at which α (h_{fb}) drops

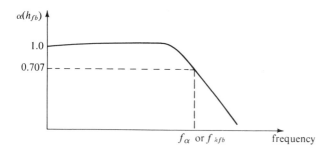

FIG. 11.55.   VARIATION OF α WITH FREQUENCY

to 0.707 of its low frequency value. The symbol f_α or f_{hfb} is given as the frequency at which this occurs. This frequency is referred to as the *common base cut-off frequency* and is primarily used with the Com. B configuration.

Since β is related to α by

$$\beta = \frac{\alpha}{1 - \alpha}$$

the value of β will also decrease with frequency but at a much faster rate. The symbol f_β or f_{hfe} is given as the frequency at which $\beta(h_{fe})$ drops to 0.707 of its low frequency value, and is called the *common emitter cut-off frequency*. This is indicated in Figure 11.56.

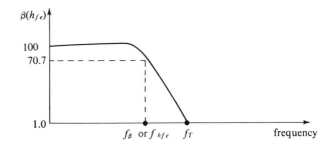

FIG. **11.56.** VARIATION OF β WITH FREQUENCY

For a given transistor, this frequency will be much lower than f_{hfb}. In fact they are related by

$$f_{hfe} = f_{hfb}(1 - h_{fb}) \tag{11.67}$$

▶ EXAMPLE 11.45

A transistor with a low-frequency α of 0.98 has an f_{hfb} of 10MHZ. Determine the value of f_{hfe}.

$$f_{hfe} = 10\text{MHZ}(1 - 0.98) = 200\text{KHZ} \qquad ◀$$

This example illustrates the fact that current gain in the Com. E and Com. C configurations will begin dropping at a much lower frequency than the current gain in the Com. B configuration. Another frequency parameter of importance for Com. E operation is given the symbol f_T and is the frequency at which β has decreased to a value of one (shown in Figure 11.56). Such a frequency as f_T is considered because in many Com. E circuits (not necessarily amplifiers) the value of β need only be greater than one for useful operation. The value of f_T is approximately given by

$$f_T \approx \frac{f_{hfb}}{1.2} \tag{11.68}$$

EXAMPLE 11.46

For the transistor of the previous example determine the value of f_T.

$$f_T = \frac{f_{hfb}}{1.2} = 8.33 \text{MHZ} \qquad \blacktriangleleft$$

The other high frequency factor is the effect of junction capacitances. An equivalent capacitance exists across both the *E-B* and *C-B* junctions. C_{ob} is the symbol given the output capacitance of the transistor in the Com. B mode and is essentially the capacitance of the *C-B* junction and any stray or wiring capacitance. It is illustrated in Figure 11.57, and it can be seen that it essentially

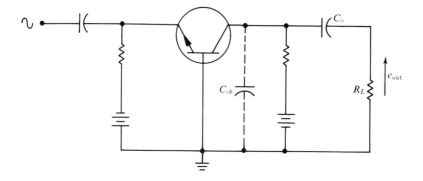

FIG. 11.57.   COM. B OUTPUT CAPACITANCE

shunts the load (at high frequencies C_o is an a-c short). This indicates that at high frequencies the impedance of C_{ob} will become small enough to shunt signal current away from the load, reducing e_{out}. The value of C_{ob} depends on doping, *C-B* junction geometry and on the d-c voltage across the *C-B* junction (recall Section 5.14) and is usually around a few pf (10^{-12} farads).

C_{oe} is the corresponding symbol for the output capacitance in the Com. E mode and is a little more complex than C_{ob} since the output is taken from collector to emitter. The capacitance between collector and base and between base and emitter both enter into the output capacity in the Com. E configuration. There is a relationship between C_{oe} and C_{ob} given below which indicates that the output capacitance in the Com. E configuration is much greater than in the Com. B.

$$C_{oe} = \frac{C_{ob}}{1 - h_{fb}} \qquad \textbf{(11.69)}$$

► EXAMPLE 11.46

A transistor with $\alpha = 0.98$ has a $C_{ob} = 4\text{pf}$ at $V_{CB} = 10\text{v}$. Determine C_{oe}.

$$C_{oe} = \frac{C_{ob}}{1 - \alpha} = \frac{4\text{pf}}{0.02} = 200\text{pf} \qquad ◄$$

Output capacitance in the Com. C amplifier is relatively insignificant since the output is taken at the emitter, a very low output impedance point. For this reason, Com. C amplifiers usually have the best high frequency response of the three amplifier configurations.

There are other high frequency effects, but the two just discussed are the most significant. It should be pointed out that many factors go toward determining the high frequency limit of a transistor amplifier and there are numerous methods of increasing this limit. These methods appropriately belong in a circuit analysis text and will not be covered here.

11.26.   Summary of Transistor Amplifier Configurations

Table 11.7 below summarizes the three transistor amplifier configurations and compares their relative characteristics.

TABLE 11.7

Characteristic	Common Base	Common Emitter	Common Collector
Current gain	less than one	high	high
Voltage gain	high	high	less than one
Power gain	moderate	highest	low
Input impedance	very low	moderate	high
Output impedance	high	moderate	very low
Input terminal	emitter	base	base
Output terminal	collector	collector	emitter
Phase shift (mid-band)	0°	180°	0°
Bias stability	good	poor (base current bias)	good
Frequency response	good	fair	best

GLOSSARY

α: a-c common base current gain

r_{ib}: common base transistor input impedance

β: a-c common emitter current gain

r_{ie}: common emitter transistor input impedance

Bias (quiescent values): d-c values of transistor currents and voltages

Bias (Q) point: d-c operating point (no signal)

Z_{ib}: common base amplifier input impedance

r_{ob}: common base transistor output impedance

Z_{ob}: common base transistor amplifier output impedance

Z_{ie}: common emitter amplifier input impedance

r_{oe}: common emitter transistor output impedance

Z_{oe}: common emitter amplifier output impedance

Q-point stability: ability of Q-point to remain constant under variations in temperature

Base current bias: method of biasing a common emitter amplifier with a
constant base current

Base voltage bias: biasing a Com. E amplifier with a constant base
to ground voltage

Z_{ic}: common collector amplifier input impedance

Z_{oc}: common collector amplifier output impedance

Emitter follower: another name for common collector amplifier

Equivalent circuit: combination of linear circuit elements which represent the operation of the transistor in a given set of
conditions

r_e: *E-B* junction a-c resistance

r_c: *C-B* junction a-c resistance

r_b: base region bulk resistance

h-parameters: parameters of the transistor hybrid equivalent circuits
(Section 11.23)

Mid-band frequencies: range of frequencies over which gain is relatively constant

$f_\alpha(f_{hfb})$:   frequency at which α has dropped to 0.707 of its low frequency value

$f_\beta(f_{hfe})$:   frequency at which β has dropped to 0.707 of its low frequency value

f_T: frequency at which β has dropped to one

$C_{ob}(C_{oe})$:   common base (emitter) output capacitance

Questions

11.1   Which transistor voltage is the controlling voltage as far as amplification is concerned?

11.2   In the active region which transistor junction has the highest resistance?

11.3   What transistor parameter measures the a-c resistance of the E-B junction in the Com. B configuration?

11.4   What transistor parameter measures the a-c current gain from emitter to collector?

11.5   The following set of data pertains to a particular transistor.

V_{BE}	I_E	I_C	V_{CB}
0.7v	1 ma	0.99 ma	10v
0.68v	0.5 ma	0.495 ma	10v

From this data determine r_{ib} and α for this transistor.

11.6   A certain transistor has $r_{ib} = 25\Omega$ and $\alpha = 0.95$ when $V_{BE} = 0.3$v, $I_E = 1$ ma and $I_C = 0.96$ ma. Determine the increase in I_E and I_C if V_{BE} increases to 0.31v.

11.7   What transistor parameter measures the a-c resistance of the E-B junction in the Com. E configuration?

11.8   What transistor parameter measures the a-c current gain from base to collector?

11.9   A certain transistor has $r_{ie} = 1600\Omega$ and $\beta = 120$ when $V_{BE} = 0.3$v, $I_B = 100$ μa and $I_C = 1.5$ ma. Determine the decrease in I_B and I_C if V_{BE} decreases to 0.29v.

11.10   In amplifiers, what is the name given to the d-c values of current and voltage?

11.11   Sketch from memory a typical Com. B amplifier circuit.

11.12   What is the purpose of the amplifier input coupling capacitor?

11.13   What is the purpose of V_{EE} and V_{CC}?

11.14   In the Com. B amplifier circuit of Figure 11.8 the transistor has an α of 0.99. Determine i_E, i_B, and i_C if the value of i_S is 10 ma and $i_X = 0$.

11.15   How is a large output signal voltage obtained in the Com. B amplifier?

11.16   How does the input signal e_S affect the forward voltage across *E-B* junction?

11.17   What effective impedance does the input signal see in the Com. B amplifier?

11.18   Across what impedance does the a-c emitter current flow? The a-c collector current?

11.19   If the Com. B current gain is less than one, how is voltage gain obtained?

11.20   The amplifier in Figure 11.8 has the following circuit values:

$$V_{EE} = 5.0\text{v}$$
$$R_E = 470\Omega$$
$$V_{CC} = 45\text{v}$$
$$R_C = 3.3K$$

The transistor is germanium and has the following parameters at the Q-point:

$$\alpha_{\text{d-c}} = 0.99$$
$$\alpha = 0.985$$
$$r_{ib} = 10\Omega$$
$$r_{ob} = 1 \text{ meg}$$

(a) Determine the Q-point values I_E, I_C, and V_{CB}.
(b) Determine i_E if the input signal is 10 mv p-p.
(c) Determine i_C and v_{CB}.
(d) Determine A_v.
(e) Determine A_p.

11.21   For the amplifier in Question 11.20 calculate the output signal power and input signal power and determine A_p. Compare with answer to 11.20 (e) above.

11.22   Without changing transistors, how could A_v be increased for the amplifier of 11.20?

11.23   What would be the effect on the voltage gain if the signal source resistance R_S were included in 11.20?

11.24 What would be the effect on the voltage gain if the amplifier of 11.20 were capacitively coupled to a load R_L?

11.25 Calculate the input and output impedances of the amplifier of 11.20 (Z_{ib} and Z_{ob}).

11.26 Determine the overall voltage gain G_v in the amplifier of 11.20 if $R_S = 2\Omega$ and $R_L = 10K$.

11.27 What two effects accompany a large value of source resistance?

11.28 If an unloaded amplifier ($R_L = \infty$) has $A_v = 1000$, what is the maximum voltage gain it can have when it is loaded? Under what condition?

11.29 Calculate the approximate voltage gain in the circuit below if $r_{ib} = 25\Omega$, $r_{ob} = 1$ meg and $\alpha = 0.992$. (Hint: use Equation

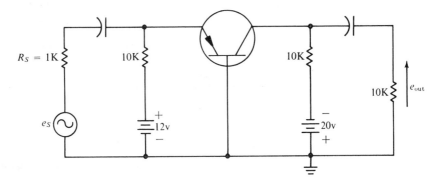

FIG. **11.58.**

11.8C). In this case the voltage gain is very low but it is relatively independent of the transistor parameters. This makes A_v less dependent on temperature and transistor replacement.

11.30 The amplifier in Figure 11.59 uses a germanium transistor with

the output characteristics of Figure 11.19. If the transistor has an $r_{ib} = 20\Omega$, determine:
(a) The waveforms of collector-base voltage and e_{out} (use graphical technique).
(b) Overall voltage gain e_{out}/e_S.

11.31 Repeat 11.30 using $e_S = 40$ mv p-p.

11.32 What effect will the inclusion of R_S (source resistance) have on voltage gain in the amplifier of Figure 11.59?

11.33 Sketch from memory a typical Com. E amplifier circuit.

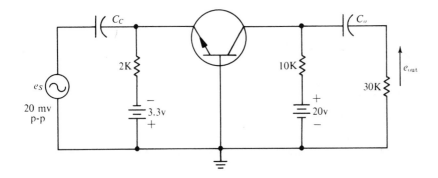

FIG. 11.59.

11.34   In the Com. E amplifier of Figure 11.23 the transistor has a β of 60. Determine i_B, i_C and i_E if i_S is 10 μa p-p and $i_x = 0$.

11.35   What effective impedance does the input signal see in the Com. E amplifier?

11.36   The amplifier in Figure 11.23 has the following circuit values:

$$V_{BB} = V_{CC} = 20v$$
$$R_B = 1 \text{ meg}$$
$$R_C = 5K$$

The silicon transistor has the following parameters at the Q-point:

$$\beta_{d\text{-}c} = 75$$
$$\beta = 70$$
$$r_{ie} = 1.5K$$
$$r_{oe} = 30K$$

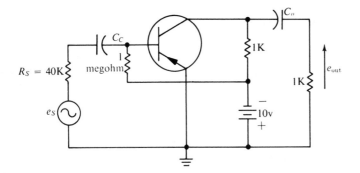

FIG. 11.60.

Determine

(a) circuit Q-point
(b) i_B, i_C and v_{CE} for $e_S = 30$ mv p-p
(c) A_v and A_p

11.37   Calculate Z_{ie} and Z_{oe} for the amplifier of Question 11.36.

11.38   Determine the overall voltage gain G_v of the amplifier of 11.36 if it is driven by a signal source of 100Ω impedance and has its output capacitively coupled to a load of $R_L = 5$K. Calculate G_i and G_p.

11.39   Calculate the approximate voltage gain in Figure 11.60 if $r_{ie} = 1$K, $r_{ob} = 25$K and $\beta = 120$. (Hint: use Equation 11.30)

11.40   The amplifier in Figure 11.61 uses a germanium transistor with the output characteristics of Figure 11.31. If the transistor has an $r_{ie} = 2$K determine:

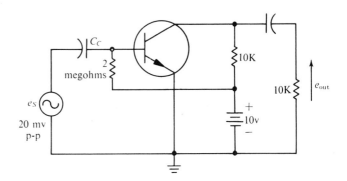

FIG. **11.61.**

(a) The waveforms of collector-emitter voltage and e_{out} (use graphical technique).
(b) Voltage gain e_{out}/e_S.

11.41   Repeat 11.40 using $e_S = 40$ mv p-p.

11.42   What type of bias is used in the Com. E amplifier in Figure 11.62? What advantage does it have over that used in Figure 11.61?

11.43   If the transistor in Figure 11.62 has $\beta_{\text{d-c}} = 60$ determine: V_B, I_E, I_C and V_{CE}.

11.44   What is the purpose of the 10 μfd capacitor in this circuit?

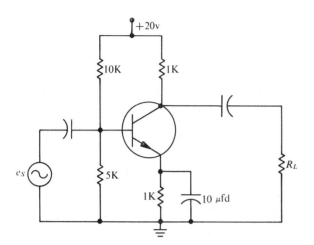

FIG. **11.62.**

11.45 For each of the following statements indicate whether it refers to Com. B or Com. E amplifiers, or both.
(a) Gives a 180° phase shift
(b) Has very low input impedance
(c) Has bias stability problems
(d) High output impedance (50K)
(e) Gives high voltage gain (500)
(f) Has highest power gain
(g) Has low current gain
(h) Will produce distortion when overdriven

11.46 Sketch from memory a typical Com. C amplifier.

11.47 Consider the Com. C amplifier in Figure 11.63. If the transistor parameters are $\beta = 120$ and $r_{ie} = 1.2K$, determine Z_B, the impedance seen looking into the transistor base for $R_L = 10K$ and for $R_L = 5K$.

11.48 Determine the input impedance of the amplifier in Question 11.47 for $R_L = 10K$ and for $R_L = 5K$.

11.49 Determine the voltage gain G_v for the same amplifier for both $R_L = 10K$ and 5K using $R_S = 2K$.

11.50 Calculate Z_{oc} for the same amplifier using $R_S = 2K$ and $r_{ib} = 40\Omega$. Repeat for $R_S = 3K$.

11.51 Will the input impedance of the amplifier in Figure 11.63 increase, decrease or remain the same under the following conditions?

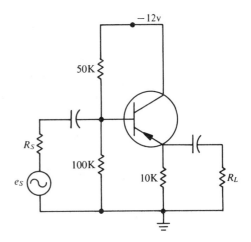

FIG. 11.63.

(a) Decrease R_L
(b) Increase R_S
(c) Increase the 50K resistor to 100K
(d) Decrease the 100K resistor to 82K
(e) Increase in transistor β

11.52   Will the output impedance of the amplifier in Figure 11.63 increase, decrease or remain the same under the following conditions?
(a) Decrease R_L
(b) Increase the 50K resistor to 100K
(c) Decrease R_S
(d) Decrease in β

11.53   Indicate which of the three amplifier configurations (Com. B, Com. C or Com. E) pertain to each of the following statements.
(a) Gives 180° phase shift
(b) Has the highest input impedance
(c) Has the lowest power gain
(d) Has high current gain (greater than 1)
(e) Has the lowest output impedance
(f) Has voltage gain less than one
(g) Has highest output impedance
(h) Gives no phase shift

11.54   How are transistor a-c equivalent circuits useful?

11.55   Draw from memory the transistor T-equivalent circuit.

11.56   Which of the transistor internal resistances r_e, r_b or r_c is usually the largest? Why?

11.57   A transistor has $r_e = 30\Omega$ at $I_E = 1$ ma. What is r_e at $I_E = 5$ ma? If the base bulk resistance (r_b) is 150Ω at $I_E = 1$ ma, what is its value at $I_E = 5$ ma?

11.58   Which of the following is most likely the value of *C-B* junction resistance (r_c): 100Ω, 10K, 100K, 1 meg?

11.59   A certain transistor has $r_b = 300\Omega$, $\beta = 100$ and $K_E = 25$ mv. Determine r_{ib} at a Q-point of $I_E = 2$ ma. Repeat for $I_E = 5$ ma.

11.60   The same transistor has an r_c of $750K$. Determine the value of r_{ob}.

11.61   For the same transistor determine r_{ie} at $I_E = 2$ ma and 5 ma. Since r_{ie} decreases with d-c emitter current, what will happen to voltage gain as I_E is increased?

11.62   Draw from memory the hybrid equivalent circuit for a transistor in the Com. E configuration.

11.63   From the following data table determine h_{ie} and h_{fe}.

V_{BE}	I_B	I_C	V_{CE}
0.68v	50 μa	4.9 ma	5v
0.69v	60 μa	5.8 ma	5v
0.69v	60 μa	5.85 ma	6v

11.64   From the same table calculate h_{oe}.

11.65   Determine the values of β, r_{ie} and r_{oe} for the transistor of the previous two questions.

11.66   Draw from memory the hybrid equivalent circuit for a transistor in the Com. B configuration. Repeat for the Com. C configuration.

11.67   A certain transistor data sheet lists the following parameters at $I_C = 1$ ma:
$$h_{fe} = 30$$
$$h_{ie} = 800 \text{ ohms}$$
$$h_{oe} = 2 \times 10^{-5} \text{ mhos}$$
$$h_{re} = 10^{-3}$$

Determine the values of the Com. B h-parameters and the T-parameters. Use Table 11.6.

11.68   What causes the low frequency loss in gain in transistor amplifiers?

11.69   The following data is listed for a particular transistor:
$$h_{fb} = 0.99$$
$$f_{hfb} = 20 \text{ MHZ}$$

Determine f_{hfe} and f_T for this transistor.

11.70 For a transistor with a given output capacitance C_{oe} how will a decrease in R_L affect the high frequency response? How will it affect mid-band voltage gain?

11.71 With the same value of R_L what type of amplifier, Com. B or Com. E, will have a better high frequency response?

11.72 If two transistors have the same value of C_{ob} but different values of β, which will have a better high frequency response in the Com. E configuration?

References

Foster, J. F., *Semiconductors, Diodes and Transistors*, Vol. 3, 7. Beaverton, Oregon: Programmed Instruction Group, Tetronix, Inc., 1964.

Malvino, A. P., *Transistor Circuit Approximations*. New York: McGraw-Hill Book Company, 1968.

Pierce, J. F., *Transistor Circuit Theory and Design*. Columbus, Ohio: Charles E. Merrill Books, Inc., 1963.

Romanowitz, H. A. and R. E. Puckett, *Introduction to Electronics*. New York: John Wiley & Sons, Inc., 1968.

Transistor Manual. Syracuse, New York: General Electric Company, 1964.

Veatch, H. C., *Transistor Circuit Action*. New York: McGraw-Hill Book Company, 1968.

The Transistor as a Switch

12.1. Introduction

An important application of the transistor is in the ever-increasing area of switching circuits. This broad category of circuits includes applications in such fields as digital computers, control systems, counting and timing systems, data-processing systems, digital instrumentation, pulse communications, radar, telemetry and television. When it is used as a switch the transistor is operated in one of two states: conducting or non-conducting. The non-conducting state is *cut-off* while the conducting state may be either in the *active* region or in the *saturation* region. The following discussion will concentrate on these two states of operation and even more importantly on the transition from one state to the other. In the process many of the transistor's switching parameters will be introduced as a means of evaluating a switching transistor's performance.

12.2. Characteristics of a Switch

In Figure 12.1 a pair of mechanical contacts form a switch. When the switch is open (as shown) the current through the resistor is equal to zero and $V_R = 0$. When the switch is closed the current becomes E/R and $V_R = E$. These results assume that the open

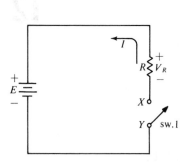

FIG. **12.1.**   MECHANICAL SWITCH

switch resistance, R_o, between points X and Y is infinite and the closed switch resistance, R_S, between X and Y is zero. This would be true only for an ideal switch. That is, an ideal switch would have an R_o/R_s ratio of infinity. Mechanical switches come close to providing this ideal ratio, but suffer from shortcomings such as slow switching speed, low reliability and contact bounce. Transistor switches cannot provide such a high R_o/R_s ratio, but to a great extent overcome the disadvantages of the mechanical switch.

The voltage V_R in the circuit has two discrete levels or states, zero and E volts. The current in the circuit also has two states, zero and E/R. In digital computer circuitry these states are used to identify bits of information and the *transition time* required to switch from one state to the other, illustrated in Figure 12.2,

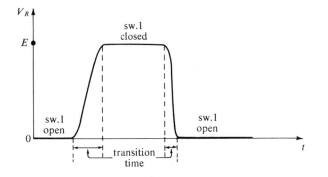

FIG. **12.2.**   ILLUSTRATION OF TRANSITION TIME BE-
TWEEN STATES

determines the speed at which computer operations can be performed. Thus, in our discussion of transistor switches, there are two areas to be investigated: the *steady-state* operation which is concerned with determining the two switching states and the *transient* operation which is concerned with operation during the transition time.

12.3. Steady-State Operation

In the circuit of Figure 12.1 a mechanical switch was used to control the current through the circuit. Figure 12.3 shows a

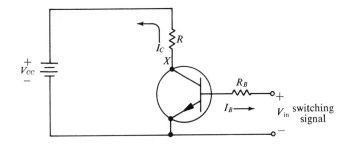

FIG. 12.3.   THE TRANSISTOR USED AS A SWITCH

corresponding arrangement in which the mechanical switch has been replaced by a transistor. The transistor is connected in the Com. E configuration which is used in practically all switching applications, since its high current gain allows large collector currents to be switched by means of a relatively small base current. As we learned in Chapter 9, the transistor can operate in either the cut-off, active, or saturation mode, depending on the status of the input base current. In switching circuits the cut-off condition is referred to as the "off" condition and the saturated condition as the "on" condition. The "active" condition retains its name. With zero base current or with the $E\text{-}B$ junction reverse-biased the transistor is turned "off" and only a small leakage current will flow from emitter to collector. With a forward-biased $E\text{-}B$ junction a base current will flow resulting in a substantial collector current. The transistor is then "active" and it will remain that way unless I_B is large enough to cause the collector current to saturate and enter the "on" state. This is more clearly demonstrated using the transistor's Com. E output characteristics in Figure 12.4. The load-line is drawn for $V_{CC} = 5v$ and $R = 500\Omega$. It can be seen that with $I_B = 0$ only a small collector current (I_{CEO}) flows and almost all of the supply voltage appears between collector and emitter. The transistor is operating in the "off" region and the

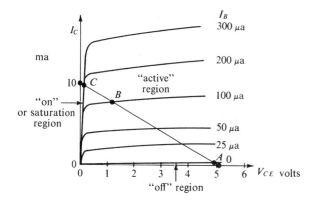

FIG. 12.4.   COMMON EMITTER CHARACTERISTICS

co-ordinates of point A determine the value of R_o for the transistor switch. For a typical silicon switching transistor $I_{CEO} = 1$ μa giving a value of $R_o = 5v/1$ $\mu a = 5$ megohms. With a base current of 100 μa the operation shifts to the "active" region where both I_C and V_{CE} are relatively large. Increasing I_B to 200 μa sends the transistor into saturation where maximum collector current flows and only a small voltage drop appears across the transistor switch. The transistor is now in the "on" region and the co-ordinates of point C give the value of R_S for the transistor switch. For the values shown $R_S = 0.2v/10$ ma $= 20\Omega$. The ratio R_o/R_S is then equal to 2.5×10^5. This ratio can be made more ideal by reverse-biasing the *E-B* junction rather than simply setting $I_B = 0$. This is normally done and results in a smaller collector leakage current in the "off" state, actually making it equal I_{CBO} which can lead to values of R_o in the neighborhood of 1000 megohms. In the "on" or saturated condition the value of collector-to-emitter voltage is given the symbol $V_{CE(sat)}$ and is normally only a few tenths of a volt. As can be seen in the figure $V_{CE(sat)}$ increases as I_C increases. As we already know, once the transistor is saturated, further increases in I_B will not increase I_C above its value at saturation, $[V_{CC} - V_{CE(sat)}]/R$ or approximately V_{CC}/R, which is independent of the base current. In the analysis and design of transistor switching circuits the transistor output curves and load-line plotting are rarely used. The approximate techniques developed in Chapter 9 are usually employed.

   It was stated in the introduction that the conducting state of a transistor switch is sometimes chosen in the "active" region (the nonconducting state is always cut-off or "off"). In these cases the transistor is said to be operating as a *non-saturated switch* as opposed to a *saturated switch* when the conducting state is in the "on" region. Circuits utilizing the transistor as a non-saturated switch typically have faster switching speeds. However, they dissipate more power, are usually more difficult to design and are less immune to noise than circuits using the transistor as a saturated switch. Some of these differences will be discussed in the following sections.

12.4. Transient Operation

The transition time between states of a transistor switch is the principal factor limiting the maximum frequency at which switching can occur. As such, it is important to understand the response of a transistor to an input pulse. Let us consider the response of the transistor switch of Figure 12.3 to a pulse of input voltage V_{in} (plotted in Figure 12.5). At $t = 0$, V_{in} is negative, reverse-biasing the *E-B* junction, and the transistor is "off" corresponding to point *A* on the load-line in Figure 12.4 with $I_B \approx 0$ and $I_C \approx 0$. The value of V_{BE} is simply $-10v$ of reverse bias. At $t = t_1$, V_{in} is suddenly increased to $+10v$. If we assume R_B is 47K, this value of V_{in} will eventually provide a base current of 200 μa to cause the transistor to turn "on" (point *C* on the load-line). However, the transistor will not respond immediately. As shown in Figure 12.5, the base-emitter voltage increases *gradually* toward its forward-bias value after V_{in} has switched. As a result the collector current will not begin increasing toward its saturation value of 10 ma until V_{BE} becomes forward-biased. Even then, I_C will increase only gradually toward 10 ma. The time interval from $t = t_1$, when V_{in} switches, to the time when the collector current rises to 10 per cent of its final value is called *delay time t_d* as indicated in Figure 12.5. The time it takes the collector current to rise from 10 per cent to 90 per cent of its final value is called *rise time t_r*. The sum of delay time and rise time is the amount of time it takes the transistor to turn "on" and is called *turn-on time t_{on}*. That is,

$$t_{on} = t_d + t_r \tag{12.1}$$

The turn-on time depends on many factors including transistor parameters and external circuit components. The principal factors determining t_{on} are (1) the transistor junction capacitances which prevent the transistor voltages from changing instantaneously (these junction capacitances must charge and discharge gradually

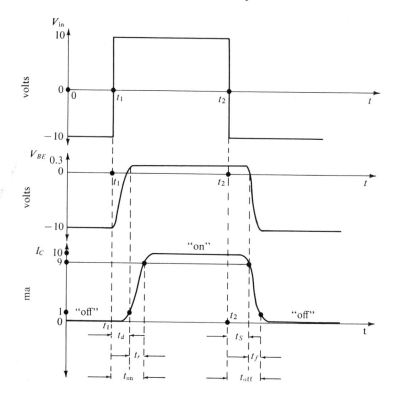

FIG. 12.5.   TRANSISTOR SWITCHING WAVEFORMS

through the circuit resistances) and (2) the time required for the emitter current to diffuse across the base region into the collector region once forward bias is established.

Values of t_{on} ranging from 75 to 300 nanoseconds (10^{-9} seconds) are typical and can vary even for the same transistor under different circuit conditions.

Once the collector current reaches its steady-state value of 10 ma it will remain there as long as V_{in} stays at 10v. At $t = t_2$, when V_{in} suddenly returns to -10v, the transistor does not respond immediately. As can be seen in Figure 12.5 a certain amount of time elapses before I_C even begins to decrease. The *storage time* t_s is defined as the time it takes for the collector current to drop to 90 per cent of its "on" value once the input has switched. The *fall time* t_f is defined as the time it takes the collector current to drop from 90 per cent to 10 per cent. The total *turn-off time* t_{off} is the sum of storage time and fall time. That is,

$$t_{off} = t_s + t_f \qquad (12.2)$$

The fall time is determined mainly by the same factors which were mentioned in conjunction with turn-on time. The storage time, however, deserves special consideration. It comes about because of the fact that when the transistor is in the "on" state, before switching has occurred, it is saturated. In saturation the *C-B* junction is forward-biased and the collector will inject carriers into the base region in the same way that the emitter does. These charges injected into the base recombine there and are called *stored charges*. When the transistor is being turned "off" these stored charges must return to the collector region. This process takes time and the movement of these charges maintains the flow of collector current. After all of the stored charge has been removed from the base the collector current will begin to decrease. The storage time depends on the transistor doping profile but is also dependent on how saturated the transistor is in the "on" state. That is, if I_B is greater than the minimum value needed to cause I_C to saturate, the transistor will be essentially *overdriven* or *oversaturated* and the stored charge will be greater resulting in a longer storage time. For the circuit in question $I_B = 200 \ \mu a$ in the "on"-state whereas a base current of 160 μa would have been sufficient to cause saturation (Figure 12.4)

Typical values for t_{off} are in the range of 100-300 nanoseconds and, again, depend not only on the transistor but on other circuit parameters. The total circuit switching time T_t is defined as:

$$T_t = t_{\text{on}} + t_{\text{off}} \tag{12.3}$$

and is a figure of merit. Its value essentially limits how many times per second the circuit can be pulsed. The smaller the value of T_t, the higher the frequency of switching which the circuit can follow.

The previous description of switching action concerned a saturated switch. If, instead, a non-saturated switching circuit were considered, such as one which switched from point A to point B on the load-line in Figure 12.4, the description would be slightly altered. The parameters t_d, t_r and t_f would be essentially unchanged but t_s would be very small since no saturation occurs. As such, the turn-off time and thus T_t would be shorter for unsaturated switches. Thus, unsaturated switching circuits can operate at higher switching frequencies which is the main reason for their use.

12.5.   Power Dissipation in Switching Transistors

At the off-point (Figure 12.4) V_{CE} is large and I_C is a small leakage current. For a typical silicon unit at 25°C, $I_{CEO} = 1 \ \mu a$. Thus at this point the transistor power dissipation P_D is approximately 5v × 1 μa = 5 μw. As temperature increases the leakage current will increase giving a higher P_D. At the on-point, V_{CE} is very small and I_C is large. $V_{CE(\text{sat})}$ is approximately 0.2v and $I_C = 10$ ma giving a power dissipation of 2 mw. These figures show one of the main advantages of using the transistor as a saturated switch, namely, there is very little power dissipation in both the "on" and "off" states.

However, we must consider what happens in the short amount of time it takes the transistor to switch from "off" to "on" and vice-versa. During this transient period the transistor will be passing through the "active" region and the power dissipation will increase since neither I_C or V_{CE} are close to zero. If the transistor spends little time in the "active" region this momentary increase in dissipation will not greatly increase the average of the power dissipation. If the transient time is comparable to the time spent in the "on" and "off" states the average power dissipation will increase. This is illustrated in Figure 12.6. In part (A) the transient time is small compared to the steady-state time resulting in low average dissipation, whereas in part (B) increasing the frequency (that is, pulsing the transistor more times per second) increases the relative amount of time spent in the "active" region thus increasing average dissipation. In both cases the average dissipa-

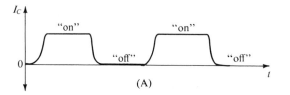

(A)

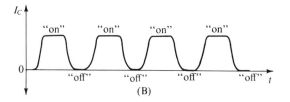

(B)

FIG. 12.6. EFFECT OF FREQUENCY ON POWER DISSIPATION (A) LOW FREQUENCY—LOW DISSIPATION (B) HIGH FREQUENCY—HIGH DISSIPATION

tion will be lower than the peak dissipation which occurs in the transient interval. For this reason large currents and voltages can be handled by saturated switches without exceeding $P_{D(\max)}$ which is the maximum d-c or average power dissipation. Of course, the voltage should be limited to a safe value below the breakdown voltage and the current below $I_{C(\max)}$. At all times average dissipation must be kept below the $P_{D(\max)}$ at the ambient temperature being used.

If we consider the unsaturated switch it is obvious that since one of the states is in the "active" region more power will be dissipated. For example, in Figure 12.4 at point B the power dissipation is approximately 8 ma $\times$ 1v = 8 mw. For this reason unsaturated switching circuits will have a higher average dissipation than saturated switching circuits. This is one of the chief drawbacks to using unsaturated switches. As it turns out, it is a compromise of speed for power when deciding on the type of circuit to use.

12.6.   Switching Circuit Applications

The most common transistor switching circuit is the *inverter* shown in Figure 12.7. This circuit is essentially the same type as the one examined in the previous sections except that a d-c reverse bias supply V_{BB} is applied at all times through a resistor R_{BB} to keep the transistor "off" in the absence of a signal V_{in}. The signal then serves to turn the transistor "on" producing current through R_C.

To examine the operation of this circuit it is beneficial to use Thevenin's theorem to obtain the equivalent base drive circuit

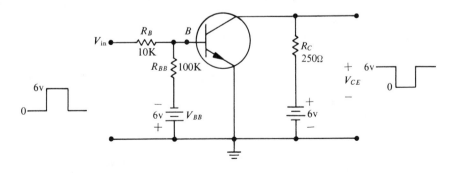

FIG. 12.7.   INVERTER CIRCUIT

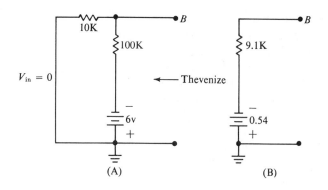

FIG. 12.8.   THEVENIZING FOR $V_{in} = 0$ VOLTS

for the two conditions on the input V_{in} (zero or 6 volts). If we consider the situation with $V_{in} = 0$ the input circuit becomes that shown in Figure 12.8A. Thevenizing between base and ground, the value of Thevenin resistance R_{TH} is 10K‖100K = 9.1K and value of Thevenin voltage E_{TH} is

$$\frac{-6v \times 10K}{110K} = -0.54v$$

resulting in the Thevenin equivalent circuit in Figure 12.8B. This tells us that when $V_{in} = 0$ the base is essentially reverse-biased by $-0.54v$ through 9.1K and the transistor is turned "off". It is essential that some reverse bias be applied to hold the transistor "off" since the collector leakage current will be smaller in this condition than in the no-bias condition ($V_{BE} = 0$). This is important especially in germanium transistors and at high temperatures. In silicon units the V_{BB} supply may be eliminated except at elevated temperatures. With the transistor "off," I_C is essentially zero and V_{CE}, the output, is at +6 volts.

When V_{in} switches to +6v the input circuit becomes that shown in Figure 12.9A. Thevenizing once again between base and ground R_{TH} is still 9.1K but E_{TH} is now

$$E_{TH} = -6v + \frac{12v \times 100K}{110K} = +4.9v$$

Thus the transistor is forward-biased by 4.9 volts through 9.1K. If we assume that the transistor is germanium, the base current will be approximately $4.6v/9.1K \approx 0.5$ ma. The transistor collector current will of course depend on $h_{FE}(\beta_{d-c})$. If we assume $h_{FE} = 60$ then the collector current would be 30 ma. However, $I_{C(sat)} = 6v/250\Omega = 24$ ma for this circuit. Thus the transistor is saturated

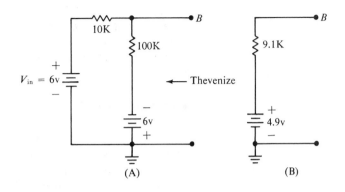

FIG. 12.9.　　THEVENIZING FOR $V_{in} = 6$ VOLTS

and $V_{CE} = V_{CE(sat)} \approx 0$. Referring to the input and output wave-forms in Figure 12.7 it is clear how the name *inverter* came about. The circuit *inverts* the positive-going input pulse to produce a negative-going output pulse.

Besides being used extensively in computer circuitry, the inverter is often used as a means of switching a large amount of power to a load (relay, lamp, motor etc.) with only a small amount of input power. In the example above the power in the load when the switch is "on" is

$$P_{load} = 6v \times 24 \text{ ma} = 144 \text{ mw}$$

while the input power being supplied by the input signal is

$$P_{in} = V_{in} \times I_B = 6v \times 0.5 \text{ ma} = 3 \text{ mw}$$

Thus, a relatively small input power can control a much larger power to a load. The power gain here is 144 mw/3 mw = 48. Much greater power gains than this can be obtained using higher gain transistors.

An important consideration in the design of saturated switches such as that in Figure 12.7 is the variation in h_{FE} from transistor to transistor. Because of this variation the circuit has to be designed so that even the lowest h_{FE} transistor will saturate when the input signal appears.

▶ EXAMPLE 12.1

In the circuit of Figure 12.7 the transistor used has a range of h_{FE} from 30 to 120 at $I_C = 24$ ma. Is this circuit properly designed?

When V_{in} is at 6v, a base current of 0.5 ma is supplied. To produce saturation I_C must equal 24 ma. The smallest h_{FE} which will provide 24 ma when $I_B = 0.5$ ma is $24/0.5 = 48$. Thus this circuit will not saturate if the transistor's h_{FE} lies between 30 and 48.

◄

► EXAMPLE 12.2

How may the circuit be modified so as to ensure saturation over the possible range of h_{FE} for the transistor used?

Since $I_{C(sat)} = 24$ ma and $h_{FE(min)} = 30$, then the largest base current needed for saturation is

$$I_{B(max)} = \frac{24\ \text{ma}}{30} = 0.80\ \text{ma}$$

If we can ensure that the base current will be, say, 1 ma when $V_{in} = 6$v, then saturation will occur even for the lowest h_{FE} transistor. To do this we can reduce R_B. Since with $R_B = 10K$, I_B was 0.5 ma, we can use $R_B = 5K$ and approximately produce the desired 1 ma base current.

◄

Although the saturated switching circuit produces low power dissipation, for very high switching speeds unsaturated switching circuits must be used to eliminate the storage time delay when the transistor is turned "off". One of the simplest unsaturated circuits is shown in Figure 12.10. Here again when the input signal goes positive and supplies base current, collector current will flow. All the collector current will flow through $R_C (I_1 = I_C)$ as long as diode D_1 is reverse biased which occurs when $V_{CE} \geq V_1$. If V_{CE} drops

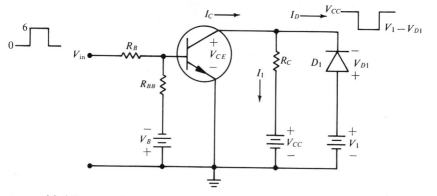

FIG. 12.10.   COLLECTOR CLAMPING TO AVOID SATURATION

below V_1 diode D_1 will be forward-biased and will conduct. When D_1 conducts then V_{CE} will be "clamped" to the voltage $V_1 - V_{D1}$ where V_{D1} is the diode's forward drop. Any increase in collector current will result in more diode current I_D. The voltage V_{CE} and thus I_1 will stay the same as I_C increases. In this way V_{CE} can be made to remain above $V_{CE(sat)}$ thus avoiding saturation. The transistor will operate in the "active" region when V_{in} goes positive. Of course, with $V_{in} = 0$ the transistor is "off," $V_{CE} = V_{CC}$, and the diode is reverse-biased.

This method of avoiding saturation has some drawbacks including the fact that the collector current is not limited resulting in high transistor dissipation and the fact that the diode switching time slows the operation down. More efficient unsaturated circuits are now used which alleviate these problems to a great extent.

▶ EXAMPLE 12.3

Using the circuit values of Figure 12.7 for the circuit in Figure 12.10, determine the transistor power dissipation when $V_{in} = 6v$. Use $V_1 = 1.7v$ and a silicon diode. Compare with the power dissipation in the saturated circuit of Figure 12.7. Assume $V_{CE(sat)} = 0.1v$.

From previous calculations the base current will be 0.5 ma and the collector current will be 30 ma. Without the clamping diode the transistor would, of course, saturate. However, as V_{CE} drops due to the increase in I_C it will not be allowed to drop to $V_{CE(sat)} = 0.1v$. Instead, it will be clamped to about 1v by the action of the diode which will begin conducting heavily at $V_{CE} = 1.7v - .7v = 1v$. Once the diode begins conducting, any collector current, above what is needed to cause $V_{CE} = 1v$, will flow through the diode. Since the diode drop will essentially be constant at 0.7v, the value of V_{CE} will stay at 1v even if I_B and I_C are increased. The current through R_C will remain fixed since V_{CE} is fixed. In this circuit $I_C = 30$ ma and $V_{CE} = 1v$. Thus, the value of I_1 is

$$\frac{5v}{250\Omega} = 20 \text{ ma}$$

Since $I_C = I_1 + I_D$, the diode current $I_D = 10$ ma. These values are shown in Figure 12.11.

The transistor's collector dissipation is given by $V_{CE} \times I_C$ (treat the collector-emitter terminals as a resistor). In this case

$$P_D = 1v \times 30 \text{ ma} = 30 \text{ mw}$$

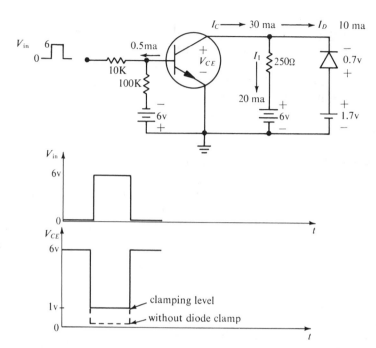

FIG. 12.11.   EXAMPLE 12.3

In the corresponding circuit of Figure 12.7 the transistor power dissipation would be

$$P_D = V_{CE(\text{sat})} \times I_{C(\text{sat})}$$
$$= 0.1\text{v} \times 24 \text{ ma} = 2.4 \text{ mw}$$

since with no clamping diode the transistor would saturate.   ◄

GLOSSARY

Transition time: time required for a switch to switch from one state to another

Steady-state operation: when the switch is resting in one of its states

Transient operation: when the switch is in the process of changing states

"On" state: transistor saturated

"Off" state: transistor cut-off

"Active" state: transistor conducting but not saturated

Saturated switch: transistor operating in either "off" or "on" states

Non-saturated switch: transistor operating in either "off" or "active" states

Delay time t_d: time required for collector current to rise to 10 per cent of its final value

Rise time t_r: time required for collector current to rise from 10 per cent to 90 per cent of its final value

Turn-on time t_{on}: sum of delay time and rise time

Storage time t_s: time required for collector current to drop to 90 per cent of its "on" value

Fall time t_f: time required for collector current to drop from 90 per cent to 10 per cent of its "on" value

Turn-off time t_{off}: sum of storage time and fall time

Total switching time T_t: sum of t_{on} and t_{off}

Questions

12.1 What are the comparative advantages and disadvantages of mechanical and transistor switches?

12.2 In Figure 12.12, what are the two states of the output voltage if the transistor is operated as a saturated switch?

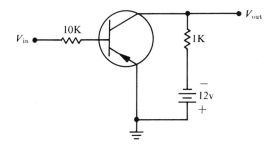

FIG. 12.12.

12.3 If the transistor in the circuit of Figure 12.12 has an $I_{CBO} = 0.1\ \mu a$ and $V_{CE(sat)} = 0.1v$ determine its R_o/R_s ratio.

12.4   Sketch the response of I_C as V_{in} switches instantaneously from +10v to −10v in the circuit of Figure 12.12. Label t_d, t_r and t_{on}.

12.5   What causes the delay in the collector current as the transistor switches from "off" to "on"?

12.6   Sketch the response of I_C as V_{in} switches instantaneously from −10v to +10v in the circuit of Figure 12.12. Label t_s, t_f and t_{off}.

12.7   What causes the turn-off delay in the collector current?

12.8   Why would the turn-off delay increase if V_{in} were switching from −15v to +10v instead of from −10v to +10v?

12.9   Why is t_{off} less in an unsaturated circuit?

12.10   Why does the average power dissipation of a transistor switch increase as the switching frequency is increased?

12.11   Which type of transistor switch dissipates more power? Why?

12.12   In the inverter circuit below, what is the minimum value of h_{FE} which the silicon transistor needs to ensure that it will be "on" when $V_{in} = -6v$?

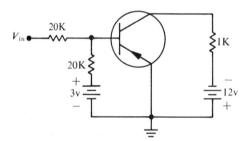

FIG. 12.13.

12.13   Calculate the power switched to the 1K load in the circuit in Figure 12.13. Calculate P_{in} and power gain.

12.14   If the transistor used in the inverter in Figure 12.13 has a value of h_{FE} twice the minimum calculated in Question 12.12, what is the minimum value of V_{in} needed to ensure saturation?

12.15   Using the value of V_{in} calculated in the previous question, repeat Question 12.13.

12.16   Discuss the comparative advantages of saturated and unsaturated switching circuits.

12.17   If, in the circuit of Figure 12.10 (Section 12.6), the value of
V_1 is 1.5v and the diode D_1 is silicon what will be the two states
of the output voltage V_{CE}?

12.18   In Example 12.3 if V_{in} is increased to 10v, determine I_B, I_C,
I_1, I_D and V_{CE}.

References

Foster, J. F., *Semiconductors, Diodes and Transistors*, Vol. 3. Beaverton,
    Oregon: Programmed Instruction Group, Tetronix, Inc., 1964.

Oppenheimer, S. L., *Semiconductor Logic and Switching Circuits*. Colum-
    bus, Ohio: Charles E. Merrill Books, Inc., 1966.

13

Transistor Technology

13.1.   Introduction

In recent years, construction of the transistor has undergone a
great many changes and improvements in order to reach its present
state of development. A number of manufacturing processes have
been devised, have lasted a few years and then have been aban-
doned as new techniques and processes have come from the
laboratory. In this chapter we will discuss some of the transistor
structures that are currently enjoying widespread use and describe
some of their comparative advantages and disadvantages. Included in this discussion will be a study of the basic structures that
are being used in integrated circuits. To make the discussion more
meaningful, we will first take a look at some of the effects of certain
transistor physical properties on its electrical characteristics.

13.2.   Effects of Transistor Physical Characteristics on Electrical Characteristics

The physical characteristics we are concerned with are the
transistor geometries and doping levels which are under control of
the transistor designer. These characteristics determine to a great
extent the behavior of electrical properties such as current gain,
frequency response, power-handling capability, switching speed

and breakdown voltages. A thorough discussion of the relation between these electrical characteristics and the transistor physical characteristics would take a prohibitively long time. The important points to be considered have been summarized in Table 13.1. In this table the desired electrical property is followed by the principal physical characteristics which produce it. For example, a high current gain is produced by doping the emitter region heavily, the base region lightly and making the base region as narrow as possible. Looking over this table it can be seen that the transistor

TABLE 13.1

Desired Electrical Property	*Necessary Physical Characteristics*
high current gain	heavy emitter doping; light base doping; thin base region
high frequency response	thin base region; small junction cross-sectional areas, light base doping and light collector doping to reduce junction capacitances
high switching speed	small junction cross-sectional areas, light base doping and light collector doping to reduce junction capacitances; heavy collector doping to reduce storage time
high current and power-handling capability	heavy emitter doping; large junction cross-sectional areas
high *C-B* junction breakdown voltage	light collector doping; wide base region; heavy base doping

designer would have to make several compromises or trade-offs in determining the best physical characteristics for a given transistor. For example, in considering switching speed a lightly doped collector will reduce *C-B* junction capacitance while, on the other hand, a heavily doped collector will help to reduce storage time.

From this table we can briefly sum up the desired attributes of the three transistor regions. First, the emitter region must be heavily doped (producing low resistivity) for high gain. It should have a large area in order to carry high currents but at the same time a small area to increase high frequency response. Some tradeoff, therefore, may be necessary between frequency response and current-carrying capacity.

The base region should have a low doping level (producing high resistivity) and should be as thin as possible for high gain and good frequency response. A very thin base, however, may result in a relatively low *C-B* junction breakdown voltage unless the collector is also doped very lightly.

Moreover, a high collector resistivity (produced by a low doping level) results in low *C-B* junction capacitance, which is a desirable feature in high-speed and high-frequency transistors. However, this high collector resistivity results in an increased storage time in saturated switching circuits. This apparent dilemma may be resolved by the introduction of gold impurities into the transistor structure which serve to reduce storage time despite high collector resistivity. Thus, it is possible to construct transistors which have high breakdown voltage, low junction capacitance and low storage time. The gold-doped transistor, on the other hand, has considerably higher leakage current and lower gain than non-gold devices. For this reason gold doping is used only for transistors intended for saturated switching, while non-gold-doped devices are used for other purposes.

13.3. The Alloy Transistor

The *alloy transistor* in Figure 13.1* is one of the earliest transistor types that is still in current use. It is relatively inexpensive, provides high low-frequency gain and can be constructed to operate at high current and power levels.

The alloy transistor is constructed by starting with a very thin crystal wafer, on the order of 0.01 inch thick, and alloying two dots of impurity material to either side of the wafer. To form a PNP structure the crystal wafer is lightly doped so it is N-type and serves as the base. At elevated temperatures a liquid solution of the base material and the P-type impurity is formed on each side which, after cooling, forms a heavily-doped P-region on each side of the base, resulting in a PNP structure. Because of the heavy doping of the emitter and collector regions and the light doping of the original base region the alloy transistor has a very high current gain. However, due to these same doping levels, *C-B* breakdown voltage is relatively low in alloy transistors.

An additional problem is caused by the lack of precise control over the alloying process which results in irregularities in alloying

---

*Figures 13.1 through 13.6 are presented through the courtesy of Tetronix, Inc.

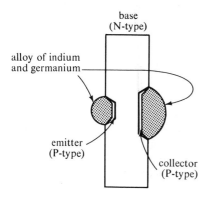

FIG. 13.1.   ALLOY TRANSISTOR

depth. The base region width is determined by the depth of the alloying process. The deeper the penetration of the alloy, the less control there is, so that very narrow base widths are difficult to produce. Thus, alloy transistors normally are low-frequency devices. A typical value of f_{hfb} for a germanium alloy transistor is 18 megHZ.

13.4.   The Microalloy Transistor

The poor high frequency response of the alloy transistor can be overcome partially by improving the alloy process resulting in

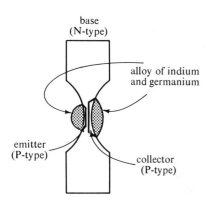

FIG. 13.2.   MICROALLOY TRANSISTOR

devices known as *microalloy transistors* (abbreviated as MATs) shown in Figure 13.2. In the improved process, to obtain a very thin, uniform base, the center of the wafer is etched to make it very thin before the dots are applied and alloyed. The etching is accomplished by concentrating a stream of acid on the two sides of the wafer and thus removing some of the wafer material. The etching process is more accurately controllable than the alloy process so that narrower base widths are possible. As a result, microalloy devices have a better frequency response than alloy types. An f_{hfb} of 40 megHZ is typical for MATs. Of course, the narrower base region makes the breakdown voltage of MATs even less than that of a plain alloy type and the thin base membrane makes the unit very fragile.

13.5.   The Microalloy Diffused Transistor

An improved version of the MAT is the *microalloy diffused transistor* (MADT) or *drift field* transistor. In this type of device, shown in Figure 13.3, the base region is not doped uniformly

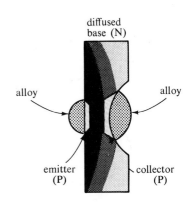

FIG. 13.3.   MICROALLOY DIFFUSED TRANSISTOR

N-type but is doped gradually, being heaviest at the emitter end and lightest at the collector end. This graduated doping is accomplished through the process of *dopent diffusion* which consists of heating the base wafer while surrounding it with the N-type impurities in gaseous form. The impurities diffuse or spread into the wafer during the process. The diffused base region is then etched and alloyed as in the MATs.

The graduated doping in the base creates a built-in electric field to help accelerate emitter-injected carriers toward the collector during transistor operation. This reduces carrier transit time through the base region thus improving high-frequency response. An increase in f_{hfb} to typically 200 megHZ can be obtained with MADTs. In addition to improved frequency response, MADTs offer higher *C-B* breakdown voltages. These overall advantages of the MADT are obtained at the expense of current gain; this gain decreases because of the heavier base doping near the *E-B* junction which enhances recombination.

13.6.   The Mesa Transistor

A major advance in high-frequency transistor design came with the development of the *mesa transistor* structure, shown in Figure 13.4. To construct a mesa, a thin layer of dopent must be diffused

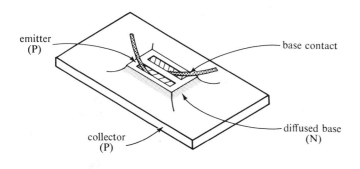

FIG. 13.4.   MESA TRANSISTOR

into a basic wafer which constitutes the collector. The diffused layer is the base region which is very lightly doped and can be as narrow as 0.0001 inch. The collector region is also very lightly doped. A metal contact is connected to the base layer for electrical connection. The emitter is alloyed into the diffused layer to form the *E-B* junction. The top of the wafer is etched away except for the portion containing the emitter and the base contact. This leaves a mesa as shown in the figure. The etching reduces the *C-B* junction area which reduces junction capacitance, since capacitance is proportional to area, while leaving the rest of the collector wafer to dissipate the heat generated by power dissipation.

The advantages of the mesa construction are a result of its extremely thin base region, its small *C-B* junction area and its light collector doping. These factors result in an extremely high frequency response and high values of *C-B* breakdown voltage. A typical mesa transistor might have an f_{hfb} of 1400 megHZ and a C_{ob} of 1.5 pf.

The principle disadvantage of the mesa transistor lies in the fact that the high resistivity collector region causes an increase in storage time and $V_{CE(\text{sat})}$ which is undesirable in saturated switching circuits. The *epitaxial mesa transistor* overcomes this problem while retaining the desirable features of the mesa transistor.

13.7.   The Epitaxial Mesa Transistor

An *epitaxial layer* is created by the process of passing a gas over a *low-resistivity* wafer until the gas has deposited a layer of *high-resistivity* material on top of the original wafer. In the epitaxial mesa transistor, shown in Figure 13.5, the collector wafer is doped

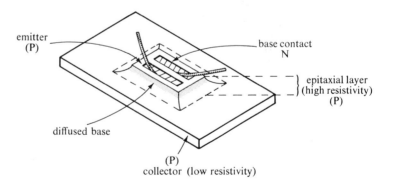

FIG. 13.5.   EPITAXIAL MESA TRANSISTOR

more heavily (which creates less resistivity) than in the mesa transistor; a high-resistivity epitaxial layer (with the same impurity as the collector is deposited on top of this wafer. The epitaxial layer causes the collector region to be lightly doped near the *C-B* junction, retaining the low *C-B* junction capacitance and high breakdown voltage of the mesa transistor, while the largest part of the collector wafer is of low resistivity thereby reducing $V_{CE(\text{sat})}$ and storage time.

13.8. The Silicon Epitaxial Planar Transistor

Despite all the improvements in electrical characteristics brought about by the development of the mesa and epitaxial mesa transistors, there still remained a drawback. The *C-B* junction, in these transistors, is exposed to the environment. This junction is highly sensitive to impingement by impurity atoms which, even in a controlled environment, can reach the junction and affect the electrical characteristics. The principal effect is an increase in leakage current. This drawback is eliminated in the *epitaxial planar transistor*, shown in Figure 13.6.

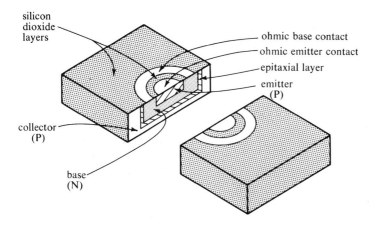

FIG. 13.6. SILICON EPITAXIAL PLANAR TRANSISTOR

The *epitaxial planar transistor* (EPT) is constructed in a manner similar to the epitaxial mesa with one notable and important difference: the *C-B* junction is buried under a layer of *silicon dioxide* to protect it from impurities. Like its mesa counterpart, the EPT begins with a heavily-doped collector wafer upon which an epitaxial layer is deposited. On top of this structure a very thin film of silicon dioxide, SiO_2, is applied. SiO_2 is an insulating material which cannot be penetrated by impurities.

The base region is formed by diffusing N-type impurities (for PNP) into the wafer. However, because the SiO_2 film impedes impurity diffusion, the film must be removed from those areas on the wafer where the base is to be diffused. This is accomplished by etching away the SiO_2 with a masked photo-resist process which results in the accurate removal of the SiO_2 film only in the region where the base diffusion is to take place. After the base impurities have been diffused into the wafer another layer of SiO_2 is grown over the entire wafer so that the *C-B* junction is *passivated*—protected against impurity penetration.

A similar process is employed for diffusing the emitter region after which an SiO_2 layer is grown over the entire surface.

Regions on the surface for the base and emitter contacts are etched using the same photo-resist process directly over the base and emitter areas.

The principal advantage of the planar structure over the mesa transistor is in the junction protection it affords. The EPT is characterized by its lower leakage current. It also has an added advantage which has made it the basic structure for silicon integrated circuits. Because the surface of the wafer (chip) is covered by a flat sheet of insulating SiO_2, passive components, such as resistors and capacitors, may be diffused into the transistor chip and interconnected with the transistor elements by a metallization pattern. This process will be discussed in greater detail in a later chapter.

13.9. Power Transistors

As we increase the power dissipation demands made on a transistor, the internal heating in the transistor itself becomes a prime consideration. We have seen that transistors are temperature-sensitive. As such, they must be prevented from overheating when large amounts of power are being dissipated. *Power transistors*, which are designed to carry high currents and dissipate large amounts of power, must be able to get rid of heat quickly and effectively.

Several methods have been used in the manufacture of power transistors. Some manufacturers have designed their transistor cases with a ribbed or fluted structure to present a large radiating surface area to the environment. This uses the same principle that fins on the cylinder of a motorcycle engine use. In extreme cases, fans or water cooling may be used to increase the rate of cooling. At present, however, the most widely-used method employs *heat sinking*. A *heat sink* is essentially a large mass of material which has a good thermal conductivity, such as copper or aluminum.

The power transistor is designed in such a way that the heat-producing element—the collector—is placed in contact with the transistor case. The case is then bolted or riveted to a comparatively large piece of metal such as a chassis or subchassis which serves as the heat sink.

Due to the obvious differences in construction, the electrical characteristics of a typical power transistor will be different from those of low power types. In Table 13.2 a comparison between the 2N250A power transistor and the 2N404A general purpose transistor is made.

First of all, the 2N250A can handle 600 times more power than the 2N404A and 70 times as much collector current. Secondly, the current gain is somewhat lower for the power transistor as is its power gain. This results mainly from the larger base region

TABLE 13.2

	2N404A	2N250A (power)
max. power dissipation	150 mw	90w
max. collector-base voltage	40v	40v
max. collector current	100 ma	7 amps
current gain (typical h_{FE})	100	60
leakage current (I_{CBO})	1 μa	1 ma
f_{hfb}	12 megHZ	4 megHZ
power gain (common emitter)	5000	1000
input impedance (common emitter)	4K	500Ω

needed to handle the increased power dissipation. Another result of this is the high leakage current of the power transistor (1 ma). The higher leakage current is not necessarily a great drawback since it must be remembered that the power transistor normally operates in the ampere range when conducting. The larger areas of the power transistor lower its junction resistances and increase its junction capacitances. This manifests itself in the form of lower input impedance and poorer frequency response for the 2N250A as compared with its low-power counterpart. The 2N250A is thus relegated to use in the audio frequency range.

13.10.   Transistor Data Sheets

To analyze or design transistor circuits intelligently one must be able to use manufacturer's data sheets to obtain information pertinent to the application. Many of the parameters which have been introduced in previous chapters appear on these data sheets as well as information concerning construction, physical characteristics and electrical characteristic curves. Two sets of typical transistor data sheets are given in Appendix II for the 2N404 (and 2N404A) transistor and the 2N250A (and 2N251A) transistor.

Refer to these data sheets for the following discussion. The first item of information presented on the data sheet is the identification of the transistor according to its JEDEC number (2N404, 2N404A), its type (PNP), its material and construction (germanium alloy transistor) and general area of application (computer and switching circuits). Following a note on environmental tests (which differ according to manufacturer) the device is usually described (TO-5 case); sometimes its outlines and dimensions are given. The lead orientation is also identified here.

The most important set of data, from a user's standpoint, is contained under the heading "absolute maximum ratings at 25°C free-air temperature." Under no circumstances should these ratings be exceeded since alteration of the transistor parameters or ultimate device failure will occur. Of particular importance is the power dissipation rating (150 mw @ 25°C) which must be derated, according to note 2, by 2.5 mw per degree of ambient temperature above 25°C for the 2N404.

▶ EXAMPLE 13.1

How much power dissipation can the 2N404 handle at $T_A = 50°C$?

$$P_{D(\text{max})}(@50°C) = P_{D(\text{max})}(@25°C) - \frac{2.5\text{ mw}}{°C} \times 25°C$$

$$= 150\text{ mw} - 50\text{ mw}$$

$$= 100\text{ mw} \qquad \blacktriangleleft$$

The "electrical characteristics at 25°C free-air temperature" include maximum and minimum values of certain transistor parameters obtained under specified conditions. The parameters listed depend on the intended application. For example, the switching parameters t_d, t_r, t_s and t_f (Chapter 12) are listed for the 2N404 and 2N404A but are not listed for the 2N250A and 2N251A power transistors. It is important to understand that these parameter values are valid only under the specified conditions. For example, a typical 2N404 will have an h_{FE} of 100 at the d-c operating point $V_{CE} = -0.15v$ and $I_C = 12$ ma and measured at

25°C. We can expect that h_{FE} will change as the d-c operating point changes as well as at higher temperatures. The same is true of many of the other parameters. For this reason typical electrical characteristic curves are usually given, among which are curves representing typical parameter variations with changes in certain conditions.

▶ EXAMPLE 13.2

What is a typical value of h_{FE} at $I_C = 12$ ma, $V_{CE} = -0.15$ and $T_A = 50°C$?

We must use the set of curves relating the normalized value of h_{FE} to T_A. In other words, these curves indicate the *relative* value of h_{FE} at different ambient temperatures. Using the appropriate curve (-0.15v, 12 ma), the value of h_{FE} is seen to increase by 20 per cent (1 to 1.2) in going from 25°C to 50°C. Thus, since h_{FE} is typically 100 at 25°C we, can expect its value to increase to 120 at 50°C. ◀

▶ EXAMPLE 13.3

What is the maximum value of I_{CBO} which can be expected at 60°C for the 2N404?

Using the curve relating I_{CBO} to T_A it can be seen that from 25°C to 60°C, I_{CBO} increases by approximately ten times (1 μa to 10 μa). Since we are looking for the maximum I_{CBO} at 60°C we can assume that if I_{CBO} were at its maximum (5 μa) at 25°C it would increase ten times so that $I_{CBO(max)}$ at 60°C is 50 μa. ◀

It may appear from the list of transistor parameters given for the 2N404 that not enough information is given in case one wished to use the 2N404 in the Com. B configuration. However, the conversion table in Chapter 11 can be used to easily convert the Com. E h-parameters to Com. B h-parameters.

▶ EXAMPLE 13.4

What are typical values of h_{fb} and h_{ib} for the 2N404 at $V_{CB} = -6$v and $I_E = 1$ ma?

The values of h_{fe} and h_{ie} are typically 135 and 4K respectively at $V_{CE} = -6$v and $I_C = 1$ ma. The value of h_{fb} is, using Equation 2 in Table 11.6,

$$h_{fb} = \frac{h_{fe}}{h_{fe} + 1} = 0.992$$

and the value of h_{ib} is, using Equation 4 in Table 11.6,

$$h_{ib} = \frac{h_{ie}}{h_{fe} + 1} = 29.4\Omega \qquad \blacktriangleleft$$

Of course, as useful as manufacturers' data sheets are, they can only predict typical or worst-case (min. and max.) transistor operation. In cases where a more accurate prediction is needed the transistor user must make his own measurements to determine the parameters he desires.

GLOSSARY

Alloy transistor: transistor structure characterized by high current gain and poor frequency response

Microalloy transistor (MAT): transistor structure characterized by better frequency response than alloy type

Dopent diffusion: the process of allowing doping impurities in the form of gas to spread throughout wafer

Microalloy diffused transistor (MADT): transistor structure similar to above two types but utilizing graduated base doping to improve frequency response

Mesa transistor: transistor structure characterized by a very thin base region and small junction capacitances thereby improving high frequency response

Epitaxial layer: a layer of high-resistivity material

Epitaxial mesa transistor: transistor structure similar to the mesa transistor but utilizing an epitaxial layer to decrease $V_{CE(\text{sat})}$ and storage time

Epitaxial planar transistor: transistor structure which utilizes diffusion of base and emitter regions into collector wafer after which surface passivation with SiO_2 is utilized to decrease leakage currents. It is the basic structure of integrated circuits.

Heat sink: large mass of heat conducting material

Questions

13.1   Discuss the desired physical attributes of the three transistor regions with respect to transistor electrical characteristics.

13.2   Briefly describe the alloy process of transistor construction.

13.3   What are some of the electrical properties of the alloy transistor?

13.4   Describe how the microalloy transistor improves frequency response over the alloy transistor.

13.5   Describe how the microalloy diffused transistor improves frequency response over the microalloy transistor.

13.6   What price is paid for the higher frequency response of MADTs?

13.7   Briefly describe the mesa process of transistor fabrication.

13.8   What are some of the advantages of the mesa transistor? What are its main drawbacks?

13.9   Describe how the epitaxial mesa transistor overcomes the mesa's drawbacks.

13.10   Briefly describe the epitaxial planar transistor structure.

13.11   What are the principal advantages of the EPT?

13.12   What are the chief differences between power transistors and low power transistors?

13.13   Refer to the transistor data sheets in Appendix II. From the data sheet for the 2N250A determine the following:
(a) $P_{D(max)}$ at 50°C.
(b) Average I_{CBO} at $V_{CB} = -20$v and $T_A = 50$°C.
(c) Minimum h_{FE} at $V_{CE} = -1.5$v and $I_C = 3$ a.

13.14   From the data sheet for the 2N404A determine the following:
(a) Typical total switching time T_t.
(b) Typical h_{FE} at $V_{CE} = -0.15$v, $I_C = 12$ ma. (25°C)
(c) Typical h_{FE} at $V_{CE} = -0.15$v, $I_C = 100$ ma. (25°C)
(d) Typical C_{ob} at $V_{CB} = -10$v, $f = 1$ megHZ.

13.15   Calculate A_v for a Com. E amplifier using a typical 2N404 biased at $I_C = 1$ ma, $V_{CB} = -6$v and using $R_C = 10$K.

References

Foster, J. F., *Semiconductors, Diodes and Transistors*, Vol. 3. Beaverton, Oregon: Programmed Instruction Group, Tetronix, Inc., 1964.

Stern, L., *Fundamentals of Integrated Circuits*. New York: Hayden Book Company, Inc., 1968.

Transistor Manual. Syracuse, New York: General Electric Company, 1964.

PNPN Devices

14.1. Introduction

The PNPN class of devices consists of *four* alternately doped
semiconductor layers and thus *three* P-N junctions. In contrast to
transistors, which are three-layer devices, the PNPNs are utilized
solely as semiconductor switches. The various devices in this class
find extensive application in pulse and switching circuitry, power
control, and motor speed control. In this chapter the physical
principles governing the operation of all PNPN devices will be
described, followed by a detailed discussion of the electrical characteristics of some of the more popular PNPN devices. Typical
circuit applications will be presented in which the device specifications and ratings will be utilized.

14.2. PNPNs: General Description

There are two-, three- and four-terminal PNPN devices in use
today. Although the various devices have certain distinguishing
characteristics, each essentially operates as a switch between the
two outer terminals which are called the *anode* and *cathode*. The
basic four-layer structure is shown in Figure 14.1 with the anode
terminal shown coming from the outer P-region and the cathode
terminal from the outer N-region. The operation of a PNPN

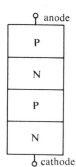

anode

| P |
| N |
| P |
| N |

cathode

anode

cathode

FIG. 14.1.   PNPN DEVICES ARE SWITCHES

device resembles that of a mechanical switch between anode and cathode. In other words, it has two operating states: "off" or high resistance, and "on" or low resistance. The various PNPN devices differ mainly in the method used to control or actuate the switching. However, unlike the mechanical switch or the transistor switch, the PNPN switch has the characteristic of *latching*. Latching simply means that once the switch has been closed (the device is "on"), removal of the control or actuating signal does not cause the switch to re-open. This is analogous to manually closing a push-button switch and then not having it re-open when the push-button is released. Because of this latching characteristic, PNPN devices must be turned "off" by some other means. In the following sections we will investigate this characteristic and how it is used in various applications.

14.3.   Structure and Basic Operation of PNPNs

The symbolic structure of the basic four-layer PNPN switch is shown in Figure 14.2. Note that the three junctions are labelled $J1$, $J2$ and $J3$ respectively. A simple, but useful, method of describing the operation of PNPN devices is to consider the PNPN bar to be composed of a PNP structure interconnected with an NPN structure, as shown in Figure 14.3(A). Such an interconnection of a PNP and NPN structure can be represented by two transistors as in Figure 14.3(B). We can now examine the operation of PNPN devices using this analogous transistor configuration.

Referring to Figure 14.4(A), if a positive voltage is applied from anode to cathode it is apparent that junctions $J1$ and $J3$ will be forward-biased and $J2$ will be reverse-biased. Since $J2$

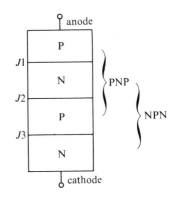

FIG. 14.2.   BASIC FOUR LAYER STRUCTURE

I_{B1} = base current of PNP

I_{C1} = collector current of PNP

I_{B2} = base current of NPN

I_{C2} = collector current of NPN

I_K = cathode current

I_A = anode current

FIG. 14.3.   EQUIVALENT REPRESENTATION OF PNPN STRUCTURE

will have a much greater resistance than either $J1$ or $J3$ in this case, we can expect that most of the voltage E will appear across $J2$ and very little current will flow from anode to cathode ($I_A = I_K \approx 0$) as long as the value of E is below the breakdown voltage of $J2$.

Keeping this in mind let us now consider the situation using the two-transistor analogy as shown in Figure 14.4(B). Both E-B junctions are slightly forward-biased since $J1$ is the E-B junction of the PNP transistor and $J3$ is the E-B junction of the

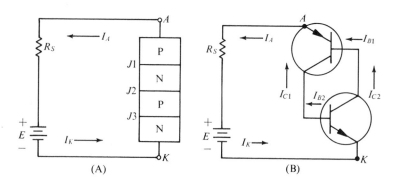

FIG. 14.4.   POSITIVE BIAS APPLIED BETWEEN ANODE AND CATHODE

NPN transistor. $J2$ is the C-B junction of both the PNP and NPN transistors and, thus, both transistors have a reverse-biased C-B junction. Both transistors, then, are biased in the active region. However, since both E-B junctions are only barely forward-biased, very little current will flow. We can determine an expression for this current by using the basic transistor equations. Consider first the PNP transistor. Its emitter current is the same as I_A, anode current. Thus, its base current can be written as

$$I_{B1} = (1 - \alpha_{\text{d-c1}})I_A - I_{CBO1} \tag{14.1}$$

where $\alpha_{\text{d-c1}}$ and I_{CBO1} are the current gain and leakage current, respectively, for the PNP transistor.

If we now consider the NPN transistor, its collector current is given by

$$I_{C2} = \alpha_{\text{d-c2}}I_K + I_{CBO2} \tag{14.2}$$

where $\alpha_{\text{d-c2}}$ and I_{CBO2} are the current gain and leakage current, respectively, for the NPN transistor. The cathode current, I_K, is the same as the emitter current of the NPN device.

We can now utilize the fact that the base current of the PNP serves also as the collector current of the NPN. That is, $I_{B1} = I_{C2}$. Equating the two previous expressions, we have

$$(1 - \alpha_{\text{d-c1}})I_A - I_{CBO1} = \alpha_{\text{d-c2}}I_K + I_{CBO2} \tag{14.3}$$

Noting that $I_A = I_K$ this equation can now be solved for I_A to give

$$I_A = I_K = \frac{I_{CBO1} + I_{CBO2}}{1 - (\alpha_{\text{d-c1}} + \alpha_{\text{d-c2}})} \tag{14.4}$$

This expression for the PNPN current is the basis for explaining the operation of all PNPN devices. In the "off" state the current given by Equation 14.4 will be very low. This may not be readily apparent, but it can be reasoned as follows: Although both transistors are operating in the active region, as mentioned previously, the E-B forward bias is very small. Now, for such low values of forward bias, the value of $\alpha_{d\text{-}c}$ for a transistor can be much lower than 1. This is especially true of silicon devices and is the reason why silicon rather than germanium PNPN devices are in use today. For example, if $\alpha_{d\text{-}c1} = 0.4$ and $\alpha_{d\text{-}c2} = 0.5$, the value of anode current given by Equation 14.4 is equal to ten times the sum of the leakage currents. Using a typical value of 0.1 μa for I_{CBO1} and I_{CBO2} the anode current becomes 2 μa. This would be the "off" current of the PNPN device. If the value of E is 50 volts and the "off" current is 2 μa this gives a resistance of $50\text{v}/2\,\mu\text{a} = 25$ megohms between anode and cathode.

Examination of Equation 14.4 will reveal how the device turns "on," which is the essence of PNPN operation. If, through some process, the values of $\alpha_{d\text{-}c1}$ and $\alpha_{d\text{-}c2}$ could be increased so that $(\alpha_{d\text{-}c1} + \alpha_{d\text{-}c2})$ is equal to 1, the device current will increase indefinitely. Actually the current will be limited by the series resistance in the circuit such as R_S in Figure 14.4. When this occurs, both transistors reach saturation in which the junction voltage drops are all small. This may be seen by referring to Figure 14.4(B). In the "on" state anode current will be approximately E/R_S. This is the emitter current of the PNP transistor and produces saturation resulting in a large I_{C1} which becomes I_{B2} and produces saturation in the NPN transistor. Since both transistors are saturated in the "on" state, the anode to cathode voltage drop is low, being equal to the sum of one E-B forward voltage drop and one $V_{CE(\text{sat})}$ typically resulting in a total of 0.8v. The "on" state resistance is very small and for some PNPN devices can go as low as 0.01 ohm. Once the device reaches the "on" state the values of $\alpha_{d\text{-}c1}$ and $\alpha_{d\text{-}c2}$ remain very low since both transistors are saturated (I_C is much lower than I_E).

There are several ways of increasing the sum $(\alpha_{d\text{-}c1} + \alpha_{d\text{-}c2})$ so that an "off" device may be *triggered* "on." The most common include increasing device temperature, increasing the forward bias on one of the transistor E-B junctions and increasing anode-to-cathode voltage. The latter method causes an increase in the C-B junction reverse bias of the transistors which, as we know, causes an increase in current gain.

Before investigating the various devices which employ one or more of these methods of triggering, a word must be said about what occurs when the voltage at the anode is made negative with respect to the cathode. In this case both transistors are biased at cut-off (E-B junctions $J1$ and $J3$ reverse-biased) and only a small reverse leakage current will flow. The entire voltage appears across *J*1 and *J*3 and when this voltage increases sufficiently to cause *J*1 and *J*3 to reach avalanche breakdown, the device behaves in the same way as any P-N diode which has reached breakdown. The device is normally not meant to operate in avalanche breakdown. Biasing with negative anode-to-cathode voltage is called *reverse* bias for the PNPN structure while the bias used in Figure 14.4 is called *forward* bias. The PNPN structure only behaves as a switch when it is in the forward bias condition.

14.4.   PNPN Four Layer Diodes: Characteristics and Operation

The *four-layer diode* was invented by W. Shockley, who made a lasting name in the semiconductor field. In fact, it is often referred to as a *Shockley diode*. Its construction is essentially that shown in Figure 14.2 and discussed in the previous section. In the previous section it was determined that the four-layer device will switch from high resistance, "off," to low resistance, "on," if the sum of the alphas is increased to 1. In the four-layer diode this is accomplished by increasing the anode-to-cathode forward voltage until switching occurs. Referring to Figure 14.4, increasing the value of *E* increases the amount of reverse bias on the center junction *J*2, which serves as the *C-B* junction for both transistors. The increase in *C-B* reverse bias causes the transistor alphas to increase. When the point is reached where $\alpha_{d-c1} + \alpha_{d-c2} = 1$, switching occurs. This may be visualized more clearly by plotting the *I-V* characteristic curve of the four-layer diode. This is done in Figure 14.5, where the circuit symbol for the four-layer diode is also shown.

The four-layer diode's characteristic curve can be explained as follows: For low values of forward anode-to-cathode voltage, V_D, the device is in the "off" state and only a small leakage current will flow. As V_D is increased it eventually reaches the value at which switching occurs. This value is called the *forward switching voltage* and is given the symbol V_S. At this voltage, point *A*, the diode will rapidly switch (shown by dotted line) from its high-resistance region to its low-resistance region, point *B*. In the "on" region the characteristic is similar to that of a forward-biased P-N diode in which high currents can flow at a low voltage drop. In this state the diode voltage drop, V_F, will be very small, typically between 0.5 and 2.0 volts. The diode will remain in the "on" state as long as the current through it is kept above the

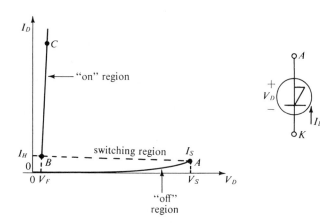

FIG. 14.5. FOUR-LAYER DIODE SYMBOL AND I-V CHAR-
ACTERISTIC CURVE

holding current, I_H, which is the value of current needed to *hold*
the diode "on." At currents below this value, the sum of the
alphas for the NPN and PNP transistors drops below 1 and the
device reverts back to its "off" state. Another diode parameter
of importance is I_S, the diode current at the switching point A.
It is called the *switching current* and, as we shall see, is important
in circuit applications.

A better understanding of four-layer diode operation may be
obtained by considering a numerical example. Refer to Figure
14.6 in which a typical four-layer diode is used in a simple circuit.
The diode's parameters are also given in the figure. Assume that
the voltage E is below 30v, say 20v. In this case the diode will be
in its "off" state with only a small leakage current flowing which
is typically 10 μa. We can write, using Kirchhoff's voltage law, that

$$V_D = E - I_D \times 1K \qquad (14.5)$$

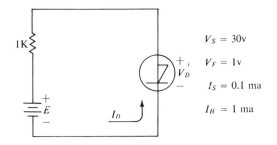

$V_S = 30v$	
$V_F = 1v$	
$I_S = 0.1$ ma	
$I_H = 1$ ma	

FIG. 14.6. SIMPLE FOUR-LAYER DIODE CIRCUIT

Thus, V_D will be approximately 20v since the voltage drop across the 1K resistor will be negligibly small (10 mv).

As E is increased the diode will remain "off" until E becomes large enough to cause the diode voltage to become equal to the switching voltage, 30v. The value of E which will accomplish this will be equal to 30v plus the small drop across the series resistor. This resistor drop will be equal to 1K times the switching current $I_S = 0.1$ ma which flows at the switching point (point A in Figure 14.5). This results in a value of $E = 30.1$v needed to cause the diode to reach 30v at which time it will rapidly switch to its "on" state. In the "on" state the diode voltage drops to approximately 1 volt (V_F). In this state the current will increase since all but 1 volt of the supply voltage will now be dropped across the 1K resistor. If $E = 30.1$v, then the current I_D will be $(30.1$v $- 1$v$)/$ 1K $= 29.1$ ma. Thus, current will begin to flow in the circuit as soon as E is increased to 30.1v, switching the four-layer diode "on."

Once the diode switches "on" it will remain "on" until the current is made to decrease below the holding current, $I_H = 1$ ma. This means that E can be decreased below 30.1v and the diode will remain "on". For example, if E is now decreased to 20v, the current will be $(20$v $- 1$v$)/1$K $= 19$ ma which is higher than the holding current and the diode will remain "on." The smallest value of E which will hold the diode "on" will be equal to that value which produces 1 ma of current. That is,

$$E_{\min} = I_H \times 1\text{K} + V_F$$
$$= 1 \text{ ma} \times 1\text{K} + 1\text{v} = 2\text{v}$$

Any value of E below this value, say 1.9v, will cause the current to drop below 1 ma and the device will turn "off." It will then remain in the "off" state until E is increased to 30.1v.

This complete sequence of switching from "off" to "on" to "off" is summarized in Table 14.1 below for the circuit values used above.

TABLE 14.1

E	V_D	I_D		Diode state
20 v	20 v	10	μa	"off"
30.1v	1 v	29.1	ma	"on"
20 v	1 v	19	ma	"on"
2 v	1 v	1	ma	Just "on"
1.9v	1.9v	10	μa	"off"

► EXAMPLE 14.1

In the circuit of Figure 14.6, if the 1K resistor is increased to 10K, will the diode turn "on" at $E = 30.1v$?

To turn the diode "on" we must have

$$E = 10K \times I_S + V_S$$
$$= 1v + 30v = 31v \qquad \blacktriangleleft$$

Thus, $E = 30.1v$ is not sufficient to switch the diode "on."

► EXAMPLE 14.2

Using the 10K resistor, if the diode is switched "on" by increasing E to 31v, then how low must E be made to turn the diode "off" again?

To turn the diode "off" E must drop below

$$E = 10K \times I_H + V_F$$
$$= 10v + 1v = 11v \qquad \blacktriangleleft$$

When the anode of the four-layer diode is biased negative relative to the cathode, it behaves essentially like a normal reverse-biased P-N junction. That is, it will block reverse current until its reverse breakdown voltage is exceeded.

In certain applications a four-layer diode which will act as a switch in both directions, forward and reverse, is desirable. For this reason the *bilateral four-layer diode* has been developed. This

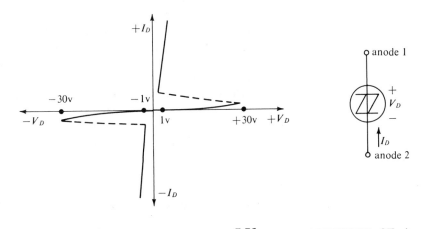

FIG. 14.7. SYMBOL AND *I-V* CHARACTERISTIC OF A
BILATERAL FOUR-LAYER DIODE

device, illustrated in Figure 14.7, behaves exactly the same as the unilateral four-layer diodes discussed thus far, except that it does so for both polarities of device voltage. For example, the device pictured in Figure 14.7 has a switching voltage of 30v of either polarity. These devices are constructed so that a PNPN structure exists in both directions giving the characteristics shown in the figure.

14.5.   Four Layer Diodes: Parameters, Ratings

Four-layer diodes are currently available with switching voltages in the range from tens of volts to a few hundred volts. The switching current, I_S, is normally, at most, a few hundred microamperes; the holding current, I_H, varies depending on the type, in the range from several milliamperes to several hundred milliamperes.

Temperature affects the value of V_S only slightly, causing it to decrease at higher temperatures. Typically it may drop by 10 per cent in going from 25°C to 100°C. The holding current also decreases at higher temperatures but more rapidly. It may change as much as 50 per cent over the range from 25°C to 100°C. This means that at higher temperatures the device will remain "on" for lower values of device current.

Limitations on the four-layer diode are mainly those of power dissipation and current. Typical medium power devices have maximum ratings of 150 mw and 150 ma d-c at 25°C. However, peak power and current ratings may exceed these values by 50 to 100 times depending on repetition rate and pulse duration.

As far as switching speed is concerned, the four-layer diode will normally turn "on" faster than it will turn "off". Typical values might be 0.2 μsec (microsecond) for turn-on time and 0.4 μsec turn-off time. These values, however, are highly dependent on circuit values.

There are several other devices which are essentially the same as the four-layer diode. The most prominent of these are the *Silicon Unilateral Switch* (SUS) and the *Silicon Bilateral Switch* (SBS). The SUS behaves essentially like the unilateral four-layer diode while the SBS is similar to the bilateral four-layer diode.

14.6.   The Rate Effect

The four-layer diode characteristic curve shown in Figure 14.5 is valid only when the applied anode-to-cathode voltage changes

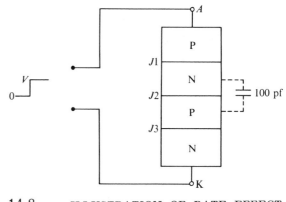

FIG. 14.8.   ILLUSTRATION OF RATE EFFECT

slowly. When a rapidly rising voltage is applied to the diode, a *rate effect* occurs that tends to turn the diode "on" at a lower value of voltage.

The cause of this rate effect is the capacitance of the reverse-biased *J2* junction, which is typically about 100 picofarads (pf). This is illustrated in Figure 14.8. When a rapid change in voltage is applied to the diode a current will flow through the capacitance which is proportional to the rate of change of the voltage. That is,

$$I_{cap} = C \frac{\Delta V}{\Delta t} \qquad (14.6)$$

For example, for a $C = 100$ pf and a voltage which is changing at the rate of 10 volts/μsec,

$$I_{cap} = 100 \text{ pf} \times 10 \frac{\text{volts}}{\mu\text{secs}} = 1000 \ \mu a$$

Because of this capacitive current, the current of the NPN and PNP transistors increases. This will cause the values of α_{d-c1} and α_{d-c2} to increase. Thus, switching will occur at a lower value than V_S. In fact, for a very rapid voltage rise, switching may occur at anode voltages as low as 3 or 4 volts.

This rate effect is very important in the operation of most PNPN devices since it is often the cause of "false triggering" which can occur when a fast rise-time transient (noise voltage) appears at the anode or when a supply voltage is switched into the circuit.

14.7.   Four-Layer Diodes: Circuit Applications

Four-layer diodes are suitable for many switching applications. The following two examples will illustrate their use.

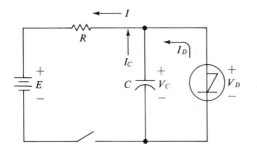

FIG. 14.9.   RELAXATION OSCILLATOR

    Consider the circuit shown in Figure 14.9. This particular circuit is called a *relaxation oscillator*. It essentially takes a d-c input voltage and produces an oscillating output signal. To operate properly the supply voltage E must be greater than the diode's switching voltage V_S.

    Let us assume that the switch is open and the capacitor is uncharged so that $V_C = V_D = 0$ volts. If the switch is now closed the capacitor will begin to charge up toward the supply voltage through the series resistor R. While this is going on, the diode is in the "off" state so that $I_D \approx 0$. Thus, while the capacitor is charging, the circuit can be redrawn as in Figure 14.10(A) with the diode removed. During this time interval the capacitor voltage V_C will be increasing toward E volts with an exponential time constant equal to RC as shown in Figure 14.10(B). If it were not for the diode, the capacitor would eventually reach E volts after about 5 time constants.

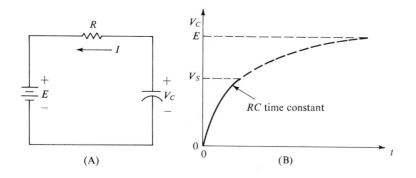

FIG. 14.10.   RELAXATION OSCILLATOR REDRAWN DURING CAPACITOR CHARGING INTERVAL

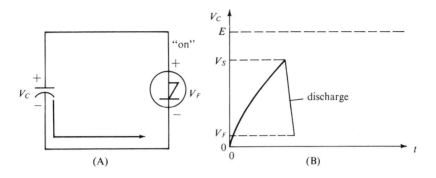

FIG. **14.11.**   CAPACITOR DISCHARGING THROUGH "ON" DIODE

The diode, however, will only block current as long as its voltage is below its switching voltage. Since E is made larger than V_S the capacitor voltage (and thus V_D) will eventually reach the value of V_S. When this occurs the diode will switch to its "on" state essentially presenting a low resistance across the capacitor. The capacitor will now discharge through the "on" diode. This is illustrated in Figure 14.11(A). The discharge time as shown in Figure 14.11(B) will be very fast since the diode is in its low resistance state. The capacitor will discharge to almost zero volts (actually to V_F, the diode's "on" voltage) and its discharge current will hold the diode "on." After the capacitor completes its discharge, the current through the resistor R and supply voltage E supply current to the diode. If this current is less than the diode's holding current, I_H, the diode will turn "off." The value of this current I will be

$$I = \frac{E - V_F}{R} \qquad (14.7)$$

and it should be made less than I_H. Thus,

$$\frac{E - V_F}{R} < I_H \qquad (14.8)$$

When the diode turns "off," it reverts back to its high resistance state and the situation returns to that in Figure 14.10 where the capacitor again begins charging toward E volts. The above sequence will then repeat itself indefinitely. The waveform of voltage across the capacitor and diode will be that shown in Figure 14.12. It is a repetitive waveform with the capacitor charging and discharging periodically. Equation 14.8 must be

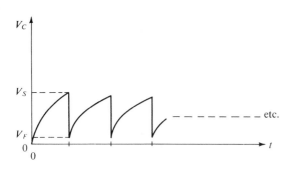

FIG. 14.12.   OSCILLATOR OUTPUT WAVEFORM

satisfied so that the diode turns "off" after the capacitor discharges and the cycle can be repeated.

The frequency of the waveform is essentially determined by the charging time of the capacitor since the discharge time is so short. The charge-up time depends on E, V_S and R and can be obtained from a universal time constant chart or from the expression

$$T_{\text{charge}} = RC \times \ln\left(\frac{E}{E - V_S}\right) \qquad (14.9)$$

The frequency of the oscillations will be the reciprocal of Equation 14.9. That is,

$$f = \frac{1}{RC \times \ln\left(\dfrac{E}{E - V_S}\right)} \qquad (14.10)$$

It is apparent from 14.10 that the frequency of oscillations is dependent on all the circuit variables. The amplitude of the oscillations, however, depends only on the diode parameter V_S and is essentially constant with frequency since the capacitor must always charge to V_S before discharging.

The most convenient way to vary the frequency of this circuit is to vary the value of R. Increasing R will increase charging time and thus decrease the frequency, and vice-versa. However, there are limits on the value of R. If R is made too small then Equation 14.8 will not be satisfied and the diode will never turn "off" once it has been turned "on." On the other hand, if R is made too large the diode will never turn "on" since at its switching point a current I_S must be supplied. To ensure that this does not occur, then

$$\frac{E - V_S}{R} > I_S \qquad (14.11)$$

or, in other words, the current through R when the diode is at V_S must be greater than I_S.

Equations 14.8 and 14.11 may be arranged to give the minimum and maximum values of R for given values of E, C and diode parameters. The results are

$$R_{min} = \frac{E - V_F}{I_H} \qquad\qquad \textbf{(14.12A)}$$

and

$$R_{max} = \frac{E - V_S}{I_S} \qquad\qquad \textbf{(14.12B)}$$

Keeping the value of R between these values will ensure oscillation.

▶ EXAMPLE 14.3

A relaxation oscillator of the type shown in Figure 14.9 uses a voltage supply of 40v, a 1 μfd capacitor, a 100K resistor and a four-layer diode with $V_S = 20$v, $I_S = 0.1$ ma, $I_H = 1$ ma and $V_F = 1$v. Determine the frequency of oscillation, if any.

To determine whether the circuit will oscillate at all, the values of R_{min} and R_{max} must be calculated.

$$R_{min} = \frac{40v - 1v}{1 \text{ ma}} = 39\text{K}$$

$$R_{max} = \frac{40v - 20v}{0.1 \text{ ma}} = 200\text{K}$$

Since our resistor is 100K, the circuit will oscillate. The frequency will be given by Equation 14.10.

$$f = \frac{1}{(100\text{K} \times 1 \text{ }\mu\text{fd}) \times \ln(2)}$$
$$= 14.5 \text{ HZ} \qquad\qquad ◀$$

The frequency of oscillation may also be controlled by varying the power supply voltage. Again, however, Equations 14.8 and 14.11 must be satisfied to ensure oscillation. These equations may be rearranged to give

$$E_{min} = V_S + R\,I_S \qquad\qquad \textbf{(14.13A)}$$

and

$$E_{max} = V_F + R\,I_H \qquad\qquad \textbf{(14.13B)}$$

for oscillations to occur.

▶ EXAMPLE 14.4

What are the limits on E for the circuit of Example 14.3? What is the range over which frequency may be varied by varying the value of E?

$$E_{min} = 20v + (100K \times 0.1 \text{ ma}) = 30v$$

and

$$E_{max} = 1v + (100K + 1 \text{ ma}) = 101v$$

Using $E = E_{min} = 30v$ the frequency will be, using Equation 14.10

$$f_{min} = 8.7 \text{ HZ}$$

and for $E = E_{max} = 101v$ the frequency will be

$$f_{max} = 50 \text{ HZ} \qquad ◀$$

A similar circuit that is often used in timing applications is shown in Figure 14.13. The function of this circuit is to provide a

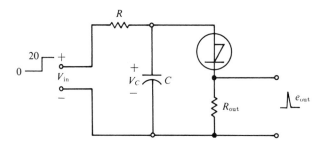

FIG. 14.13.   TIME DELAY CIRCUIT

sharp positive pulse output that occurs a certain time delay after the application of input voltage. The operation of this circuit is similar to the oscillator previously discussed except that a small resistor R_{out} is placed in series with the diode. This means that the capacitor discharge current also flows through R_{out}, producing a pulse across it. The pulse will occur a pre-determined amount of time after the application of power. The time delay will be essentially the capacitor charge-up time given by Equation 14.9.

$$T_{delay} = RC \times \ln\left(\frac{E}{E - V_S}\right) \qquad (14.14)$$

The value of R_{out} must be small to assure a fast capacitor discharge to provide a sharp pulse. Values between 10 and 100 ohms are typical. The output pulse amplitude will be approximately equal to V_S.

Usually only one pulse is desired rather than a series of pulses as would occur in an oscillator. For this reason, it is desirable to choose R so that the diode will remain "on" after the first pulse and no further pulses will occur. Once R is chosen, then C can be chosen to give the necessary time delay. Figure 14.14 shows the waveform relationships for this circuit.

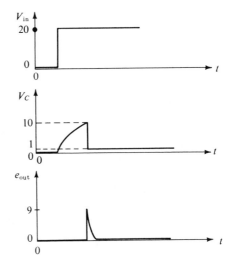

FIG. 14.14.   TIME DELAY CIRCUIT WAVEFORMS

► EXAMPLE 14.5

Using a diode with $V_S = 8$v, $I_S = 0.1$ ma, $V_F = 1$v and $I_H = 2$ ma determine values of R and C for a 5 msec time delay if V_{in} equals 16v.

The value of R must be small enough so that only *one* pulse occurs and then the diode latches "on." For this

$$\frac{V_{in} - V_F}{R} > I_H$$

or

$$\frac{19v}{R} > 2 \text{ ma}$$

We can use $R = 8$K. The value of C will be chosen to give the desired time delay. We have

$$5 \text{ msec} = RC \times \ln(2)$$
$$= 0.69 \times 8K \times C$$

or, solving for C,

$$C = 0.91 \ \mu\text{fd} \qquad\qquad ◄$$

14.8.   The Silicon Controlled Rectifier: Basic Operation

The *silicon controlled rectifier* (SCR) is a PNPN device with three terminals: anode, cathode and *gate*. Its gate terminal is attached to the P-region closest to the cathode. The SCR construction is illustrated in Figure 14.15 along with the circuit symbol for the

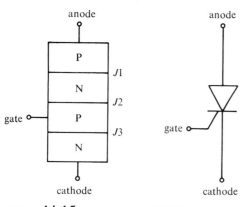

FIG. 14.15.   SCR CONSTRUCTION

SCR. The gate terminal is sometimes referred to as the *cathode gate* to distinguish it from a second gate which is used in certain other PNPN devices.

The two transistor equivalent for the SCR can be used to explain its basic operation and is shown in Figure 14.16. It is

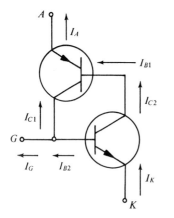

FIG. 14.16.   TWO-TRANSISTOR EQUIVALENT

essentially the same as that of the four-layer diode except that the base of the NPN transistor is accessible via the gate terminal. In fact, when the gate is not used (when it is open circuited), the SCR operates the same as the four-layer diode. The gate, however, allows us to turn the device "on" (low resistance between anode and cathode) by a means other than increasing the anode-to-cathode voltage.

Recall from Section 14.3 that to cause switching in a PNPN device the sum of the transistor alphas must be increased to 1. In the SCR this is accomplished by supplying gate current, in the direction shown, by forward biasing the E-B junction ($J3$) of the NPN transistor (gate made positive relative to cathode). This gate current I_G increases the base current I_{B2} of the NPN transistor. This in turn will cause an increase in I_{C2} and I_{B1} which, therefore, increases I_{C1}. Thus both transistors will be conducting more current. As a result, the values of their respective alphas will increase. For a given value of anode-to-cathode forward voltage the gate current can be increased to the point where ($\alpha_{d\text{-}c1} + \alpha_{d\text{-}c2}$) equals 1. At this point the SCR turns "on" and the resistance between anode and cathode drops to a low value similar to the four-layer diode.

This may be made clearer upon inspection of a set of typical SCR I-V characteristics shown in Figure 14.17. Referring to the figure it can be seen that with $I_G = 0$ the anode-to-cathode characteristic is similar to that of the four-layer diode. That is, with the anode positive relative to the cathode so that $V_{AK} > 0$, the

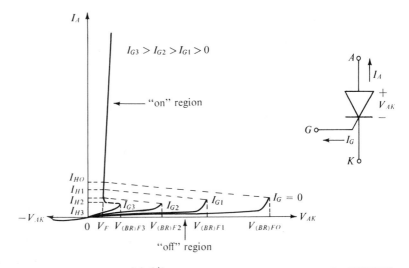

FIG. 14.17.   SCR CHARACTERISTIC CURVES

SCR will block current, making I_A low, until the value of V_{AK} is increased to the *forward breakover voltage*, $V_{(BR)FO}$, at which time the SCR turns "on" and the anode to cathode resistance becomes very low.

With the application of a gate current, I_{G1}, the operation is essentially the same except that switching takes place at a lower value of V_{AK}. Increasing the gate current to I_{G2} causes the forward breakover voltage to decrease even further [$V_{(BR)F2}$]. Eventually a value of I_{G3} is reached at which switching will occur at a very low value of voltage [$V_{(BR)F3}$], typically 2-3 volts. Thus, the gate current controls the value of anode-to-cathode voltage at which switching will occur, hence the name silicon *controlled* rectifier.

The reverse characteristic of the SCR ($V_{AK} < 0$) is essentially that of a P-N diode except that the reverse leakage current is higher for positive values of I_G. For this reason, when an SCR is reverse-biased, I_G is usually kept at zero to reduce leakage current.

An important property of the SCR is its latching ability. That is, after the application of a gate current has triggered the SCR "on," the gate current may be removed and the SCR will remain "on" due to the inherent feedback between the two transistors. Thus, only a pulse of gate current is needed to turn the SCR on. This is illustrated in Figure 14.18. Here, the current through the

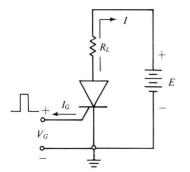

FIG. 14.18.   TURNING ON SCR WITH GATE PULSE

SCR will be only a leakage current as long as the gate current is zero. When a pulse of voltage which is positive relative to the cathode is applied at the gate, the resulting gate current triggers the SCR "on." The current through the SCR will then be limited only by the load resistor R_L and will be approximately E/R_L.

14.9.   SCR Ratings and Characteristics

Circuit designers have available a choice of SCRs whose current capabilities generally range from a few hundred milliamperes to several hundred amperes, and whose voltage capabilities range up to 1000 volts or more. There are SCRs which are designed for fast switching speed, others which need only a low gate current to trigger them "on" and thus have a high gate sensitivity, and still others with characteristics that make them particularly suitable for certain applications. As such, designers and others who select an SCR for a particular application must be familiar with the device's electrical parameters and characteristics and especially its maximum ratings. The following list contains some of the more important SCR ratings and parameters with their symbols and definitions:

Repetitive Peak Reverse Voltage, $V_{ROM(rep)}$:   maximum allowable instantaneous value of repetitive reverse (anode negative) voltage that may be applied to SCR anode with gate open-circuited ($I_G = 0$). This rating should never be exceeded even though reverse breakdown may not occur.

Non-repetitive Peak Reverse Voltage, $V_{ROM(non-rep)}$:   maximum allowable instantaneous value of reverse voltage, of a non-repetitive nature, that may be applied to the SCR with $I_G = 0$. This rating applies to any transient voltage less than 5 msec in duration, and is always greater than $V_{ROM(rep)}$.

Peak Forward Blocking Voltage, V_{FOM}:   maximum instantaneous value of forward blocking voltage (anode positive) which will not switch the SCR to the "on" state with the gate circuit open.

Peak Forward Blocking Voltage, V_{FXM}:   same as V_{FOM} except that a resistor, R_{GK}, is connected between gate and cathode. V_{FXM} is larger than V_{FOM}.

Forward Breakover Voltage, $V_{(BR)FO}$:   voltage at which SCR switches into the conductive state with gate circuit open.

Forward Breakover Voltage, $V_{(BR)FX}$:   same as $V_{(BR)FO}$ except that a resistor, R_{GK}, is connected between gate and cathode. $V_{(BR)FX}$ is larger than $V_{(BR)FO}$.

Average Forward Current, $I_{F(AV)}$:   maximum continuous d-c current which may be permitted to flow in the "on" state under stated conditions.

rms Forward Current, I_f: maximum continuous *rms* current which may be allowed to flow in the "on" state under given conditions.

Peak One-Cycle Surge Forward Current, $I_{FM(surge)}$:   the highest instantaneous value of forward current that may be permitted to flow through the SCR non-repetitively. The peak surge current may recur without damage when sufficient time has elapsed to permit the SCR to recover.

Peak Forward (or Reverse) Gate Voltage, V_{GFM} (or V_{GRM}): maximum allowable peak voltage between gate and cathode when the gate is made positive (or negative) relative to the cathode.

Peak Gate Power Dissipation, P_{GM}:   maximum instantaneous value of power dissipation permitted between gate and cathode terminals.

Average Gate Power Dissipation, $P_{G(AV)}$:   maximum value of average power dissipated between gate and cathode.

Instantaneous "on" voltage, V_F: voltage drop between anode and cathode in "on" state at a given current level.

Instantaneous Forward Blocking Current, $I_{FO}(I_{FX})$:   instantaneous anode current in "off" state at stated conditions of forward voltage and temperature. I_{FO} is with gate open; I_{FX} is with R_{GK} between gate and cathode. I_{FX} is less than I_{FO}.

Instantaneous Reverse Blocking Current, $I_{RO}(I_{RX})$:   counterpart of I_{FO} (I_{FX}) under reverse bias.

Gate Trigger Current (Voltage), $I_{GT}(V_{GT})$:   gate current (voltage) needed to trigger the SCR with anode terminal at $+6$ volts with respect to cathode terminal at stated temperature conditions.

Holding Current, I_{HO} (I_{HX}):   value of anode current in the "on" state needed to hold the SCR "on" at a given temperature. I_{HO} is used when the gate is open; I_{HX} indicates that R_{GK} is between the gate and the cathode. I_{HO} is lower than I_{HX}.

Turn-on Time, t_{on}:   roughly equal to the time that elapses between the triggering of the SCR and its transition to the "on" state.

Turn-off Time, t_{off}:   time interval required for SCR to go from "on" state to "off" state under stated circuit conditions.

These are the most important SCR characteristics. The meanings of some of these parameters and ratings will become clearer in the following sections.

14.10. SCR Gate Triggering

The SCR, like the four-layer diode, can be triggered "on" by increasing its anode-to-cathode voltage above the breakover voltage. However, this method is not used in SCR applications since gate triggering offers so many advantages. The main advantage of gate triggering lies in the high power gain which allows a low power level at the gate to control a large power level to a load. In power control circuitry this mode of triggering makes the most use of the SCR.

The conventional SCR is triggered by causing current to flow between the gate and cathode of the device. Therefore, the SCR's triggering characteristics can be described in terms of the gate-cathode electrical characteristics at given temperature and anode-cathode bias conditions. The gate-cathode section in the SCR is essentially a P-N junction and its characteristics are similar to those of a P-N junction until the SCR is triggered "on." The SCR will trigger when the gate-cathode junction is sufficiently forward-biased and the anode is positive relative to the cathode. It should be pointed out that the gate-cathode junction is somewhat different from ordinary low-current P-N junctions mainly due to the larger physical size needed to handle high currents; the junction area is very large, typically 0.02 sq. in.

Because of the nature of the manufacturing process, a certain spread of gate-cathode characteristics is likely to be found even between SCRs of the same type. Figure 14.19 shows a typical gate characteristic for a 7-amp SCR as it would normally be supplied

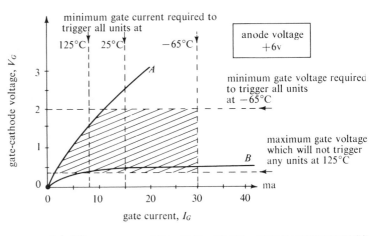

FIG. 14.19.   TYPICAL SCR GATE CHARACTERISTICS

on the manufacturer's data sheet. The two curves shown indicate the limits of the possible gate characteristics. That is, any SCR of this type would have an $I_G - V_G$ curve somewhere between curves *A* and *B* over the limits of junction operating temperature (typically $-65°$ to $125°C$).

A given SCR will trigger at a definite gate current, I_{GT}, and gate-cathode voltage, V_{GT}. The basic function of the trigger circuit is to simultaneously supply I_{GT} and V_{GT}. The shaded area shown in Figure 14.19 contains all the possible trigger points of all SCRs of this type between the temperature limits of $-65°C$ to $125°C$. From the figure it can be seen that the maximum gate current needed to trigger any SCR of this type is 8 ma at $125°C$, 15 ma at $25°C$ and 30 ma at $-65°C$. In other words, the maximum I_{GT} needed to trigger any of these SCRs decreases as junction temperature increases. This indicates that an SCR is *easier to trigger at higher temperatures*. This is to be expected since the alphas will increase with temperature thus requiring a smaller I_G to bring about triggering.

It is also indicated in Figure 14.19 that at $-65°C$ the minimum gate voltage needed to trigger all units of this type is 2v. That is, the maximum value of V_{GT} at $-65°C$ is 2v. At higher temperatures this will decrease to typically 1v at $25°C$ and 0.5v at $125°C$. Another important value is that of the maximum gate voltage that will *not* trigger any units at $125°C$. In the figure this value is indicated to be 0.3v. This means that the minimum value of V_{GT} that can trigger any of these SCRs is 0.3v. The importance of this value will become apparent when we consider typical SCR circuits.

TABLE 14.2

Gate Triggering Characteristics			$(V_{AK} = +6v)$
I_{GT} (ma)			
Min.	Typ.	Max.	Conditions
—	10	15	$T_J = 25°C$
—	20	30	$T_J = -65°C$
—	4	8	$T_J = 125°C$
V_{GT} (volts)			
—	0.7	1	$T_J = 25°C$
—	1	2	$T_J = -65°C$
0.3	0.5	—	$T_J = 125°C$

Since the shaded area in Figure 14.19 contains all possible trigger points (I_{GT}, V_{GT}), the trigger circuit should supply values of I_{GT} and V_{GT} *outside* this area in order to reliably trigger *all* SCRs of this type. Of course, care must be exercised in ensuring that the maximum gate current, I_{GFM}, maximum gate voltage, V_{GFM}, and maximum gate power dissipation, P_{GM}, are not exceeded.

These gate triggering values are usually specified in another manner on SCR data sheets. Table 14.2 shows the same information in tabulated form. Again, note that as temperature increases, a smaller I_{GT} and V_{GT} are required for triggering.

14.11. Gate Triggering Pulse Width

The values of I_{GT} and V_{GT} needed to trigger the SCR as stipulated in the last section are assumed to be either d-c values or pulses with sufficient pulse width. It takes a certain amount of time, t_{on}, for the SCR anode current to increase to its final value once a gate trigger is applied. For this reason, a very short pulse at the gate may not turn the SCR "on" even if its amplitude is greater than V_{GT}. The pulse at the gate must be long enough for the SCR anode current to build up to a value called the *latching current*, I_L. When the latching current level is reached the SCR will turn "on" and stay "on" even if the gate pulse terminates at the same instant. The value of I_L can usually be assumed to be about 3 times the holding current value.

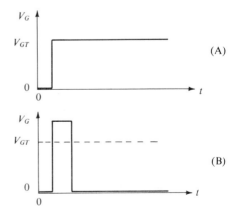

FIG. 14.20.   ILLUSTRATION OF EFFECT OF GATE PULSE WIDTH

The SCR's turn-on time will decrease for a higher amplitude gate trigger. Thus, the gate pulse can be made narrower if its amplitude is increased accordingly. Occasionally, SCR data sheets present curves indicating the required gate pulse width for various pulse amplitudes.

For example, referring to Figure 14.20, a d-c gate voltage signal such as that shown in part (A) of the figure may be sufficient to trigger the SCR. However, if a pulse of gate voltage is used, a higher amplitude may be required as in part (B). If the pulse is wide enough, the amplitude need not be any larger than the d-c value V_{GT}.

14.12.   Gate Triggering Turn-on Gains

It may be beneficial at this time to point out some of the SCR's advantages. In typical operation the gate current needed to trigger an SCR is less than 1 per cent of the anode current that flows when the SCR becomes fully conductive, providing a current gain of greater than 100. Gate voltage needed to trigger is normally around 1 volt, whereas the voltage across the load might be 100 volts once the SCR is "on". Thus, voltage gains of 100 or greater are possible. This results in a power gain of $100 \times 100 = 10,000$. The fact that the gate signal may be of much shorter duration than the anode current makes the ratio of load power to gate power even greater. In fact, power gains on the order of one million are not unusual. In view of the inherent large turn-on power gain, very low-power-level trigger circuitry can be used for reliable turn-on of SCRs. Typically, a trigger circuit using half-watt resistors, low-voltage capacitors, and a small, switching-type transistor can turn on an SCR controlling 100 kw of power in its anode circuit.

Because of its large power gains and its ability to be triggered by a short pulse the SCR (and related devices) has become the most widely used power control device. In contrast to a typical silicon power transistor, an SCR may supply 5 amps of current to a load when it receives a 50 ma gate current pulse for a few microseconds whereas the transistor might require up to 250 ma of *continuous* base current to achieve the same result.

14.13.   SCR Turn-Off Considerations

The SCR is a latching device that will remain in its low-impedance "on" state as long as anode current is maintained above the holding current. Unlike a junction transistor, where removal of the base current will bring collector current to zero, removal of SCR gate current will *not* reduce its anode current and turn the device "off." In other words, the gate has no control over the conventional SCR once the device has been triggered "on." There are exceptions to this among some of the smaller, low-current SCRs and special gate turn-off devices.

To turn the SCR "off" the sum of the transistor alphas must decrease below unity. The transistor alphas will decrease as the current through them decreases. Reducing anode current sufficiently, then, will turn the SCR "off." This reduction may be accomplished in various ways including mechanically opening the anode circuit, reverse-biasing the anode to cathode, diverting anode current or using an auxiliary circuit. Regardless of the method used, a certain amount of time, t_{off}, is needed for the SCR to go from "on" to "off" and this should be considered when turning an SCR "off." A typical value of t_{off} is 25 μsec and this usually limits the SCR to operating frequencies below 30 or 40 KHZ. The value of t_{off} increases with the amount of SCR "on" current.

At this point it may appear that by reverse biasing the gate-cathode the SCR could be made to turn "off" since the *E-B* junction of the NPN transistor would seemingly be reversed-biased. This would be true if the SCR truly consisted of two conventional junction transistors. However, due to large differences in junction sizes and doping, turning "off" the SCR in this manner will not work except for some of the very low-power devices. For this reason, the gate does not take part in turn-off action and all practical SCR power control circuits most have some provision for effecting anode current turn-off. Some of the turn-off methods will be covered in the following sections.

14.14.   The SCR Used as a d-c Switch

The SCR and related PNPN devices are often used in place of mechanical switches or relays. The advantages the SCR offers include smaller size, faster switching speed, silent operation, durability and high sensitivity. SCRs can withstand billions of switching cycles without wearing out, do not suffer from contact bounce or arcing, as relays do, and can survive shock and vibration.

The first SCR circuit we will look at is the simple d-c switch shown in Figure 14.21. Here the SCR simply acts like an "on"-

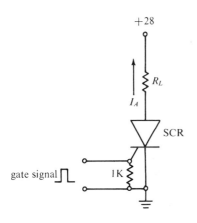

FIG. 14.21.   SIMPLE D-C SWITCH

"off" switch which controls the d-c current to the load. Upon application of the gate signal the SCR will turn "on." In this state the voltage dropped from anode to cathode will be about 1 volt (V_F). Thus, 27v will appear across R_L. The gate signal could be d-c or a pulse of sufficient amplitude and duration. The 1K resistor connected between gate and cathode is used to stabilize the SCR from turning "on" due to increases in temperature or from transients (voltage spikes) on the power supply terminal. This resistor is essentially connected between the base and emitter of the NPN transistor (recall the 2-transistor equivalent circuit) and shunts some of the current away from the base. This causes the SCR "off" current level, and thus the alphas, to be lower, making the SCR more difficult to turn "on" accidentally.

Once the gate signal triggers the SCR, it will continue conducting as long as the anode current is greater than the holding current and the gate will no longer have any control over the SCR current. To turn the SCR "off" the anode current must be reduced or interrupted. A mechanical switch in series with R_L could be opened momentarily to allow I_A to become zero. Upon reclosing the switch the SCR would stay in the "off" or forward blocking state until the gate signal appeared again. This process is called *resetting* the SCR.

The load may be purely resistive, it may be a lamp, a heater, a d-c motor field winding or even a relay. In cases where the load is inductive, as in a motor or relay load, special care must be taken due to the amount of time it takes current to build up in an inductance. This case is shown in Figure 14.22. The load is represented by an inductance in series with a resistance. Neglect the

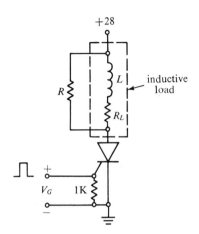

FIG. 14.22.   D-C SWITCH WITH INDUCTIVE LOAD

resistor R for the moment. If a pulse is to be used to trigger the SCR, its duration must be long enough to allow the current through the load to build up to the SCR latching current, I_L. If the pulse is too narrow the anode current will not have time to reach I_L, thus causing the SCR to turn back "off" when the gate pulse terminates. This can be overcome by using a longer gate pulse. However, in many applications a very narrow gate pulse is to be used or the gate pulse width cannot be controlled accurately. In these cases the SCR can still be turned "on" by putting a resistor R across the load. Now when the gate is pulsed turning the SCR "on," about 27 volts appears across the parallel combination of the load and R. If R is chosen correctly, the current through it will be greater than I_L, thus providing the SCR with enough current to latch "on" even though the gate pulse has terminated. The current through the load will then be able to build up to its final value ($27v/R_L$) since the SCR stays "on."

▶ EXAMPLE 14.6

The SCR in Figure 14.22 has a holding current I_{HX} of 1 ma and an "on" voltage V_F of 1 volt. What value of R is needed to ensure turn-on with a narrow gate pulse?

To latch "on" the SCR current must reach about $3 \times I_{HX} = 3$ ma. Thus

$$\frac{27v}{R} \geq 3 \text{ ma}$$

or

$$R \leq 9K \qquad\qquad ◀$$

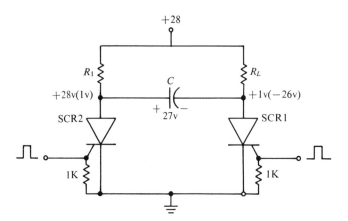

FIG. 14.23.   TURNING SCR1 "OFF" USING A SECOND
SCR

A common method of turning "off" an SCR in a d-c current is shown in Figure 14.23 in which a second SCR is used to effectively reverse-bias the main SCR. Assume SCR1 has been triggered "on" by its gate signal and current is supplied to the load. If SCR2 is "off" capacitor C will charge to 27v, as shown, since its right hand plate is connected to the anode of SCR1 which is about 1 volt above ground and its left hand plate is connected to the anode of SCR2 which is at $+28$ volts. To turn SCR1 "off" a gate pulse is applied to SCR2. This turns SCR2 "on" (since its anode is positive) causing its anode voltage to drop to about 1 volt (shown in parentheses). Since C cannot change its voltage instantaneously, the voltage at the anode of SCR1 will instantaneously become -26v (shown in parentheses), reverse-biasing the anode and turning "off" SCR1. The capacitor C will then charge through R_L to 27v of the opposite polarity placing $+28$ volts at SCR1's anode. When SCR1 is pulsed again, it will turn "on" causing SCR2 to go "off" by the same process.

14.15.   The SCR Used as an a-c Switch

SCRs are often used with an a-c voltage supply; in these applications, turn-off is accomplished automatically by the cyclical reversal of the a-c supply voltage. Consider the circuit shown in Figure 14.24. Here the anode supply is an a-c voltage e_{in}. The circuit operation can be explained with the aid of the voltage waveforms drawn in Figure 14.25.

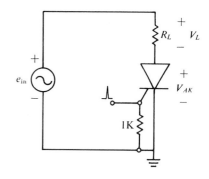

FIG. 14.24.   SCR USED IN AN A-C CIRCUIT

During the positive half-cycle of e_{in} the anode is positive relative to the cathode. If no gate signal is applied the SCR will be in the forward blocking state with $V_L \approx 0$. Thus, V_{AK} will equal e_{in}, as shown, during the interval from $t = 0$ to $t = t_1$. If at $t = t_1$ a gate pulse is applied, the SCR will be triggered "on" and its voltage will drop to about 1 volt. The load voltage then

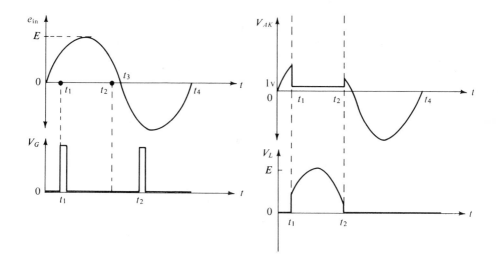

FIG. 14.25.   WAVEFORMS FOR CIRCUIT OF FIG. 14.24

becomes equal to e_{in} (minus the 1v drop across the SCR) at $t = t_1$. The SCR will remain "on" with $V_L \approx e_{in}$ until e_{in} decreases to the point where the current through R_L and the SCR drops below I_{HX} at which point the SCR will turn "off." This occurs at $t = t_2$ when the value of e_{in} is

$$e_{in} = R_L \times I_{HX} + V_F \qquad (14.15)$$

▶ EXAMPLE 14.7

At what value of e_{in} will the SCR turn "off" in the circuit of Figure 14.24 if $R_L = 100\Omega$, $I_{HX} = 10$ ma and $V_F = 1v$?

At turn-off

$$e_{in} = 100\Omega \times 10\text{ ma} + 1v$$
$$= 2v \qquad \blacktriangleleft$$

The SCR will remain "off" for the duration of the positive half-cycle with $V_L = 0$ and $V_{AK} = e_{in}$ from t_2 to t_3. At $t = t_3$ the input voltage reverses, causing the SCR to become reverse-biased (V_{AK} negative). In this state the SCR remains "off" with $V_L = 0$ and $V_{AK} = e_{in}$ even if a gate pulse occurs. The SCR will not turn "on" again until the gate is pulsed during the next positive half-cycle of e_{in}.

If we examine the load-voltage waveform it can be seen that power is not applied to the load until the gate pulse appears during the positive half-cycle. Thus, the average power in the load will depend on the point in the positive half-cycle at which the SCR is triggered "on." That is, the closer t_1 is to 0, the greater the load power will be since it will be conducting for a greater portion of the half-cycle. Various possible load voltage waveforms are shown in Figure 14.26.

In this figure the phase angle at which the SCR is triggered has been included. In part (A) of Figure 14.26 the SCR is triggered at the 45° point in the half-cycle. In other words, the *trigger angle*, α, is 45°. From the figure it should be clear that the load power *decreases* as the trigger angle *increases*. The trigger angle, α, can vary from almost 0° (maximum load power) to almost 180° (minimum load power). This method of controlling the power to the load is called *phase control*, and is used extensively in power controllers, lamp dimmers, motor controllers and in certain types of d-c power supplies.

A circuit similar to that of Figure 14.24 which uses resistance controlled gate triggering to vary the power to the load is shown in Figure 14.27. Instead of using a gate pulse to trigger the SCR,

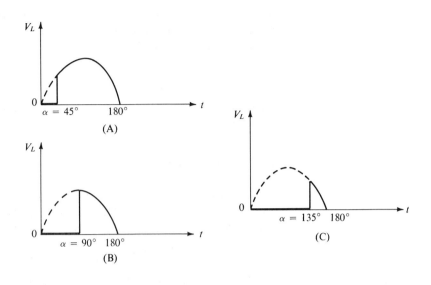

FIG. 14.26.   EFFECT OF TRIGGER ANGLE ON LOAD VOLTAGE

the gate trigger current is supplied by the input voltage e_{in} through R_1, R_2 and the series diode.

As e_{in} goes positive, current I_G will flow since the diode and the gate-cathode junction are forward-biased. This gate current will increase as e_{in} increases toward its peak until at some point I_G will equal I_{GT}, the gate current needed to trigger, and the SCR

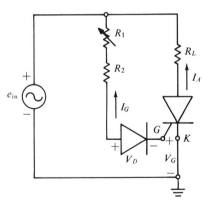

FIG. 14.27.   RESISTANCE CONTROLLED PHASE CONTROL CIRCUIT

will turn "on" applying power to the load. The instantaneous value of e_{in} that produces I_{GT} is controlled by varying R_1. This value can be determined by reasoning that e_{in} must reach a value such that

$$e_{in}(\text{to trigger}) = (R_1 + R_2)I_{GT} + V_D + V_{GT} \qquad \textbf{(14.16)}$$

where V_D is the diode forward voltage drop and V_{GT} is the gate cathode voltage when $I_G = I_{GT}$.

▶ EXAMPLE 14.8

The circuit in Figure 14.27 uses an SCR with $I_{GT} = 0.1$ ma and $V_{GT} = 0.5$v. If $R_2 = 10$K and the diode is silicon, determine the value of e_{in} needed to trigger for (a) $R_1 = 100$K and (b) $R_1 = 10$K.

(a) Using Equation 14.16 with $R_1 = 100$K we have

$$e_{in}(\text{to trigger}) = (110\text{K}) \times 0.1 \text{ ma} + 0.7\text{v} + 0.5\text{v}$$
$$= 12.2\text{v}$$

(b) With $R_1 = 10$K

$$e_{in}(\text{to trigger}) = 10\text{K} \times 0.1 \text{ ma} + 0.7\text{v} + 0.5\text{v}$$
$$= 2.2\text{v} \qquad ◀$$

The trigger angle is determined by calculating the phase angle at which e_{in} reaches the value needed to trigger. If e_{in} is sinusoidal we have

$$e_{in} = E \sin wt \qquad \textbf{(14.17)}$$

The value of wt at which $e_{in} = e_{in}$ (to trigger) is simply the trigger angle, α. Thus

$$e_{in}(\text{to trigger}) = E \sin \alpha \qquad \textbf{(14.18)}$$

Solving for α we have

$$\alpha = \arcsin \left(\frac{e_{in}(\text{to trigger})}{E} \right) \qquad \textbf{(14.19)}$$

α can vary from almost $0°$ to $90°$ and is controlled by varying R_1 which varies e_{in} (to trigger). α will increase as R_1 increases.

▶ EXAMPLE 14.9

For the circuit values of Example 14.8 determine the trigger angle in each case if e_{in} has an amplitude of 24 volts.

(a) From Example 14.8 with $R_1 = 100K$, e_{in} (to trigger) = 12.2v. Using Equation 14.19

$$\alpha = \arcsin\left(\frac{12.2}{24}\right) = \arcsin(0.508)$$
$$= 30.6°$$

(b) Similarly with $R_1 = 10K$

$$\alpha = \arcsin\left(\frac{2.2}{24}\right) = \arcsin(0.092)$$
$$= 5.2° \qquad \blacktriangleleft$$

The diode in this circuit is used to prevent the gate-cathode reverse voltage from exceeding V_{GRM} during the negative half-cycle of the input. The diode is chosen to have a PRV rating higher than the input amplitude. The value of R_2 is chosen to limit gate current below its maximum rating, I_{GFM}. Care must be taken that the amplitude E of the input voltage does not exceed the SCR's maximum forward blocking voltage, V_{FOM}, or its maximum reverse blocking voltage, V_{ROM}.

The two circuits just investigated are d-c power control circuits since the SCR can conduct only during the positive half-cycle allowing current to flow through the load in only *one* direction. The load-voltage waveform (Figure 14.26) is not pure d-c but is rather pulsating d-c. It has a non-zero average value whereas pure a-c would have a zero average value. These circuits could not be used to deliver a-c power to a load but they may be modified to do so. The circuit of Figure 14.28 is essentially the same as that of Figure 14.24 except that *two* SCRs are used in an *inverse parallel* arrangement. SCR1 will conduct when its gate is pulsed and e_{in} is in its positive half-cycle, while SCR2 will conduct when its gate is pulsed during the negative half-cycle of e_{in}. Thus, load current will flow in both directions and a-c power is applied to the load. This circuit is highly impractical since *two* separate gate trigger circuits are required. A PNPN device which can be used in place of the two SCRs will be discussed in the next section.

There are many types of gate pulse trigger circuits used in SCR circuits. One common circuit utilizes the four-layer diode time delay circuit discussed in Section 14.7. The output pulse is used to trigger the SCR gate. Another useful circuit will be discussed in conjunction with unijunction transistors in Chapter 15.

These few example applications of the SCR do not come near to exhausting its numerous capabilities and applications. Further applications can be found in the references at the end of the chapter.

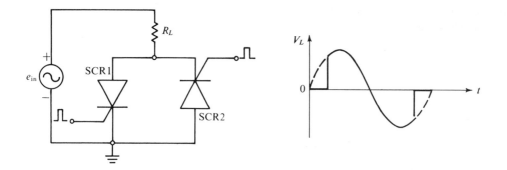

FIG. 14.28.   TWO SCRS SUPPLY A-C POWER TO A LOAD

14.16.   Other PNPN Devices

A number of other PNPN devices which are similar in operation to the SCR have gained wide acceptance in the fields of switching circuits and power control.

The *silicon controlled switch*, SCS, is basically a sensitive SCR with a smaller I_{GT}. It is smaller in size and can handle only relatively low currents (below 1 amp). It has two gate terminals (see Figure 14.29(A). One is the conventional cathode gate, the other

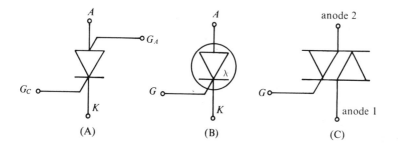

FIG. 14.29.   (A) SCS (B) LASCR (C) TRIAC

is the anode gate which is connected to the N region closest to the anode in the PNPN structure. In the SCS the cathode gate can be used to turn the device "off" as well as "on" by using a negative pulse. The anode gate can be used to turn the device "on" (negative pulse) and "off" (positive pulse). The SCS is used mostly in switching circuit applications since its switching speed is much faster than that of an SCR.

The *light-activated SCR*, LASCR, is essentially an SCR that can be triggered "on" by light energy. It is equipped with a translucent window in its casing to permit illumination of the light-sensitive area of the silicon crystal. The LASCR can also be gated "on" in the conventional manner of an SCR. Its electronic symbol is shown in Figure 14.29(B).

A *triac* is essentially a double PNPN device similar to the SCR except that it can conduct current in both directions, making it useful for controlling a-c power to a load. The triac [see Figure 14.29(C)], like the SCR, has only one gate but has two anode terminals and no cathode. The triac will conduct when anode 2 is positive relative to anode 1 and the gate is made *positive* relative to anode 1. When anode 2 is negative relative to anode 1, the triac will conduct when the gate is made *negative* relative to anode 1. Actually, the triac can often be triggered by either polarity of gate pulse although the sensitivity is greatest for the two conditions described above. The triac can be inserted in a circuit such as that in Figure 14.28 to replace the two SCRs. The advantages are obvious since only one gate trigger circuit is needed as well as one less PNPN device. Triacs are normally high-current devices and are used to control a-c power to heaters, motors, and lamps.

GLOSSARY

PNPN devices: four-layer devices of alternate doping

Latching: the characteristic of a PNPN switch which allows it to remain "on" after the excitation has been removed

Triggering: process of causing a PNPN device to switch from "off" to "on"

Forward switching voltage: anode-to-cathode voltage at which a four-layer diode. switches

Holding current: current required to maintain a PNPN switch in the "on" state

Rate effect: process by which a PNPN device switches "on" due to a rapidly rising anode-to-cathode voltage

Forward breakover voltage: anode-to-cathode voltage at which an SCR switches "on"

Latching current: current required from anode to cathode of an SCR for switching to occur

Trigger angle: phase angle of input voltage at the instant of SCR triggering

Phase control: control of power to a load by controlling trigger angle

Questions

14.1   How does a PNPN switch differ from a mechanical switch aside from physical characteristics?

14.2   Sketch the PNPN structure, label all junctions and terminals and draw its two-transistor equivalent.

14.3   What is the difference between a four-layer diode and a P-N diode?

14.4   What process produces switching in the four-layer diode?

14.5   Sketch the *I-V* characteristic of the four-layer diode. Label the voltages V_S and V_F and the currents I_S and I_H.

14.6   In the circuit of Figure 14.6, the four-layer diode has the following parameters:

$$V_S = 8v$$
$$I_S = 0.5 \text{ ma}$$
$$I_H = 1.5 \text{ ma}$$
$$V_F = 1v$$

The input voltage E is changing according to the waveform in Figure 14.30. Sketch the waveform of V_D in response to this input.

14.7   Repeat Question 14.6 using a series resistor of 10K.

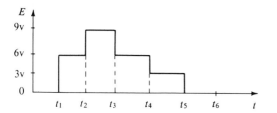

FIG. 14.30.

14.8   What is a bilateral four-layer diode?

14.9   Explain how the rate effect can cause triggering of a four-layer diode at a voltage lower than V_S.

14.10   A relaxation oscillator of the type shown in Figure 14.9 uses the diode with the parameters given in Question 14.6. If a capacitor of 0.1 μfd is used and $E = 12$v, find R_{min} and R_{max} and the resulting limits on the oscillator frequency.

14.11   Since I_H decreases with temperature what will happen to the oscillator's frequency limits at elevated temperatures?

14.12   Using the diode of Question 14.6 determine values of R and C for a time delay circuit with 10 msec delay. Use $V_{in} = 20$v.

14.13   The time delay of the circuit of Question 14.12 may be increased by increasing R or C or both. What are the considerations in deciding which one to increase to obtain more time delay?

14.14   How may the time delay circuit be modified so as to produce a periodic train of pulses?

14.15   Draw the circuit symbol for the SCR and label all terminals.

14.16   How does the SCR differ from the four-layer diode?

14.17   Sketch the *I-V* characteristic of an SCR for three values of gate current. Label all important points.

14.18   Can the gate terminal be used to trigger the SCR when its anode is negative relative to cathode?

14.19   Refer to the specification sheet for the GE C30 and C32 SCRs in Appendix II. For the C30A SCR determine the following:

(a) Minimum anode-cathode forward breakover voltage
(b) Maximum allowable repetitive reverse voltage
(c) Typical I_{GT} at 25°C
(d) Typical V_{GT} at 25°C
(e) Typical holding current at 25°C
(f) $T_{J(max)}$
(g) Maximum allowable reverse gate voltage
(h) Maximum allowable *rms* forward current

14.20   Indicate whether the values in answer to 14.19 (a), (c), (d), (e), (f), and (h), will increase, decrease or remain the same at higher junction temperatures.

14.21   Will the SCR with the gate characteristics of Figure 14.19 trigger under the following conditions?

(a) $I_G = 5$ ma, $V_G = 0.2$v, $T_J = 25$°C
(b) $I_G = 20$ ma, $V_G = 1$v, $T_J = 25$°C
(c) $I_G = 20$ ma, $V_G = 2.5$v, $T_J = -65$°C

14.22   In Figure 14.31, the SCR has a holding current of 1 ma and a latching current of 3 ma. How wide must the gate pulse be in order for the SCR to turn "on"? Assume $V_F = 1v$.

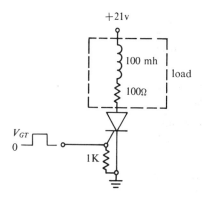

FIG. 14.31.

14.23   If a narrower gate pulse is to be used, what value of R should be used across the load?

14.24   Why is the SCR useful for supplying large amounts of power to a load?

14.25   Can most SCRs be turned "off" by reverse-biasing the gate?

14.26   One method of turning "off" an SCR is shown in Figure 14.32. The transistor is normally held "off" by reverse bias at the *E-B* junction. If the SCR is triggered it will turn "on." When V_{in} is positive the transistor will turn "on" (saturate) and divert all the anode current to the collector. This will turn the SCR "off" and it will remain "off" until its gate is pulsed again when $V_{in} = 0$.

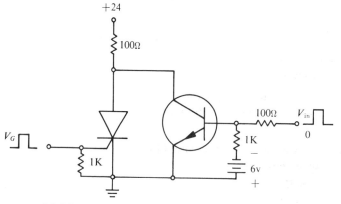

FIG. 14.32.

For this circuit determine the value of V_{in} needed to turn the SCR "off" if the transistor is silicon and has $h_{FE} = 30$.

14.27   The SCR in Figure 14.33 has a holding current of 10 ma, $V_F = 1v$ and $V_{GT} = 2v$. For the input and gate signal waveforms shown sketch the resulting load voltage waveform.

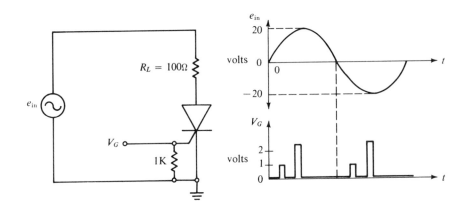

FIG. **14.33.**

14.28   The circuit of Figure 14.28 utilizes an SCR with $I_{GT} = 0.1$ ma and $V_{GT} = 0.5v$. If $R_2 = 10K$ and the diode is silicon, determine the value of R_1 needed to cause triggering when e_{in} reaches 3.2v.

14.29   If e_{in} in Question 14.28 is a 40v p-p sinewave, determine the trigger angle. If R_1 is increased what happens to the trigger angle? To the load power?

References

Heller, S., *Understanding Silicon Controlled Rectifiers*. New York: Hayden Book Company, Inc., 1968.

Romanowitz, H. A. and R. E. Puckett, *Introduction to Electronics*. New York: John Wiley & Sons, Inc., 1968.

Silicon Controlled Rectifier Manual. Auburn, New York: General Electric Company, 1964.

Sowa, W. A. and M. M. Toole, *Special Semiconductor Devices*. New York: Holt, Rinehart and Winston, Inc., 1968.

The Unijunction Transistor

15.1. Introduction

The *Unijunction Transistor*, abbreviated UJT, is a three-terminal, single-junction device. The most important electrical property of the UJT is its *negative resistance* characteristic which makes it suitable for use in oscillator, timing and multivibrator circuits. Like the PNPN device, the UJT is normally operated as a switch and, in fact, finds its most important application in SCR trigger circuits. The following discussion will concentrate heavily on the UJT's circuit operation rather than on its physical behavior.

15.2. Basic Operation

A typical UJT structure, pictured in Figure 15.1, consists of a lightly-doped, N-type silicon bar provided with ohmic contacts at each end. The two end connections are called *base* 1, designated $B1$, and *base* 2, $B2$. A small P region is alloyed into one side of the bar closer to $B2$. This P region is the UJT *emitter*, E, and forms a P-N junction with the bar.

An *interbase resistance*, R_{BB}, exists between $B1$ and $B2$. It is typically between 4K and 10K and can easily be measured with an ohm-meter with the emitter open. R_{BB} is essentially the resistance of the N-type bar. This interbase resistance can be

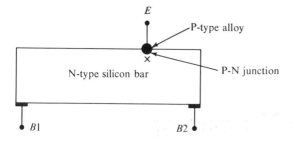

FIG. 15.1.   TYPICAL UJT STRUCTURE

broken up into two resistances, one to the left of the emitter region, called R_{B1}, and one to the right of the emitter, called R_{B2}. Since the emitter is closer to $B2$, the value of R_{B1} is greater than R_{B2} (typically 4.2K versus 2.8K).

The operation of the UJT can better be explained with the aid of an equivalent circuit. The UJT's circuit symbol and its equivalent circuit are shown in Figure 15.2. The diode represents the

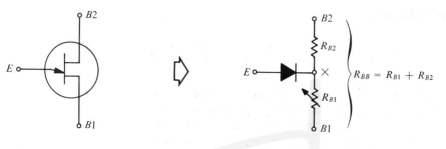

FIG. 15.2.   UJT SYMBOL AND EQUIVALENT CIRCUIT

P-N junction between the emitter and the base bar (point x). The arrow through R_{B1} indicates that it is *variable* since during normal operation it may typically range from 5K to 50Ω.

The basic UJT circuit is shown in Figure 15.3(A) and redrawn in Figure 15.3(B) using the UJT equivalent circuit. The *I-V* characteristic at the emitter (I_E versus V_E) is also shown in part (C) of the same figure. In the basic circuit $B2$ is biased positive relative to $B1$ (V_{BB}). The resistor R is a current-limiting resistor.

Consider the condition $V_{in} = 0$. In this case V_E will be 0 and, since point x is positive, the diode will be reverse-biased and only

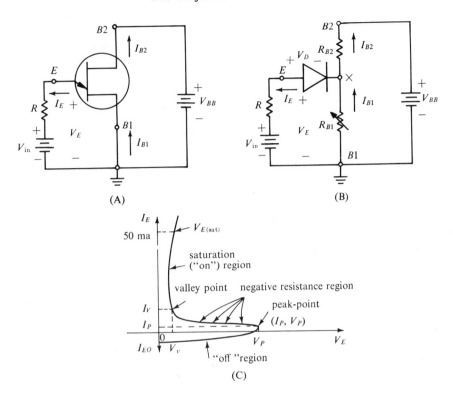

$$\text{FIG.} \quad 15.3. \qquad \text{(A) BASIC CIRCUIT (B) EQUIVALENT CIR-}$$
$$\text{CUIT (C) EMITTER } I\text{-}V \text{ CURVE}$$

an emitter leakage current, I_{EO}, will flow. This current is typically a few microamperes. The emitter diode will remain reverse-biased until V_{in} is increased to a value slightly larger than V_x. The value of V_x is obtained using the voltage divider rule as

$$V_x = \left(\frac{R_{B1}}{R_{B1} + R_{B2}}\right) V_{BB} = \left(\frac{R_{B1}}{R_{BB}}\right) V_{BB}$$
$$= \eta V_{BB} \tag{15.1}$$

where η (eta) is the voltage divider ratio and is called the *intrinsic standoff ratio*. Its value is usually in the range 0.5 to 0.8. The region of operation between $V_E = 0$ and $V_E = V_x + V_D$ is called cut-off or "off" and in this region I_E is very small. When V_{in} is increased to the point where

$$V_E = V_p = V_x + V_D$$
$$= \eta V_{BB} + V_D \tag{15.2}$$

the diode turns "on" ($V_D = 0.7v$) and forward emitter current begins to flow. This point is called the *peak point* and the emitter voltage at this point, Equation 15.2, is *Vp, peak point voltage.*

This emitter current causes holes to be injected into the *B1* region and the effect of these extra current carriers is to cause R_{B1} to decrease. Hence, as I_E is increased by increasing V_{in}, the decrease in R_{B1} will cause V_x and therefore V_E to drop. This effect of V_E *decreasing* as I_E is *increasing* is, of course, the *negative resistance* concept studied in Chapter 7 in conjunction with tunnel diodes. The negative resistance region of the curve illustrates this. As I_E is increased above a certain point (I_V) the value of V_E will begin to increase slowly with large increases in I_E. This region is called the *saturation* or "on" region and here the resistance is positive. The *valley point* occurs usually at a few ma and around 1 to 2 volts. In the saturation region the value of $V_{E(sat)}$ is defined as the emitter voltage at $I_E = 50$ ma.

The UJT is normally used as a switch operating between the cut-off region and the saturation region. At this point the student should recognize the similarities between the UJT operating characteristic and that of the four-layer diode. The major difference is that the UJT switches at a variable voltage V_p which depends on V_{BB} (see Equation 15.2). Table 15.1 below lists the four-layer diode parameters and their counterparts for the UJT. As we shall see, UJT circuits operate similarly to four-layer diode circuits.

TABLE 15.1

Four-layer diode	UJT
V_S	V_P
I_S	I_P
V_F	V_V
I_H	I_V

The *I-V* characteristic will be different for different values of V_{BB}. The curve will actually shift to the right as V_{BB} increases. This will increase V_P, V_V and $V_{E(sat)}$. Also I_V increases with V_{BB}.

15.3.   UJT Parameters and Ratings

A set of parameters and ratings for a typical UJT are listed in Table 15.2 for $T_J = 25°C$.

TABLE 15.2

Max. reverse emitter voltage (V_{B2E}):   60v
Max. interbase voltage (V_{BB}):   45v
Max. peak emitter current: 1 amp
Max. average power dissipation: 500mw
Interbase resistance (R_{BB}):   4.7K to 6.8K
Intrinsic standoff ratio (η):   0.51 to 0.62
Emitter leakage current (I_{EO}):   2 μa(max) at $V_{B2E} = 60$v
Valley current (I_V):   8 ma (min) at $V_{BB} = 10$v
Valley voltage (V_V):   1v (typical) at $V_{BB} = 10$v
Peak-point current (I_P):   12 μa (max) at $V_{BB} = 10$v

Most of the entries in the table need no further explanation. However, it should be explained that the reason for listing only a *peak*
emitter current rating lies in the fact that UJTs are normally
operated in pulsing or oscillating circuits where a continuous d-c
emitter current is not encountered.

15.4.   UJT Circuit Operation

The most common UJT circuit in use today is the relaxation
oscillator, shown in Figure 15.4. Its operation is similar to the
four-layer diode relaxation oscillator. However, its differences are
significant enough to warrant a detailed investigation of its operation.

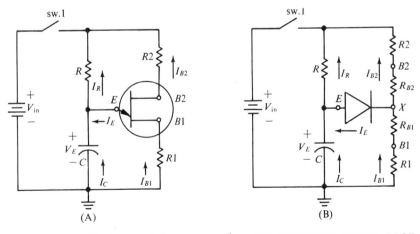

FIG. 15.4.   (A) UJT BASIC RELAXATION OSCILLATOR
(B) ITS EQUIVALENT CIRCUIT

Let us consider the situation in which the capacitor is at zero volts and the switch is suddenly closed at $t = 0$ applying V_{in} to the circuit. Since $V_E = V_C = 0$, the UJT emitter diode is reverse-biased and the UJT is "off." The amount of reverse bias is V_x volts which can be obtained using the voltage divider rule

$$V_x = \frac{(R_1 + R_{B1})V_{in}}{R_1 + R_{B1} + R_2 + R_{B2}} \tag{15.3}$$

In many cases $R1$ and $R2$ are much smaller than R_{B1} and R_{B2} and V_x becomes approximately equal to ηV_{in} (Equation 15.1).

In this condition the only emitter current flowing will be a small reverse leakage, I_{EO}. Also, R_{B1} will be at its "off" value (typically 4K). Thus, we can consider the emitter to be open ($I_E \approx 0$) and the capacitor will begin to charge toward the input voltage V_{in}. The capacitor voltage increases with a time constant of RC as illustrated in Figure 15.5(A). It will continue to increase until the voltage at the emitter reaches the peak-point value, V_P, given by Equation 15.2. At this time, T_1, the emitter diode becomes forward-

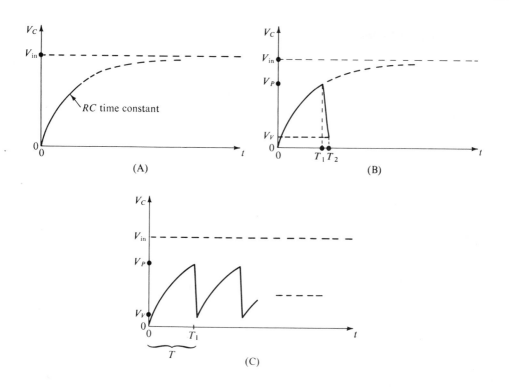

FIG. 15.5.   CAPACITOR VOLTAGE WAVEFORM

biased and the UJT turns "on" with R_{B1} dropping to a very low value (20 ohms typical). Since the diode is now forward-biased, the capacitor will discharge through the low resistance path containing the diode, R_{B1} and R_1.

The capacitor discharge time constant is normally very short compared to its charging time constant [see Figure 15.5(B)]. An analytical expression for the discharge time constant is difficult to obtain since R_{B1} will continually change as the current I_E decreases. The discharging capacitor provides the emitter current needed to keep the UJT "on" and it will remain "on" until I_E drops below the valley current I_V (note the similarity to I_H) at which time the UJT will turn "off." This occurs at time T_2 when the capacitor voltage has dropped to the valley voltage V_V (typically 1 to 2 volts). At this time R_{B1} returns to its "off" value, the diode is again reverse-biased, and $I_E \approx 0$.

The capacitor will begin charging toward V_{in} once again and the previous chain of events will repeat itself indefinitely as long as power is applied to the circuit. The result is a periodic sawtooth-type waveform as shown in Figure 15.5(C). To calculate the frequency of this waveform we first calculate the period of one cycle. The length of one period, T, is essentially the time it takes for the capacitor to charge to V_P since the discharge time T_2 is relatively short. Thus $T \approx T_1$ and is given by

$$T = RC \ln \left(\frac{V_{in}}{V_{in} - V_P} \right) \qquad (15.4)$$

In most cases, $V_P \approx \eta V_{in} + V_D$ and the period can be written as

$$T \approx RC \ln \frac{V_{in}}{V_{in}(1 - \eta) + V_D} \qquad (15.5)$$

Often the small diode drop may be neglected to give an even more approximate expression

$$T \approx RC \ln \left(\frac{1}{1 - \eta} \right) \qquad (15.6)$$

Examination of Equation 15.6 brings out an important point, namely that T is relatively independent of supply voltage V_{in}. This characteristic is important when designing a stable oscillator circuit.

The oscillator frequency is given by $1/T$ and can be obtained using either of the three previous equations.

▶ EXAMPLE 15.1

The circuit of Figure 15.4 uses a UJT with $\eta = 0.6$, $R_{BB} = 10K$ and $V_D = 0.5v$. If $V_{in} = 20v$, $R1 = R2 = 100\Omega$, $R = 10K$ and

$C = 1$ μfd determine the amplitude of the capacitor waveform (V_P) and the oscillation frequency.

The value of V_P can be calculated using

$$V_P = \eta V_{\text{in}} + V_D$$

since $R1$ and $R2$ are $\ll R_{BB}$. Thus, we have

$$V_P = 0.6(20v) + 0.5v = 12.5v$$

The period of the waveform is approximately given by Equation 15.6 as

$$T \approx 10\text{K} \times 1 \ \mu\text{fd} \times \ln\left(\frac{1}{1 - 0.6}\right)$$
$$\approx 10 \text{ msec} \times \ln(2.5)$$
$$\approx 9 \text{ msec}$$

This gives a frequency of $1/T = 111$ HZ.   ◀

The similarity between the operation of the UJT oscillator and the four-layer diode oscillator should now be apparent. The main differences are that the UJT circuit has a *frequency* relatively independent of V_{in} while the four-layer diode oscillator has an *amplitude* (V_s) which is independent of V_{in}.

The UJT relaxation oscillator circuit can also supply pulse waveforms. If the output is taken from B1, the result is a train of pulses occurring during the discharge of the capacitor through the UJT emitter. The waveform of V_{B1} is illustrated in Figure 15.6(A). The amplitude of the B1 pulses is always less than V_P but is greater for larger values of C. The voltage at B1 during the UJT "off" time will be very small and is determined by the voltage divider formed by $R1$, R_{BB} and $R2$ [see Figure 15.4(B)]. That is,

$$V_{B1}(\text{``off''}) = \frac{R1(V_{\text{in}})}{R1 + R_{BB} + R2} \qquad (15.7)$$

This voltage is important in certain applications as we shall see.

The rise time of the pulses at B1 is very short (less than 1 μsec) but the fall time depends on the values of C and $R1$. A larger value of C or $R1$ will cause a slower capacitor discharge and a longer falltime.

If the output is taken at B2 a waveform of negative-going pulses is obtained as shown in Figure 15.6(B). This results from the decrease in R_{B1} when the UJT turns "on." This increases I_{B2} which increases the drop across R2 and thus reduces V_{B2}.

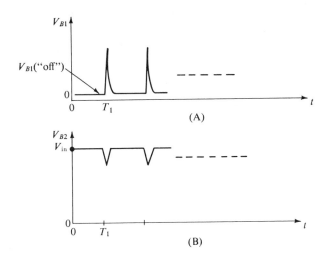

FIG. 15.6.   WAVEFORMS AT (A) $B1$ AND (B) $B2$

The amplitude of these pulses is usually about a couple of volts but can be increased by increasing $R2$.

The frequency of oscillations is normally controlled by varying the charging time constant RC. There are, however, limits on R as there were in the four-layer diode circuit. These limits are dictated by the same considerations (which will not be repeated here) and are

$$R_{\min} = \frac{V_{\text{in}} - V_V}{I_V} \qquad \text{(15.8A)}$$

$$R_{\max} = \frac{V_{\text{in}} - V_P}{I_P} \qquad \text{(15.8B)}$$

Keeping R between these limits will ensure oscillation. If R is greater than $R_{\max}$, the capacitor never reaches V_P since the current through R is not large enough to both charge the capacitor and supply I_P to the UJT. The UJT will stay in the "off" state.

If R is smaller than $R_{\min}$, the capacitor will reach V_P and discharge through the UJT but the UJT will not turn "off," since the current through R is greater than the I_V needed to hold the UJT "on." In some circuits this is useful where only *one* output pulse is desired after application of power. A time delay circuit similar to that using the four-layer diode is a good example. The time delay is equal to *one* period (Equation 15.6).

▶EXAMPLE 15.2

For the circuit values given in Example 15.1 determine the limits on the charging resistor R and the resulting limits on frequency. The UJT has $I_V = 10$ ma, $V_V = 2$v and $I_P = 5$ μa.

$$R_{min} = \frac{20v - 2v}{10\ ma} = 1.8K$$

and

$$R_{max} = \frac{20v - 13.5v}{5\ \mu a} = 1.5\ megohms$$

Using these values to calculate T,

$$T_{min} = 1.8K \times 1\ \mu fd \times \ln(2.5) = 1.6\ msec$$

and

$$T_{max} = 1.5\ meg \times 1\ \mu fd \times \ln(2.5) = 1.35\ sec$$

This results in

$$f_{max} = 625\ HZ$$

and

$$f_{min} = 0.74HZ \qquad\qquad ◀$$

Examination of Equation 15.8 indicates that to obtain a greater upper limit on frequency (a lower R_{min}) the value of I_V should be made larger. Similarly, to obtain a smaller lower limit on frequency (a higher R_{max}) the value of I_P should be made smaller. UJTs with I_V as high as 8 ma and I_P as low as 2 μa are presently available.

The frequency may also be varied by varying C. The lower limit on C is normally around 0.001 μfd, while the upper limit depends on the size of $R1$ (which limits discharge current). In most applications of this circuit the value of C is kept fixed and a variable resistor is used for R.

The temperature stability of the UJT relaxation oscillator frequency is normally very good. This is because η varies only slightly with temperature and the only variation in V_P is due to the small decrease in V_D (2 mv/°C) with temperature. Its stability of frequency with variations in temperature and supply voltage coupled with its simplicity and low cost make the UJT oscillator a popular circuit for timing and pulsing applications.

15.5.   The UJT as an SCR Trigger

The circuit examined in the previous section is often used as the gate trigger source in SCR applications. The basic circuit is shown in Figure 15.7 where the $B1$ pulse output is used to trigger the SCR a predetermined interval of time after the switch is closed. That is, the first $B1$ pulse occurs T seconds after the 28v is supplied to the UJT circuit. After the SCR has been triggered "on" subsequent pulses at its gate have no effect.

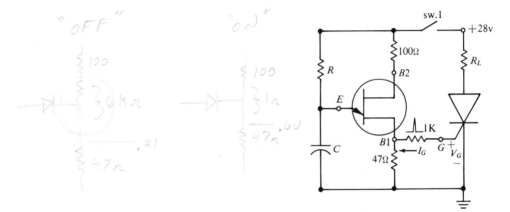

FIG. 15.7.   UJT OSCILLATOR AS GATE TRIGGER SOURCE

An important design consideration in this type of circuit concerns premature triggering of the SCR. The voltage at $B1$ when the UJT is "off" (Equation 15.7) must be smaller than the voltage needed to trigger the SCR, otherwise the SCR will be triggered immediately upon switch closure with no delay. Thus, we have the requirement

$$V_{B1}(\text{"off"}) < (I_{GT} \times 1K + V_{GT}) \qquad (15.9)$$

▶ EXAMPLE 15.3

The UJT in Figure 15.7 has $R_{BB} = 6K$ and the SCR has $I_{GT} = 0.1$ ma and $V_{GT} = 0.5v$. Determine whether the circuit will cause premature SCR triggering.

Using Equation 15.7, we have

$$V_{B1}(\text{"off"}) = \frac{47\Omega \times 28v}{6147\Omega} = 0.21v$$

The requirement of Equation 15.9 is

$$V_{B1}(\text{"off"}) \le (0.1 \text{ ma} \times 1K + 0.5v) = 0.6v$$

Our value of 0.21v satisfies this requirement.   ◄

▶ EXAMPLE 15.4

The same UJT of the previous example has $\eta = 0.7$, $V_D = 0.7v$, and $I_V = 3$ ma. Choose values for R and C to give a 10 msec delay in the circuit of Figure 15.7.

The value of R is to be chosen to produce only one $B1$ pulse. We have

$$V_P = 0.7 \times 28v + 0.7v$$
$$= 20.3v$$

Thus

$$R \le R_{\min} = \frac{28v - 20.3v}{3 \text{ ma}}$$
$$= 2.57K$$

If we choose $R = 2.2K$, the value of C is obtained using Equation 15.6.

$$C = \frac{10 \text{ msec}}{2.2K \times \ln(3.3)}$$
$$= 3.8 \text{ }\mu\text{fd}$$ ◄

The UJT oscillator is also used in triggering the SCR in a-c circuits such as that shown in Figure 15.8. In this circuit, the a-c input voltage supplies the load power and also drives the UJT

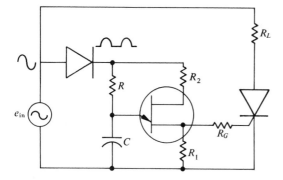

FIG. **15.8.**   UJT AS A GATE TRIGGER IN AN A-C SCR
CIRCUIT

circuit. The diode is used to rectify the negative half-cycle of the input before it reaches the UJT. The circuit operation is similar to the d-c circuit of Figure 15.7 except that the UJT triggers the SCR during each input cycle in order to provide continuous power to the load. This circuit has the capability of varying the load power by varying the RC time constant which controls the trigger angle for each cycle. Trigger angle variations covering almost the entire range from 0° to 180° are possible with this circuit, thus giving it more capability than the SCR power control circuit discussed in Chapter 14.

GLOSSARY

Unijunction transistor: switching device consisting of a silicon N-type bar and one alloyed P-N junction

Base 1, base 2: terminals at either end of the N-type bar

Emitter: terminal at alloyed P-region

Interbase resistance (R_{BB}): resistance between base 1 and base 2 ("off" state)

Intrinsic standoff ratio (η): ratio of the distribution of interbase resistance on either side of the emitter

Peak-point voltage (V_P): voltage needed at the emitter relative to base 1 to turn UJT "on"

Peak-point current (I_P): emitter current at peak-point voltage V_P

Valley voltage (V_V): emitter voltage in the "on" state

Valley current (I_V): emitter current at the valley voltage V_V

Questions

15.1   In the circuit of Figure 15.3 if the UJT has $R_{B1} = R_{B2} = 5K$ and $V_D = 0.7$v calculate the peak-point voltage V_P. What value of V_{in} is needed to turn the UJT "on"?

15.2   After the UJT is turned "on" what happens to the value of R_{B1}?

15.3   How can the value of V_P be varied for a given UJT?

15.4 A UJT with the following parameters is used in the relaxation circuit of Figure 15.4:

$$R_{B1} = 6K$$
$$R_{B2} = 3K$$
$$V_D = 0.7v$$
$$I_V = 4 \text{ ma}$$
$$V_V = 1v$$
$$I_P = 10 \mu a$$

The circuit values are $R1 = 100\Omega$, $R2 = 50\Omega$, $R = 10K$, $C = 2 \mu fd$, and $V_{in} = 24v$.

(a) Determine V_P.

(b) Determine whether R is within the limits for oscillation. If it is, determine the oscillator frequency.

(c) Sketch and label accurately the capacitor voltage waveform.

15.5 Repeat Question 15.4 using $R = 5K$.

15.6 Determine the range of frequencies which can be obtained by varying R in the circuit of Question 15.4. How may this range of frequencies be raised to the KHZ level?

15.7 The UJT of Question 15.4 is used in the SCR trigger circuit of Figure 15.7. The values of R and C are to be chosen so that the SCR is triggered 10 msec after the switch is closed. Only *one* gate pulse is desired. Determine suitable values for R and C.

15.8 The SCR in the previous problem only requires $V_{GT} = 0.2v$ and $I_{GT} = 10 \mu a$. Will the SCR trigger prematurely? What is the maximum value of $R1$ which can be used in this circuit without causing premature triggering?

References

Silicon Controlled Rectifier Manual. Auburn, New York: General Electric Company, 1964.

Sowa, W. A. and M. M. Toole, *Special Semiconductor Devices.* New York: Holt, Rinehart and Winston, Inc., 1968.

Transistor Manual. Syracuse, New York: General Electric Company, 1964.

16

Field-Effect Transistors

16.1.   Introduction

The *field-effect transistor* (FET) actually preceded the junction transistor; it was invented by Lilienfeld in 1928. However, due to the limited development of the physics involved in the field-effect, the vacuum tube and then the junction transistor (1948) overshadowed field-effect devices. Finally, in the early 1960s the FET emerged as an important member of the semiconductor family. Today, the junction FET (JFET) and the insulated gate FET (IGFET) are rapidly replacing both vacuum tubes and junction transistors in applications requiring a high input impedance.

The advantages FETs have over vacuum tubes are their small size, low power consumption and lack of a filament, whereas the advantages they have over junction transistors include high input impedance, high power gain and reduced noise (random electrical fluctuations). The FET also offers fabrication advantages over junction transistors which makes it particularly suitable to integrated circuitry.

Briefly, the FET is a *majority* carrier device in which the current flow is controlled by an electric field which is perpendicular to the conduction path. The electrical characteristics of FETs are similar to those of a vacuum tube pentode and, as such, many FET circuits resemble their vacuum tube counterparts. The material in this chapter will serve to introduce the student to the various and often confusing types of FETs and their circuit operation. Emphasis is placed on those concepts which are new and which may not relate to the student's previous studies.

16.2.   Junction Field-Effect Transistors (JFET)

In its simplest form the JFET starts with nothing more than a bar of N-type silicon which behaves like a resistor between its two terminals, *source* and *drain* [Figure 16.1(A)]. This N-type bar is

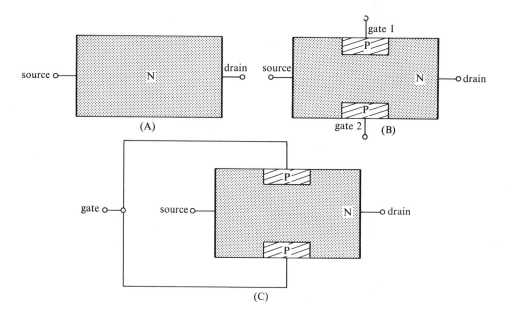

FIG. 16.1.   BASIC N-CHANNEL JFET STRUCTURE

called the *N-channel*. By introducing P-type regions on either side of the channel the structure of Figure 16.1(B) results. These P regions are called *gates* and are usually connected together. The result is the *N-channel JFET* as shown in Figure 16.1(C). The gate terminal is analogous to the grid of a vacuum tube, and, like the grid, it is used to control the current flow from source (cathode) to drain (plate).

The N-channel JFET is normally operated with the drain positively biased relative to the source as shown in Figure 16.2(A). This potential produces majority electron flow from source to drain, which passes through the channel between the P-regions.

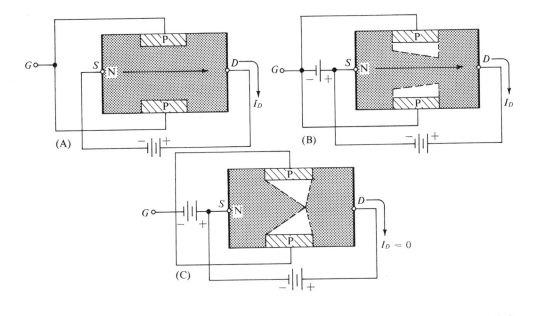

FIG. 16.2. EFFECT OF GATE-SOURCE VOLTAGE: (A)
NO BIAS (B) SMALL REVERSE BIAS (C)
PINCH-OFF

This current is called the drain current, I_D, and is analogous to
plate current I_P in a tube.

If a *reverse* bias is applied between gate and source the magnitude of the current through the channel will be reduced. This
is caused by the formation of depletion regions at the P-N junctions
which penetrate into the channel [Figure 16.2(B)]. Recall that
these depletion regions are regions where *no* charge carriers exist,
and thus the width of the conductive portion of the channel is
decreased. This increases the channel resistance, because resistance
varies inversely with cross-sectional area, and reduces I_D.

If the reverse bias is made sufficiently large the depletion
regions will extend into the channel and meet, thus *pinching off*
all current flow [Figure 16.2(C)]. This pinch-off condition occurs
when the gate-source voltage reaches the *pinch-off voltage* V_P,
that is, when $V_{GS} = V_P$. For N-channel JFETs V_P is negative,
typically -3v. Notice, in Figure 16.2, that the depletion region
is wedge-shaped. That is, it extends further into the channel at
the drain end than at the source end. This is because the reverse
bias between gate and drain is greater than between gate and
source and thus causes a larger depletion region at the drain end.

It is important to note that with reverse bias between gate and source only a very small leakage current, typically 10 nano-amperes, will flow in the gate terminal. Since the gate will normally be used as the input terminal, this indicates a very high input resistance, usually about 100 megohms.

Up to now the discussion has centered about an N-channel, P-gate JFET. P-channel, N-gate JFETs are also used and the previous discussion would be essentially the same except that all polarities would be reversed. N-channel JFETs have an advantage over the P-channel type since the current carriers are conduction electrons which have a greater mobility than holes and therefore operate better at high frequencies. It is also interesting to note that in the N-channel type the voltages between gate-source and drain-source are of the same polarity as in vacuum tubes. The electronic circuit symbols for the N-channel and P-channel JFETs are shown in Figure 16.3 along with their proper bias polarities. Note that the gate arrow points into the N-channel and out of the P-channel.

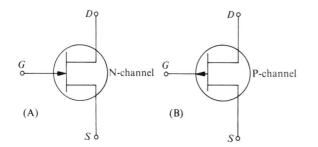

FIG. 16.3.   JFET CIRCUIT SYMBOLS (A) N-CHANNEL (B) P-CHANNEL

We can now investigate the drain family of characteristic curves for a typical N-channel JFET (Figure 16.4). If we consider first the curve for zero gate bias, $V_{GS} = 0$, it can be seen that drain current I_D increases substantially as the drain-source voltage V_{DS} is increased up to a certain point (point A) where $V_{DS} = 6v$. Above 6v the effect of V_{DS} on I_D is very slight. In fact, at about $V_{DS} = 15v$ the drain current levels off at 9.2 ma, and further increases in V_{DS} have no effect on I_D until the gate-drain break-down occurs. The region of the curve to the right of point A is called the *pinch-off region* since at about $V_{DS} = 6v$ the reverse bias on the drain end of the gate P-N junction is enough to pinch

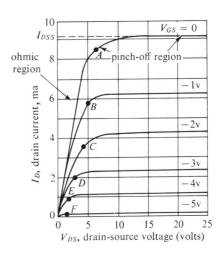

FIG. 16.4.   TYPICAL DRAIN FAMILY OF CURVES

off the channel and prevent drain current from increasing further. The region of the curve to the left of point A is called the *ohmic region* since in this region the channel acts almost like a linear ohmic resistance.

A special significance is attached to the current in the pinch-off region when $V_{GS} = 0$ and it is given the symbol I_{DSS}, the drain-source current at pinch-off when the gate is shorted to the source. It is usually measured well into the pinch-off region. In this case, $I_{DSS} = 9.2$ ma at $V_{DS} = 15$v.

If the gate reverse bias is increased to $V_{GS} = -1$v, the $I_D - V_{DS}$ curve shifts downward due to a narrower conducting channel. The pinch-off region at this gate voltage begins at $V_{DS} = 5$v (point B) and the drain current levels off at 6.25 ma at pinch-off. Similar results occur at larger values of V_{GS}. These results are tabulated in Table 16.1 where for each value of V_{GS} the corresponding values of V_{DS} at pinch-off are given as well as the pinch-off current I_{DP} measured at $V_{DS} = 15$v.

Looking at the table, notice that at $V_{GS} = -6$v the JFET is pinched off entirely with no current flowing for any value of V_{DS}. This value of V_{GS} is the pinch-off voltage V_P needed to cut-off all channel current. That is, $V_P = -6$v or 6 volts reverse bias from gate to drain is needed to reach pinch-off. Thus, when V_{GS} is 0v, V_{DS} must be 6v for pinch-off and when V_{GS} is -1v, V_{DS} must be 5v and so on. In other words, for pinch-off to occur

$$V_{GS} - V_{DS} = V_P \qquad (16.1)$$

TABLE 16.1

Gate-source bias V_{GS}	V_{DS} needed to pinch off	Pinch-off current I_{DP} at 15v
0v	6v	9.2 ma (I_{DSS})
−1v	5v	6.3 ma
−2v	4v	4.1 ma
−3v	3v	2.4 ma
−4v	2v	1.2 ma
−5v	1v	0.3 ma
−6v (V_P)	0v	0

To recapitulate on this pinch-off concept, the channel will become pinched off, where I_D levels off, when the gate-drain reverse bias equals V_P, which is in this case −6v. The pinch-off current will decrease for more negative values of V_{GS} until at $V_{GS} = V_P$ no current will flow; that is, the pinch-off current = 0.

If a graphical plot is made of the variation in pinch-off current I_{DP} with gate-source bias V_{GS} the result is that shown in Figure 16.5. This curve is often referred to as the *transfer characteristic* and it turns out that for most JFETs it is approximately in the shape of a parabola whose equation is

$$I_{DP} = \left(1 - \frac{V_{GS}}{V_P}\right)^2 \times I_{DSS} \qquad \textbf{(16.2)}$$

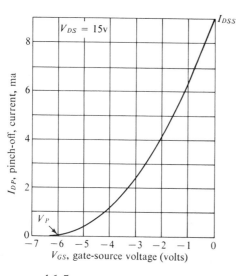

FIG. 16.5.   PINCH-OFF   CURRENT   (I_{DP})   VARIATION WITH V_{GS} (TRANSFER CHARACTERISTIC)

In this case $I_{DSS} = 9.2$ ma and $V_P = -6$v so that we have

$$I_{DP} = \left(1 - \frac{V_{GS}}{-6v}\right)^2 \times 9.2 \text{ ma}$$

For example, this equation predicts that at $V_{GS} = -3$v the value of pinch-off current will be

$$I_{DP} = \left(1 - \frac{1}{2}\right)^2 \times 9.2 \text{ ma}$$

$$= 2.3 \text{ ma}$$

From the curve the correct value of I_{DP} at -3v is seen to be about 2.4 ma.

One more word should be said about the JFET characteristic curves: the value of V_{GS} need not always be *negative* for the N-channel device. In fact, V_{GS} can be made slightly positive (usually less than $+0.5$v) resulting in another curve in Figure 16.4 somewhat above the $V_{GS} = 0$ curve. However, making V_{GS} positive will forward-bias the gate-source P-N junction and eventually cause a large gate current to flow. This will greatly lower the input resistance at the gate and may cause damage since the gate is not designed to carry any considerable amount of current. Thus, care must be taken that V_{GS} never goes above $+0.5$v.

Of course, the above discussion on JFET characteristic curves is equally applicable to P-channel devices. A set of typical P-channel drain characteristics can be obtained by changing the polarity signs on V_{GS} and V_{DS} in Figure 16.4. The same holds true for Table 16.1 and Figure 16.5.

16.3.   JFET Ratings and Parameters

As with all semiconductor devices, the JFET ratings include maximum current, voltage and power limitations. The most important JFET voltage ratings are BV_{DGO}, the drain-gate reverse breakdown voltage and BV_{DSX}, the drain-source breakdown voltage which, of course, should not be exceeded. Another rating is $V_{BR(GSS)}$, gate-source breakdown voltage which is usually the same value as BV_{DGO}. A typical value for all these ratings is 30 volts.

An important JFET parameter is its gate leakage current, I_{GSS}, which is normally measured at a reverse-bias value which is at least 50 per cent of the gate-source breakdown rating. It is usually measured at two temperatures including 25°C and an elevated temperature. A typical JFET can have an I_{GSS} of 0.1 na

($10^{-4}\mu$a) at 25°C whereas at 150°C it might increase to 100 na. This low input current requirement results in very high input impedances at the gate (typically 100 megohms or greater).

The parameters V_P* and I_{DSS} which were discussed in the previous section are important from the standpoint that they essentially determine the JFET's transfer characteristic (Equation 16.2). The transfer characteristic is a measure of the device's ability to *amplify* since it indicates how the output current, I_{DP}, is controlled by the gate-source voltage V_{GS}. Another useful parameter, which is essentially a measure of the JFET's amplification, can be obtained from the transfer curve. The *forward transfer admittance* (transadmittance), y_{fs}, is defined as the ratio of the change in drain current to the change in gate voltage which produced it. It is measured at a constant value of V_{DS} in the pinch-off region. The expression for y_{fs} is

$$y_{fs} = \frac{\Delta I_D}{\Delta V_{GS}}\bigg|_{V_{DS}} \qquad (16.2)$$

Referring to Figure 16.5, it can be seen that the value of y_{fs} will decrease for larger values of V_{GS} since the transfer curve is steepest at $V_{GS} = 0$ and slowly levels off as V_{GS} approaches the pinch-off voltage V_P.

▶ EXAMPLE 16.1

From Figure 16.5 determine approximate values of y_{fs} near $V_{GS} = 0$ and near $V_{GS} = -2.5$.

The following values are obtained from the transfer characteristic:

I_{DP}	V_{GS}	
9.2 ma	0	volts
7.7	−0.5	
4.1	−2	
2.4	−3	

Using the first two entries

$$y_{fs}(V_{GS} = 0) \approx \frac{1.5 \text{ ma}}{0.5\text{v}} = 3000 \ \mu\text{mhos}$$

Using the last two entries

$$y_{fs}(V_{GS} = -2.5\text{v}) \approx \frac{1.7 \text{ ma}}{1\text{v}} = 1700 \ \mu\text{mhos}$$ ◀

---

*Some manufacturers use the symbol V_{GS} ("off") in place of V_P.

The transadmittance y_{fs} is the counterpart of the transconductance g_m of vacuum tubes and in some cases the two symbols are used interchangeably. A larger value of transadmittance indicates a greater degree of control the gate voltage has over the drain current. Presently, values of transadmittance up to 10,000 μmhos are possible.

The value of transadmittance at $V_{GS} = 0$ is often given the symbol y_{fs0} and can also be calculated by using the relationship

$$y_{fs}0 = \frac{2I_{DSS}}{V_P} \qquad (16.3)$$

This relationship indicates that JFETs with lower pinch-off voltages will have higher gain.

▶ EXAMPLE 16.2

Recalculate the transadmittance of the JFET of Figure 16.5 using Equation 16.3

$$y_{fs}0 = \frac{2 \times 9.2 \text{ ma}}{6\text{v}} = 3067 \ \mu\text{mhos}$$

This agrees closely with the graphical result of Example 16.1. ◀

The FET parameter which is analogous to plate resistance r_p in a vacuum tube is the drain-source resistance r_{DS} which is simply the a-c channel resistance at a given point on the drain characteristic curve. That is,

$$r_{DS} = \frac{\Delta V_{DS}}{\Delta I_{DS}}\bigg|_{V_{GS}} \qquad (16.4)$$

Referring to the drain characteristics of Figure 16.4 it can be seen that in the ohmic region r_{DS} will be much lower (1K) than in the pinch-off region (500K). Like a pentode, the FET is normally operated in the high a-c resistance region when operated as an amplifier. When the FET is operated as a switch, the drain-source resistance when $V_{GS} = 0$ and $V_{DS} = 0$ is significant. Its symbol is $r_{DS}(\text{"on"})$ and essentially it is the FET resistance in the ohmic region when $V_{GS} = 0$ (FET "on"). Typically $r_{DS}(\text{"on"})$ may be a few hundred ohms.

The FET, like any P-N junction device, possesses junction capacitances which affect its high-frequency behavior. The gate-source capacitance, C_{SG}, and gate-drain capacitance, C_{DG}, are typically only a few picofarads. However, due to an effect called the *Miller effect* these relatively small capacitances can result in an FET input capacitance many times larger. These capacitances cause a decrease in FET high frequency gain.

16.4.   The Basic JFET Common-Source Amplifier

Figure 16.6(A) shows a simple N-channel JFET common-source amplifier. The gate-source circuit contains a d-c bias battery of -2.5volts. With no input signal present, the amplifier Q-point is found by constructing the d-c output load-line determined by V_{DD}, the drain-source supply, and R_L. Using the FET characteristics of Figure 16.4, this load-line is drawn in Figure 16.6(B)

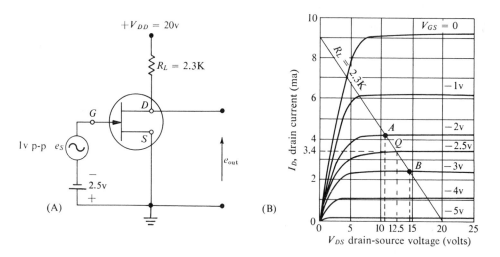

FIG. 16.6.   (A) BASIC JFET AMPLIFIER (B) LOAD-LINE

The Q-point is obtained as the intersection of the load-line and the curve corresponding to $V_{GS} = -2.5$volts. The values at the Q-point are $I_{DQ} = 3.4$ ma and $V_{DQ} = 12.5$ volts. Notice that this Q-point is well into the pinch-off region.

With a 1-volt p-p input gate signal, e_s, the total gate-source voltage will consist of a -2.5 volt d-c level with the 1 volt p-p signal riding on it. This will cause the gate-source voltage to vary between -2 volts and -3 volts. As a result the operating point will move along the load-line between points A and B. The output voltage, then, will swing approximately between 10.5 volts (A) and 14.5 volts (B). The input and output waveforms are shown in Figure 16.7. Notice that the output voltage swing is four times greater than the input and is 180° out of phase with it.

To maintain a non-distorted output, the operation must obviously be confined to the pinch-off region. It should also be

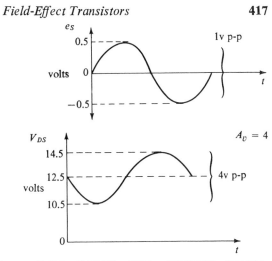

FIG. 16.7.   AMPLIFIER INPUT AND OUTPUT WAVE-
FORMS

apparent that to obtain maximum gain, the Q-point should be chosen closer to $V_{GS} = 0$ to take advantage of the greater spacing between the curves (higher y_{fs}).

An approximate expression for voltage gain, which can be used when the load resistor is much smaller (10 times or more) than r_{ds} in the pinch-off region, is given by

$$A_v = \frac{e_{out}}{e_s} \approx y_{fs} \times R_L \qquad (16.5)$$

We may use this expression to calculate the gain of the amplifier in question. We must use the value of y_{fs} calculated at or near the Q-point. In Example 16.1, y_{fs} ($V_{GS} = -2.5$ volts) was calculated as 1700 μmhos. Thus, we have

$$A_v \approx 1700 \times 10^{-6}\text{mhos} \times 2300 \text{ ohms}$$
$$\approx 3.91$$

which agrees closely with our graphical result.

If the amplifier were biased closer to $V_{GS} = 0$, the larger y_{fs} would result in a greater A_v. In fact, the amplifier could be biased at $V_{GS} = 0$ as long as the input signal is kept below about 1 volt p-p so as to prevent forward biasing of the gate-source diode.

The amplifier circuit of Figure 16.6 is highly impractical and would probably never be used since more efficient biasing methods can be employed which eliminate the gate bias supply. However, the signal operation and amplification are essentially the same in the more practical amplifier. As such, the previous discussion should give a clear idea of *how* the JFET amplifies. In general, voltage gains in FET amplifiers will not be as high as in junction transistor amplifiers. On the other hand, the FET's power gain is much greater due to the low input current (high input impedance), a typical value being 100,000.

For a more detailed coverage of JFET circuits, the student should consult the references at the end of the chapter. It is assumed that in subsequent course work FET circuits will receive a much more comprehensive treatment.

16.5.   JFETs: General Comments

A few remarks should be made in order to compare the JFET to the junction transistor. Briefly, the JFET has much lower voltage-gain capabilities but, as was pointed out, can produce tremendous power gains. The JFET has a very high output impedance in the common-source configuration (approximately equal to r_{DS}) comparable to the Com. B transistor output impedance.

The frequency response of the JFET is not, as yet, comparable to that of the high-frequency junction transistors. However, temperature and noise effects are considerably less in the JFET. Finally, the JFET has not yet developed to the point where "power FETs" are available that even approach the power capabilities of the power transistors. When they become available, power FETs are expected to offer some significant advantages over their predecessors.

16.6.   Insulated   Gate   Field   Effect   Transistors (IGFETs)

The insulated gate FET (IGFET) is similar to the JFET but operates with a slightly different mechanism. Consider Figure 16.8 which shows the structure of an N-channel IGFET. The structure begins with a high-resistivity P-type substrate; two low-resistivity N-type regions are diffused into the substrate as shown. Then the surface of the structure is covered with a layer of insulating silicon dioxide. Holes are cut into the oxide layer allowing contact to the N regions (source and drain). Then a metal contact area is placed over the oxide, covering the entire channel from source to drain. The contact to this metal area is the gate terminal. Note that there is no physical contact between the gate and P substrate due to the insulation afforded by the silicon dioxide.

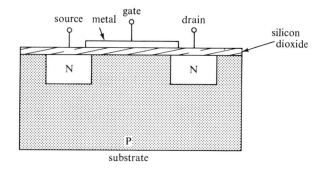

FIG. 16.8.   STRUCTURE OF AN N-CHANNEL IGFET (MOSFET)

Since the source and drain are separated by the P-type substrate, the source-to-drain current will be extremely low because there are essentially two P-N junctions connected back to back. However, the gate can be used to produce a conductive channel from source to drain. The metal area of the gate, the silicon dioxide layer, and the semiconductor channel form a capacitor. The gate area is the top plate and the P substrate forms the bottom plate. For the structure of Figure 16.8 consider a positive gate potential (see Figure 16.9). The positive charge at the metal side of the metal-oxide-semiconductor (MOS) capacitor induces a corresponding negative charge at the semiconductor side.

As the positive voltage at the gate is increased, the negative charge induced in the semiconductor increases until the region beneath the oxide becomes an N-type semiconductor region.

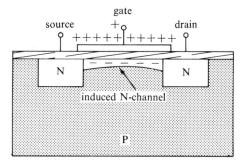

FIG. 16.9.   POSITIVE GATE VOLTAGE INDUCES AN N-TYPE CHANNEL

Current can now be made to flow from source to drain through the induced N-channel. The device current flow has thus been *enhanced* by the gate potential. In fact, making the gate voltage even more positive will induce a larger N-channel and therefore increase source-to-drain current.

The IGFET in Figure 16.9 is said to be operating in the *enhancement mode* since device current is *enhanced* by the application of gate voltage. This is opposite to the operation of the JFET, in which device current was *depleted* by the application of gate voltage. JFETs operate in the *depletion mode*. The complete designation for the IGFET of Figures 16.8 and 16.9 is *N-channel enhancement IGFET*, or, because of the MOS capacitor, *N-channel enhancement MOSFET*. Both designations are in common usage.

An electronic symbol for an N-channel enhancement IGFET is shown in Figure 16.10(A) along with the normal voltage polari-

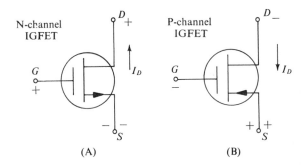

(A)   (B)

FIG. **16.10.**   ELECTRONIC SYMBOLS FOR (A) N-CHANNEL
                    AND (B) P-CHANNEL IGFET

ties. Note that the gate input resembles a capacitor representing the MOS capacitor of the IGFET. The arrow in the source lead points away from the N-channel. P-channel enhancement IGFETs are also manufactured and their electronic symbol and polarities are shown in Figure 16.10(B).

A typical set of drain characteristic curves for the N-channel enhancement device is shown in Figure 16.11. The pinch-off and ohmic regions correspond to those discussed for the JFET. It is significant to note that drain current does not flow until V_{GS} is made at least 5 volts positive. This voltage is called the *threshold voltage* $V_{GS}(th)$ and indicates the minimum positive gate voltage required to induce a significant N-channel. It is also significant that the gate-source voltage and drain-source voltage are of the same polarity. This makes biasing IGFET amplifiers much simpler than for JFET or vacuum tube amplifiers where the bias voltages

Field-Effect Transistors

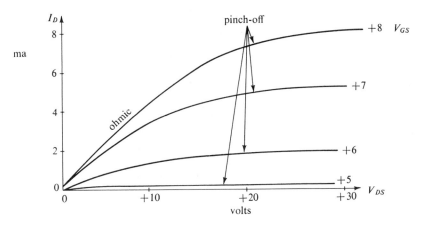

FIG. **16.11.**   TYPICAL   N-CHANNEL   ENHANCEMENT
IGFET DRAIN CHARACTERISTICS

are of opposite polarity. A typical set of P-channel enhancement
IGFET drain characteristics can be obtained by simply changing
the polarity of V_{GS} and V_{DS} in Figure 16.11.

The IGFET just described was of the enhancement type. A
depletion type of IGFET is also available (N-channel only, due to
manufacturing difficulties) which is constructed so it is similar to
the enhancement type of Figure 16.8, except for the fact that a
moderate resistivity N-channel is permanently diffused between
the source and drain. This initial N-channel allows current to
flow from source to drain without gate voltage. As in the en-

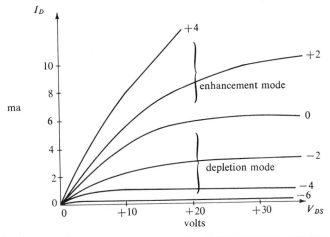

FIG. **16.12.**   TYPICAL N-CHANNEL DEPLETION IGFET
DRAIN CHARACTERISTICS

hancement device, a positive gate voltage will enhance current flow by widening the already formed N-channel. On the other hand, a negative gate voltage will reverse the process and will cause the N-channel to become depleted of conduction electrons, thereby effecting a decrease in device current. Thus, the depletion type of IGFET will operate with both polarities of gate voltage. This is illustrated in Figure 16.12 where a set of typical N-channel depletion IGFET drain characteristics are shown. Unlike the enhancement type, drain current will flow for $V_{GS} = 0$. As V_{GS} is increased negatively the drain current will decrease (as in the N-channel, JFET depletion type) until at $V_{GS} = -6$ volts the channel becomes pinched off and $I_D \approx 0$. As V_{GS} is increased positively the drain current will increase, as in the N-channel IGFET enhancement type. When operated in the depletion region the IGFET can replace the JFET. The ability of the depletion type IGFET to conduct for both polarities of gate input permits amplifier biasing at $V_{GS} = 0$ (highest gain region) without a limitation on gate signal voltage.

16.7.   Summary of FET Types

At this point it will be helpful to pause and summarize the basic differences encountered, thus far, among the different types of FET. Table 16.2 lists the various FETs and the corresponding information concerning mode of operation and bias polarities. Note that there is no entry in the table for P-channel depletion mode IGFETs since this type of FET is not manufactured.

From the table, it can be concluded that all N-channel FETs are operated with a positive drain-to-source voltage while all P-channel FETs utilize negative drain-to-source voltage. Also, it

TABLE 16.2

FET Type	Operating Mode	V_{DS} Polarity	V_{GS} Polarity	N or P Channel
JFET	depletion	positive	negative can go slightly positive)	N
JFET	depletion	negative	positive (can go slightly negative)	P
IGFET	enhancement	positive	positive only	N
IGFET	enhancement	negative	negative only	P
IGFET	depletion (and enhancement)	positive	positive (enhancement) negative (depletion)	N

can be seen that a FET operating in the depletion mode (JFET or IGFET) always uses a gate-to-source voltage opposite in polarity to V_{DS}. On the other hand, a FET operating in the enhancement mode uses a gate-to-source voltage of the same polarity as V_{DS}.

16.8.   IGFETs: General Comments

The gate leakage current I_{GSS} for an IGFET is so small as to be practically immeasurable. This is due to the insulating layer of silicon dioxide between the gate and substrate. Gate input resistances on the order of 10^{15} ohms are typical. This is much higher than even the JFET. The input capacitances between gate and source (C_{GS}) and gate and drain (C_{GD}) are smaller than those of the JFET. This helps account for the superior frequency response of IGFETs.

As a result of this low gate capacitance and high gate resistance, the gate is easily charged to a voltage (about 30 volts) which may exceed the breakdown voltage of the silicon dioxide layer which serves as the capacitor dielectric. Static charges generated by a technician may be sufficient to puncture the insulator and ruin the device. For this reason it is advisable to work with a grounded soldering iron, and guard against static charges from measuring instruments. Many IGFETs are packaged with all the leads temporarily shorted together to prevent damage during handling.

Enhancement-type IGFETs are relatively independent of temperature with some rated as high as 200°C. In general, IGFETs are less sensitive to temperature than other semiconductor devices.

The IGFET does have a better frequency response than the JFET but is not yet comparable to the high-frequency junction transistor. Therefore, IGFETs are presently unsuitable for very high-frequency RF work and are slower in switching applications than junction transistors. The major reason for the poor high-frequency performance is, of course, the gate capacitance. As technology advances, it is reasonable to expect that this effect will be reduced, resulting in IGFETs with higher frequency responses.

If high speed is not essential the switching applications of the IGFET are enormous. Extremely small, complex arrays of IGFET circuits can be integrated with less complications than comparable junction transistor arrays. Power dissipation in integrated IGFET arrays is extremely small. IGFET integrated circuits are just now making an impact in airborne avionic systems, earth satellites, medium-speed computers and desk calculators.

GLOSSARY

Field effect: the effect of varying the conductivity of a current path by the application of a perpendicular electric field

Junction field effect transistor (JFET):   field effect device utilizing reverse biased P-N junction gate

Channel: semiconductor conductive path

Drain, source: alternate ends of the channel

Gate: control terminal in FETs which produces the electric field

Pinch-off: conduction existing when gate voltage is sufficient to cut-off all drain current flow or when drain to source voltage is sufficient to cause drain current to level off

Pinch-off voltage (V_P):   gate-to-source voltage which causes pinch-off

Transfer characteristic: curve relating pinch-off drain current to gate to source voltage

Transadmittance (y_{fs}):   FET parameter which is a measure of its ability to amplify

Insulated gate field effect transistor (IGFET):   field effect device utilizing insulated capacitor gate

MOS (metal-oxide-semiconductor):   structure of the capacitor input of an IGFET

Depletion mode: operation of an FET with an increase in gate-source voltage to *decrease* drain current

Enhancement mode: operation of an FET with an increase in gate-source voltage to *increase* drain current

Threshold voltage $V_{GS}(th)$:   gate to source voltage needed to produce drain current in an enhancement IGFET

Questions

16.1   What is the principal current carrier in the N-channel JFET? The P-channel JFET?

16.2   Sketch the symbol for the N-channel JFET showing the proper bias polarities. Do the same for the P-channel JFET.

16.3   How does an increase in gate-source reverse bias affect the drain current in a JFET?

16.4   Why is the input resistance of the JFET so high?

16.5   Sketch a typical set of characteristics for a P-channel JFET. Label the ohmic and pinch-off regions.

16.6   A certain N-channel JFET has $V_P = -5v$. At what value of V_{DS} will the drain current level off (reach pinch-off) with $V_{GS} = -2v$? With $V_{GS} = 0v$? With $V_{GS} = -5v$?

16.7   The FET of the previous question had $I_{DSS} = 10$ ma. Using Equation 16.2, calculate I_{DP} at $V_{GS} = 0, -1v, -2v, -3v, -4v, -5v$. Sketch the device's transfer characteristic.

16.8   Using the data sheets for Motorola 2N4220 and 2N4222 N-channel JFETs in Appendix II determine the following for the 2N4220.
     (a) Maximum allowable V_{DS}
     (b) Maximum allowable I_D
     (c) Maximum allowable P_D
     (d) Maximum gate leakage current at 25°C; at 150°C
     (e) Minimum and maximum I_{DSS}
     (f) Typical y_{fs} at $V_{GS} = 0$
     (g) Typical r_{ds}("on")

16.9   If the 2N4220 were biased at $V_{GS} = 0$, what would be a typical voltage gain using $R_L = 20K$ in the basic JFET amplifier? (Hint: Use Equation 16.5)

16.10   From the transfer characteristic of Figure 16.5 determine the approximate value of y_{fs} at $V_{GS} = -3.5v$. Then, determine the voltage gain of the amplifier of Figure 16.6 when it is biased at $V_{GS} = -3.5v$ both graphically and by using Equation 16.5.

16.11   Why is it advantageous to bias a JFET amplifier close to $V_{GS} = 0$? What are the restrictions when this is done?

16.12   A particular JFET has $I_{DSS} = 5$ ma and $y_{fs0} = 2000$ μmhos. What is its V_P? This method of determining V_P is often used since I_{DSS} and y_{fs0} can be easily measured experimentally, while V_P is somewhat more difficult because of the gradual decrease in I_D as V_{GS} approaches V_P (see Figure 16.5.)

16.13   Sketch the symbol for the N-channel enhancement IGFET showing the proper bias polarities. Repeat for the P-channel enhancement IGFET.

16.14   Indicate whether the drain current will increase, decrease, or remain the same when the gate voltage of the following FETs are made more negative:
     (a) N-channel JFET

     (b) P-channel JFET
     (c) N-channel enhancement IGFET
     (d) P-channel enhancement IGFET
     (e) N-channel depletion IGFET

16.15   Why is the input resistance of the IGFET so high?

16.16   Explain the difference between *depletion* and *enhancement*.

16.17   Sketch a typical set of drain characteristics for a *P-channel enhancement* IGFET.

16.18   Repeat 16.17 for an *N-channel depletion* IGFET.

16.19   What type of FET can be used with *both* polarities of gate voltage?

16.20   Identify the FET types in Figure 16.13.

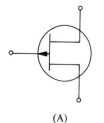   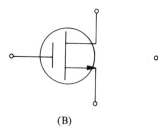

(A)   (B)   (C)

FIG. 16.13.

16.21   Indicate which of the following statements refer to JFETs and which refer to IGFETs:
     (a) has lower gate leakage current
     (b) has higher input resistance
     (c) has higher input capacitance
     (d) has better frequency response
     (e) can operate in the enhancement mode

References

Gosling, W., *Field-Effect Transistor Applications*. New York: John Wiley & Sons, Inc., 1965.

Richman, P., *Characteristics and Operation of MOS Field-Effect Devices*. New York: McGraw Hill Book Company, 1967.

Sevin, L. J., *Field-Effect Transistors*. New York: McGraw-Hill Book Company, 1965.

Sowa, W. A. and M. M. Toole, *Special Semiconductor Devices*. New York: Rinehart and Winston, Inc., 1968.

17

Special Semiconductor Devices

17.1. Introduction

The devices studied in the previous chapters use the properties of semiconductor material and the characteristics of P-N junctions to perform circuit functions such as rectification, amplification, and switching. In addition to these more widely-used devices, a number of other useful semiconductor devices have only recently been invented; but they already promise to rival in importance those covered in the previous chapters. Some of the special devices described in this chapter are based on the properties of the P-N junction while others use some of the more unusual properties of semiconductor crystals.

Even upon completion of this chapter, the student will not have been exposed to all the useful semiconductor devices available today. The amazingly rapid advances in semiconductor technology are a tribute to the seemingly unlimited ingenuity of scientists and engineers. One can only hope to keep pace with advances in this field by means of technical publications, special seminars and manufacturers' advertisements. The coverage in this chapter will serve only to introduce the various devices and their operating principles.

17.2. Phototransistors

The construction and basic circuit of a phototransistor is shown in Figure 17.1. The phototransistor is similar to a PNP junction

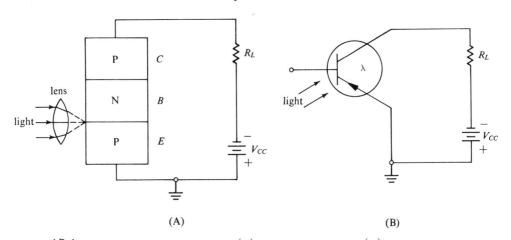

(A)   (B)

FIG. 17.1.   PHOTOTRANSISTOR (A) CONSTRUCTION (B)
                 ELECTRONIC SYMBOL

transistor. In normal operation the collector is negatively biased
relative to the emitter as in the Com. E configuration. However,
unlike the normal junction transistor, the *E-B* junction is left
unconnected, so it has no bias. Light is focused on the *E-B* junction; under the influence of this light a photovoltaic effect (Chapter
8) takes place which forward-biases the *E-B* junction. The effect
is the same as if a forward voltage were applied between base and
emitter. With variations in light intensity, corresponding variations in *E-B* voltage and, thus, in emitter current are produced.
This results in a collector current and load voltage which vary
with light intensity.

   Besides the photoelectric effect in the *E-B* region, transistor
action takes place with the result being the same as if a junction
photovoltaic cell were driving a Com. E transistor circuit. Thus,
using a phototransistor, currents of several milliamperes can be
achieved, while the photovoltaic cell produces typically 100 μa.
The load, which may be a relay, can be driven directly by the
phototransistor, whereas with a photovoltaic cell an amplifying
stage must be used.

   The phototransistor, which can typically operate at frequencies
in the range of tens of kilohertz, has applications typical of other
photo devices. One major application is in reading punched cards
in a digital computer.

17.3.   Light-emitting Diodes: Junction Lasers

In a forward-biased P-N junction the electrons which diffuse
into the P region will recombine with holes there. In certain semi-

conductors, most notably GaAs (gallium arsenide), recombinations take place from the conduction band to acceptor levels located near the valence band (Chapter 4). Each such recombination represents an electron losing energy. This energy is emitted in the form of light energy whose frequency is proportional to the energy lost by the recombining electron. In GaAs the emitted light is in the infrared region. P-N junctions in which this mode of recombination takes place can function as efficient light sources whose intensity can be easily and rapidly varied by varying the forward current.

Since each electron recombination is independent of all other recombinations, the light is emitted randomly and is similar to that from fluorescent lamps. However, by suitably arranging the junction geometry, the emitted light can be used to stimulate further emission, essentially causing a phenomenon called "light amplification by stimulated emission of radiation", commonly shortened to *laser*. The characteristics of the light emitted from a laser are very different from those of conventional light sources. Laser light is emitted at one frequency rather than a range of frequencies. This is analogous to the difference between a pure audio tone (say 1 KHZ) and the complex tones of the human voice. Furthermore, the light beam from a laser is strictly parallel with no beam spread.

These characteristics mean that the laser beam may be focused with a lens to a very minute spot size. This concentration of light energy in a minute area is so high that temperatures great enough to destroy any material are easily attained. The laser beam may be used to cut or drill through the hardest of materials with great precision. Such beams have also been used in surgery to cauterize and cut tissue with much more than human precision and delicacy.

The single-frequency laser beam may be used to carry information from a television transmitter simply by modulating (varying) the current in accordance with the signal to be transmitted. The information-handling capacity of laser beams is almost unlimited, and because of their narrow beam spread they are expected to play a vital role in space communications.

17.4.   Thermistors

The temperature-sensitive property of semiconductors has up to now been considered a disadvantage due to the circuit design complications it may cause. However, this property has found useful application in devices called *thermistors*. Thermistors are simply *thermally sensitive resistors*.

Intrinsic semiconductor material exhibits a negative temperature coefficient (NTC). That is, its resistance decreases with increases in temperature. A typical resistance-versus-temperature curve of an NTC thermistor is shown in Figure 17.2. The NTC thermistors are the most common type and are usually manufactured from certain metallic oxides that belong to the semiconductor family.

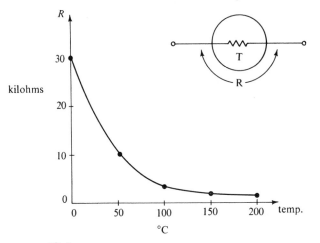

FIG. 17.2.   TYPICAL RESISTANCE-VERSUS-TEMPERATURE CURVE FOR AN NTC THERMISTOR

Certain thermistors are produced which have a characteristic of increasing resistance with temperature. Such devices are positive temperature coefficient (PTC) thermistors and are often made of doped silicon.

Because of their extreme temperature sensitivity, thermistors find many applications. In the area of temperature measurement and control, thermistors are often used to sense temperature variations and convert these variations to an electrical signal which is then used to control the heating device. The temperature can be measured over a wide range ($-70°C$ to $150°C$). Thermistors are available in a broad range of resistance values so that they can be made compatible with almost any circuit or instrument. The thermistor is much more sensitive and reliable than mercury switches or bimetals and operates over a continuous range; it is not limited to "on" and "off" as are other thermal switches.

Another major application of thermistors lies in the area of temperature stabilization of semiconductor circuits. Here, the thermistor is used to compensate for temperature variations of other semiconductor devices in a given circuit. A simple illustra-

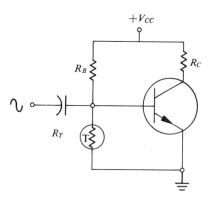

FIG. 17.3.   THERMISTOR USED TO STABILIZE Q-POINT

tion of this function is shown in Figure 17.3 where an NTC thermistor is placed between base and ground of a base-current biased Com. E amplifier stage. Its function is to stabilize the Q-point from variations due to temperature. As the temperature increases, the transistor's $\beta_{\text{d-c}}$ increases, causing I_C to increase. The thermistor resistance, however, will decrease and cause current to be shunted away from the base. This reduces the base current and collector current thereby counteracting the effect of the increasing $\beta_{\text{d-c}}$.

Other applications of thermistors include the measurement of RF power, voltage regulation and timing and delay circuits.

17.5. The Hall Effect Generator

When a current is made to flow through a semiconductor bar placed in a magnetic field, a voltage is developed at right angles to both the current and the magnetic field. This voltage is proportional to the current and the intensity of the magnetic field. This is called the *Hall effect*.

Consider the semiconductor bar in Figure 17.4 which has contacts on all four sides. If a voltage E_L is impressed across two opposite contacts (A and B) a current will flow. If now a magnetic field B is placed perpendicular to the bar, as shown, an electric potential E_H is generated between the other contacts (C and D). This voltage E_H, which can be detected with a simple voltmeter, is a direct measure of the magnetic field strength.

A Hall effect generator may be used as a magnetometer to detect and measure magnetic fields. It is capable of measuring magnetic field strengths that are one million times smaller than

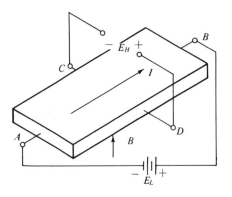

FIG. 17.4.   HALL EFFECT DEVICE

that of the earth. Its sensitivity, small size and simplicity make the Hall effect magnetometer an attractive device. Other uses for the Hall effect device are in the area of semiconductor measurements (mobility, charge concentration etc.)

17.6.   Strain Gages

Semiconductors are not only sensitive to light, heat and magnetic fields, but also to mechanical forces. If a long thin rod of silicon is pulled from end to end, its resistance increases considerably because the mechanical force pulls each silicon atom slightly further away from its adjacent atoms than normal. This increases the width of the forbidden energy gap and correspondingly decreases the number of electrons and holes thus increasing the resistivity of the rod. Because the number of carriers varies greatly with the width of the forbidden gap, silicon and other semiconductors make very sensitive *strain gages*, devices used to measure small changes in the lengths of solid objects.

Strain gages, of course, are used extensively by civil engineers to test the tensile strength of materials and to aid in determining the change in length of various structures. The typical silicon strain gage will change its resistance by about 6 per cent for a 0.05 per cent change in its length. This resistance change is easily measured, so it is possible to detect very minute changes in length. The silicon strain gage is much more sensitive than devices made of other materials. Its major drawback is its temperature sensitivity. This effect can usually be minimized by using a silicon thermistor in the circuit so that the temperature effects cancel out.

17.7.   Varactor Diodes

Varactor diodes are high-frequency devices designed to utilize the property of P-N diodes which causes junction capacitance to decrease with increasing reverse bias (see Section 5.14). Varactors are normally made of silicon due to its low reverse leakage current. They find extensive applications in automatic frequency controls, generation of frequency modulated signals, frequency multiplication and division, and in variable RC and LC filters.

GLOSSARY

Phototransistor: a photo detector that incorporates transistor action to provide an amplified output

Junction laser: light emitting diode that emits single-frequency, parallel-beam light

Thermistor: heat-sensitive resistor

Hall effect: effect of magnetic field on current flowing through a semiconductor

Strain gage: device used to measure minute changes in length

Varactor: a P-N diode that utilizes the variation of junction capacitance with reverse voltage

Questions

17.1   How is a phototransistor superior to a junction photovoltaic cell?

17.2   What causes light energy to be emitted in a junction laser?

17.3   Compare a laser beam of light to a conventional light beam.

17.4   Why are thermistors superior to mercury thermostats and bi-metal thermostats?

17.5   Why are silicon strain gages superior to other types?

17.6 Which of the following devices utilizes a P-N junction?
(a) thermistor
(b) Hall effect generator
(c) varactor
(d) junction laser
(e) strain gage
(f) phototransistor

References

Brophy, J. J., *Semiconductor Devices*. New York: McGraw-Hill Book Company, 1964.

Carrol, J. M., *Tunnel-Diode and Semiconductor Circuits*. New York: McGraw-Hill Book Company, 1963.

Romanowitz, H. A. and R. E. Puckett, *Introduction to Electronics*. New York: John Wiley & Sons. Inc., 1968.

18

Introduction to Integrated Circuits

18.1.   Introduction

The terms *microelectronics* and *integrated circuits* are often used interchangeably. Strictly speaking, this is not correct. *Micro-electronics* refers to the general area concerned with extremely small electronic components and circuit assemblies, whereas an *in-tegrated circuit* is a special class of microelectronics and refers to a circuit that has been fabricated as an inseparable assembly of electronic components in a single structure. Integrated circuits (ICs) completely eliminate the use of individual electronics parts, such as resistors, capacitors, diodes, and transistors, as the building blocks of an electronic circuit.

Basically, there are two general classes of ICs: the *semicon-ductor monolithic* integrated circuit and the *thin-film* integrated circuit. In addition, there are several variations and combinations of these basic structures, each with specific advantages and dis-advantages from the standpoints of circuit design, applications and economy.

This chapter will introduce the student to the most commonly-used structures and those showing promise of implementation in the near future while pointing out the comparative advantages of each type. A much more detailed discussion of integrated circuit technology can be found in the various references cited.

18.2.   Monolithic Integrated Circuits

The basic semiconductor IC is a monolithic device; that is, all circuit elements are fabricated inseparably on or within a continuous piece of material. In the present state of technology, this material is silicon. The technology of monolithic ICs is based on the silicon diffused planar process (Chapter 13), in which all process steps are performed on one surface of the silicon slice and all the contacts to the various components are made at the same surface. Interconnection between the components is made by depositing a metallic wiring pattern on the oxide-covered surface of the silicon wafer.

The geometries of each individual component (transistors, diodes, resistors, and capacitors) of a given IC are designed so that they can all be formed simultaneously. In fact, all the elements of a complete circuit can be diffused into a single wafer with exactly the same processes and in almost the same amount of time required to make a single transistor.

The basic structure of a monolithic IC is illustrated in Figure 18.1. It consists of three layers of different materials. The relatively

silicon dioxide

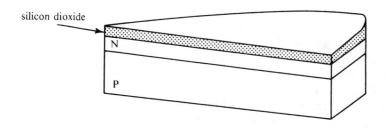

FIG. 18.1.   BASIC MONOLITHIC IC STRUCTURE

thick bottom layer is of P-type silicon, onto which is grown a thin epitaxial (high-resistivity) layer of N-type silicon. This P-N structure is topped with a thin layer of silicon dioxide.

In *all-diffused monolothic* structures all the component parts are formed within the thin N-type region. The P region is not an active part of the circuit. Its primary function is to serve as a substrate in order to give the structure mechanical ruggedness. It serves an additional purpose by providing a simple means of electrically isolating (insulating) the various diffused components.

The silicon dioxide layer has two specific functions. It protects the semiconductor surface against contamination by external impurities, and it provides the means for selectively diffusing the various components into the wafer beneath.

Since each component is formed within an N region, it is necessary to isolate the various N regions from each other in order to isolate each component. Two methods of providing this isolation are illustrated in Figure 18.2. The first method, called P-N

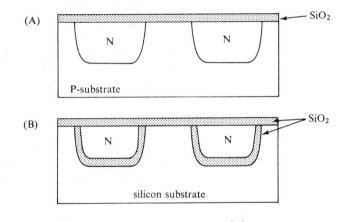

FIG. 18.2.   ISOLATION TECHNIQUES (A) P-N DIODE ISOLATION (B) SILICON-DIOXIDE ISOLATION

diode isolation, is shown in Figure 18.2(A) and uses the high resistance of a reverse-biased P-N junction. Current will not flow from one N region to the other since they are separated by the P region substrate which essentially forms two back-to-back diodes. In practice, the substrate is tied to the most negative voltage in the circuit so that each N region is reverse-biased relative to the substrate. In this way, each N region is insulated from the substrate and from the other N regions. This method does have drawbacks due to the imperfect isolation afforded by a reverse-biased diode and especially due to the junction capacitances across each isolation diode. These capacitances limit the circuit operating speed.

The second method of isolation is shown in Figure 18.2(B) and is called *silicon-dioxide isolation*. A layer of silicon dioxide around each N region produces the desired isolation. The substrate is undoped silicon. This type of isolation has several advantages over the first type. First of all, the isolation is much more perfect because the silicon dioxide is a better insulator than a reverse-biased P-N junction. In addition, there is no capacitance between the N regions and the substrate. This improves high-frequency operation. Another advantage lies in the greater versatility in the types of circuits which can be manufactured.

Counteracting these advantages is the added complexity of the fabrication process. Even when developed for mass production, the additional process steps add to the manufacturing costs. These costs, of course, are passed on to the IC user.

The components normally associated with a monolothic IC are transistors, diodes, resistors and capacitors. The transistor represents the most complicated component and all the other parts can be fabricated in conjunction with one or more of the transistor processes. This is illustrated in Figure 18.3 where a typical cross section of the basic monolithic components is shown.

The technique for fabricating IC transistors is similar to the planar transistor (Chapter 13) as shown in Figure 18.3(A). The NPN transistor structure is formed by successive impurity diffusions into the top of the substrate. The silicon dioxide layer is appropriately etched to allow diffusion into the proper portion of the substrate. After the diffusion is complete the top surface

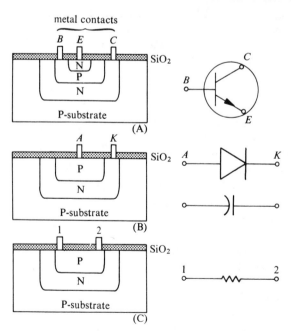

FIG. 18.3.   TYPICAL IC COMPONENTS: (A) TRANSISTOR (B) DIODE AND CAPACITOR (C) RESISTOR

is covered with silicon dioxide for protection and metal contacts are made to the various transistor regions.

Integrated circuit diodes are formed by simply utilizing the P-N junctions of the integrated transistor. In Figure 18.3(B), the *C-B* junction of the transistor is used as the diode. The anode of the diode is formed during the transistor base diffusion. The cathode of the diode is the collector region. Contacts are made to these two regions and brought to the top surface. This type of diode is used for general applications. When high speed switching is required, the *E-B* junction of the transistor is used as a diode.

There are two basic methods of forming monolithic capacitors. The first method, shown in Figure 18.3(B), utilizes the junction capacitance of a reverse-biased P-N diode. In this method, the capacitance is limited to about 100 pf and is dependent on the reverse voltage across the junction. Despite these limitations, it has the advantage that it can be produced by diffusion simultaneously with the other components.

The other type of capacitor utilizes the metal-oxide-semiconductor (MOS) structure similar to that used as the gate of IGFETs. MOS capacitors provide somewhat higher values of capacitance but are still limited to several hundred picofarads. They offer the principal advantages of being nonpolar (voltages of either polarity may be used) and independent of voltage. In addition, they have lower leakage and can normally operate at higher voltages than the diffused capacitor.

Integrated circuit resistors utilize the resistivity of the doped silicon. A resistor is formed by diffusing an impurity into the silicon wafer. By controlling the concentration of the impurity and the depth of diffusion the resistance values can be controlled. Most resistors are formed during the diffusion of the base [see Figure 18.3(C)] since this is the highest resistivity region. For very low values of resistance the emitter region is used since it has a much lower resistivity. For reasons associated with the diffusion process, it is difficult to reproduce resistors with tolerances closer than ±10 per cent. However, the ratio of resistor values made on the same wafer can be reproduced to within ±1 per cent tolerances. For this reason, IC designers use resistance ratios rather than absolute values of resistance as the controlling factor.

18.3. Formation of a Complete Monolithic IC

To help illustrate the formation of a complete IC, a simple circuit will be investigated. Refer to Figure 18.4. The first step in the

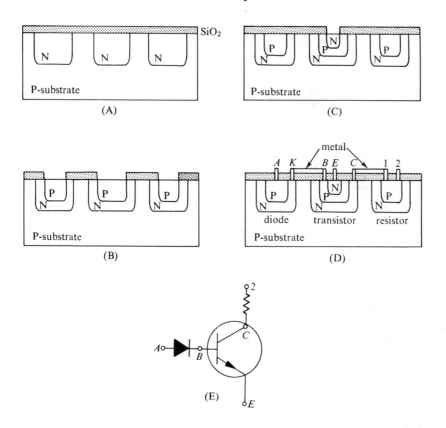

FIG. 18.4.   IC PROCESS STEPS: (A) ISOLATION OF N REGIONS (B) P-TYPE BASE DIFFUSION (C) N-TYPE EMITTER DIFFUSION (D) CONTACT FORMATION AND INTERCONNECTION (E) CIRCUIT SCHEMATIC

formation of the IC is the isolation of the various N regions as shown in Figure 18.4(A). In general, they will not be the same size depending on the components each region is used for. One N region is needed for each component. Step two in the process [Figure 18.4(B)] is the diffusion of the P-type base region. This is accomplished by etching away the appropriate areas of silicon dioxide and allowing P-type impurities to diffuse into each N region. As far as the resistor and diode are concerned the process is complete. The transistor, however, must still be provided with its emitter region. This is accomplished in the third step [Figure 18.4(C)] of the process in which N-type material is diffused into the P region (base) to form the emitter. In this step the diode and resistor are not affected because the silicon dioxide layer masks these regions from any impurity diffusion.

The last step, as shown in Figure 18.4(D), forms the contacts of the various components and a metallization pattern is then deposited to connect the components according to their circuit arrangement. The final circuit is shown schematically in Figure 18.4(E).

From this example, it can be seen that the number of process steps needed to produce an integrated circuit is the same as required to produce a transistor (except for the isolation step). This is true no matter how complicated the circuit is. A complete circuit may total 50 components and can be fit into an area of 50 mils-square (0.05 in. × 0.05 in.). A circular silicon wafer of 1.25 inches diameter can contain nearly 350 of these circuits.

Thus, a large number of circuits can be formed on one silicon wafer in the same process steps shown in Figure 18.4. After the circuits have been formed they are usually tested right on the wafer before being separated into individual chips. The testing usually consists of d-c probe measurements. After testing, the individual circuits on the wafer are separated into individual circuit wafers. This is usually done by scribing and breaking the wafer.

The individual circuit wafer is then prepared for assembly in a package. The wafer is mounted to either a metal or glass base and electrical connections are made from the wafer contacts to the external package leads. This process is usually thermal compression bonding with gold wire of 1 mil diameter. Finally, the package is sealed by molding in plastic or by welding on a metal lid or can.

18.4. Thin-Film Integrated Circuits

Thin-film circuits begin with a substrate made of an insulating material such as ceramic or glass. Upon this substrate *passive* circuit components such as resistors and capacitors and their metal interconnections are deposited by various techniques including vacuum evaporation, sputtering and silk screening. Also added to the substrate are discrete *active* elements such as transistors and diodes which are needed to complete the circuit. These are added separately since a process has not yet been developed which will successfully permit the deposition of active elements on the insulating substrate. This is the major drawback of thin-film circuits. The addition of the discrete active components requires extra production steps which increases costs and reduces reliability.

Thin-film components are formed by evaporation, sputtering or silk screening of films of thicknesses between 100 to 1000 angstroms upon a ceramic or glass substrate. Resistors are formed by depositing nichrome, tantalum or tin-oxide, in strip form on the surface of the substrate. The resistance is controlled by varying the length, width and film thickness. Values between 10 ohms and 1 megohm can thus be obtained.

Thin-film capacitors are prepared by forming a thin dielectric layer between two conductive plates. The dielectric material, dielectric thickness and plate dimensions are varied to obtain the desired value of capacitance. Typical dielectric materials are tantalum oxide, silicon dioxide and glass. One common thin-film technique is to use tantalum for all the resistors and capacitors. A thin tantalum film is deposited on the substrate. The pattern of resistors and capacitors is etched into the tantalum. The portions used for capacitors are then oxidized to form the tantalum oxide dielectrics. The top plates of the capacitors and the connecting paths between components are then deposited. A typical thin-film structure is illustrated in Figure 18.5.

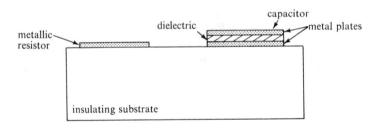

FIG. 18.5.   TYPICAL THIN-FILM STRUCTURE

The active devices are not produced using thin-film techniques. Therefore, they must be added separately to the substrate. A number of methods for accomplishing this have been used. One technique is to attach the transistor or diode chip to the thin-film substrate and then to make the various circuit interconnections by means of thermal compression bonding of fine wires from the chip to the thin-film components.

In comparing thin-film ICs with semiconductor monolithic ICs two advantages of the thin-film structures are significant:

(1) The thin-film components can be made with a wider range of values, to closer tolerances and with better electrical characteristics such as less capacitor leakage and better temperature stability.

(2) Since any active component that can be manufactured in discrete form can be utilized in thin-film circuits, the conversion of circuit designs from discrete to thin-film structures is greatly simplified. Even though extremely large values of resistance and capacitance are impractical in thin film circuits, such devices can be added in discrete form to the substrate. The same holds true for inductors which cannot be fabricated by any IC process. Thus, many conventional discrete circuits can be duplicated in thin-film form where the circuit will be smaller, lighter and somewhat more reliable due to reduction in component interconnections.

On the other hand, in comparison with monolithic ICs, thin-film circuits have certain disadvantages:

(1) They are larger in size. For example, a complete monolithic integrated circuit can be fabricated in the same space required for a single thin-film component.

(2) They are higher in cost, mainly due to the necessity of using discrete active components which increases the number of interconnections.

(3) They are less reliable, again mainly due to the greater number of interconnections needed.

18.5.   Other IC Types

Two other IC types have been developed which essentially utilize the advantages of both thin-film and monolithic techniques. The *compatible integrated circuit* is one in which all the active elements and some of the passive elements are diffused into the basic semiconductor substrate, and additional passive elements are deposited by thin-film processes onto the silicon dioxide protective layer that covers the semiconductor elements. Then interconnections are made between the thin-film elements and the semiconductor elements.

Compatible ICs are more flexible than all-diffused monolithic ICs because they can utilize the less limited and more accurate thin-film passive components. Of course, they will be somewhat larger, more expensive and slightly less reliable due to the additional process steps.

Multi-chip (*hybrid*) *ICs* are composed of separate circuits of the thin-film and monolithic types which are placed on a ceramic substrate and interconnected. This type of IC is useful for applications where only a small number of identical circuits is required. This is because the cost of monolithic and compatible ICs is high for small quantities, while a multi-chip IC can use standard off-the-shelf monolithic and thin-film ICs and thus be less expensive.

18.6.   MOSFETs in Integrated Form

IGFETs, principally MOSFETs, are particularly suitable for monolithic ICs and appear to be the devices of the future in this respect. Some of the properties which make monolithic structures so attractive are:

(1) They need no isolation substrate region since both source and drain are inherently isolated from the substrate by their own P-N junctions. This means a smaller area is needed for MOSFETs than for junction transistors.

(2) The diffusion process is simpler for MOSFETs since only one diffusion step is needed to form the source and drain regions. This of course lowers production costs.

(3) The MOSFET can be used as a resistor with drain-to-source resistances up to the megohm range being possible by use of suitable gate voltages. MOS capacitors have already been discussed in Section 18.2.

The principle disadvantage of the MOSFET IC is its slow speed when compared to the junction transistor. As such, it does not yet compete with the transistor monolithic ICs in applications such as ultra-high-speed computers. However, it does offer economic advantages in applications where its speed of response is sufficient.

18.7.   Advantage of Integrated Circuits

Despite its rapid development in the past few years, integrated circuit technology is still considered to be in its infancy. However, even in this early stage ICs have demonstrated significant improvements over discrete circuitry. Basically these advantages include greatly reduced size and weight, lower cost, and improved reliability.

The weight and size reduction is obvious. These savings are particularly important in military and space applications where the increased sophistication of electronic control systems has caused a dramatic increase in the number of electronic circuits and components. In space applications weight is of primary importance since every extra ounce requires several more pounds of thrust to maintain it. In consumer applications weight and size are normally not primary considerations.

The cost reductions afforded by ICs are a result of many factors. A major factor is the fact that a very complex circuit can be fabricated in the same number of process steps as a conventional transistor. Another factor which adds to potential cost-savings concerns business aspects. With complete IC circuits serving as basic components, shipping charges, purchasing costs, inventory costs, incoming inspection and testing costs, and the cost of almost all the factors involved in equipment manufacturing are greatly reduced.

Perhaps the most important advantage of ICs lies in the area of reliability. The increased reliability is due to several factors, the most significant of which is the need for fewer interconnections. In earlier discrete component circuits up to 50 per cent of all circuit failures were caused by interconnections between components. Another factor concerns the low power operation of ICs. Due to their small size, ICs are more suited to low power operation. The closeness of the components within a silicon wafer reduces the chance of stray electrical pick-up, allowing very small signal operation. This low power operation means lower internal temperature rises, and consequently improved reliability. Thus, the IC offers a more reliable approach to circuit assemblies than is available using discrete components. This is by far its most important advantage both from the military and consumer application standpoint.

GLOSSARY

Microelectronics: the broad area concerned with any special component or circuit of extremely small size

Integrated circuit: an electronic circuit constructed as an inseparable assembly of components in a single structure

Monolithic integrated circuit: an electronic circuit in which all circuit elements are formed and inter-connected on or within a single piece of silicon

Thin-film integrated circuit: an electronic circuit in which thin films are used to form passive components

Diode isolation: a method of electrically isolating components in a monolithic IC by creating reverse-biased P-N diodes between all components

Silicon dioxide isolation: a method of isolation in which silicon dioxide acts as the insulator

Compatible integrated circuit: monolithic IC that utilizes thin-film passive components

Multi-chip integrated circuit: a form of IC in which separately manufactured monolithic and thin-film ICs are placed on a substrate and interconnected to perform a given circuit function

Questions

18.1   What are the two major classes of integrated circuits?

18.2   Describe the basic structure of a monolithic IC.

18.3   What are the two isolation techniques used in monolithic structures? Compare their advantages.

18.4   What are the basic monolithic components?

18.5   Which of these requires the greatest number of process steps? The least?

18.6   Compare the two types of monolithic capacitances.

18.7   What are the basic thin-film components?

18.8   What are the comparative advantages and disadvantages of thin-film and monolithic ICs?

18.9   What characteristics of MOSFETs make them attractive for ICs?

18.10   What are the principal advantages of ICs over discrete component circuits?

References

Brazee, J. G., *Semiconductor and Tube Electronics*. New York: Holt, Rinehart and Winston, Inc., 1968.

Stern, L. S., *Fundamentals of Integrated Circuits*. New York: Hayden Book Company, Inc., 1968.

Appendix I

Periodic Table
of the Elements

Much valuable information about individual elements can be obtained from the periodic table of elements. For example, if we look at the element *carbon* in the table, we find that it is listed under the column numbered IV. This indicates that the carbon element has 4 valence electrons. Similarly, *nitrogen* in column V has 5 valence electrons. Referring to carbon again, we see that it is in the row numbered 2 indicating that the carbon atom has 2 shells of electrons. Similarly, *silicon* in the row numbered 3 has 3 shells of electrons.

The individual element squares contain information on atomic number, weight, and electron shell configurations. The carbon square is repeated in Figure I.1. The number 6 represents the atomic number, C is the symbol for carbon and 12 is the atomic weight (rounded off) of carbon. The numbers 2-4 indicate the arrangement of electrons in the K,L,M,N. . . shells around the carbon nucleus. For carbon the K-shell contains 2 electrons and the L-shell contains 4 electrons. All the remaining shells are empty. To summarize, we can now construct the model of the carbon atom from the above information. The carbon nucleus has 12 particles since its atomic weight is 12. And since its atomic number is 6, there are 6 protons in the nucleus along with 6 neutrons. The complete carbon model is shown in Figure I.2.

450

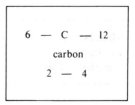

FIG. I.1.

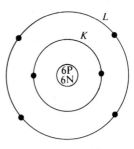

FIG. I.2.

PERIODIC TABLE

Max. No. Electrons Per Shell	Valence Shells	I	II	III	IV	V
2	1	1–H–1 Hydrogen				
8	2	3–Li–7 Lithium	4–Be–9 Beryllium	5–B–11 Boron 2–3	6–C–12 Carbon 2–4	7–N–14 Nitrogen
18	3	11–Na–23 Sodium	12–Mg–24 Magnesium	13–Al–27 Aluminum 2–8–3	14–Si–28 Silicon 2–8–4	15–P–31 Phosphorus
32	4	19–K–39 Potassium	20–Ca–40 Calcium	21–Sc–45 Scadium	22–Ti–48 Titanium	23–V–51 Vanadium
		29–Cu–63 Copper	30–Zn–64 Zinc 2–8–18–2	31–Ga–69 Gallium 2–8–18–3	32–Ge–74 Germanium 2–8–18–4	33–As–75 Arsenic 2–8–18–5
32	5	37–Rb–85 Rubidium	38–Sr–88 Strontium	39–Y–89 Yttrium	40–Zr–90 Zirconium	41–Nb–93 Niobium
		47–Ag–107 Silver	48–Cd–114 Cadmium	49–In–115 Indium 2–8–18–18–3	50–Sn–120 Tin	51–Sb–121 Antimony 2–8–18–18–5
	6	55–Cs–133 Cesium	56–Ba–138 Barium	57–La–139 Lanthanum	72–Hf–180 Hafnium	73–Ta–181 Tantalum
		79–Au–197 Gold	80–Hg–202 Mercury	81–Ti–205 Tallium	82–Pb–206 Lead	83–Bi–209 Bismuth
	7	87–Fr–223 Francium	88–Ra–226 Radium	89–Ac–227 Actinium		

OF THE ELEMENTS

VI	VII		VIII		0
					2–He–4 Helium
8–O–16 Oxygen	9–F–19 Fluorine				10–Ne–20 Neon
16–S–32 Sulfur	17–Cl–35 Chlorine				18–A–40 Argon
24–Cr–52 Chromium	25–Mn–55 Manganese	26–Fe–56 Iron	27–Co–59 Cobalt	28–Ni–58 Nickel	
34–Se–80 Selenium 2-8-18-6	35–Br–79 Bromine				36–Kr–84 Krypton
42–Mo–09 Molybdenum	43–Tc–99 Technetium	44–Ru–102 Ruthenium	45–Rh–103 Rhodium	46–Pd–106 Palladium	
52–Te–130 Tellurium	53–I–127 Iodine				54–Xe–132 Xenon
74–W–184 Wolfram (Tungsten)	75–Re–187 Rhenium	76–Os–192 Osmium	77–Ir–193 Iridium	78–Pt–195 Platinum	
84–Po–210 Polonium	85–At–210 Astatine				86–Rn–222 Radon

Appendix II

Manufacturers' Data Sheets

The material presented on the following pages is done so through the courtesy of the following:

1. Motorola Semiconductor Products Inc.

2. Texas Instruments Incorporated

3. General Electric Company

4. Radio Corporation of America Laboratories

———— Silicon Zener Diodes ————

1N**3821** thru 1N**3830**

1 W
3.3 — 7.5 V

1N3821A thru 1N3828A USN/JAN

1N3821A thru 1N3828A HI-REL

CASE 52

Low-voltage, alloy-junction zener diodes in hermetically sealed package with cathode connected-to-case. Available as standard industrial types as well as for military and high-reliability applications.

MAXIMUM RATINGS

Junction and Storage Temperature: -65°C to +175°C.
D-C Power Dissipation: 1 Watt.(Derate 6. 67 mW/°C above 25°C)

The type numbers shown have a standard tolerance on the nominal zener voltage of ±10%. A standard tolerance of ±5% on individual units is also available and is indicated by suffixing "A" to the standard type number.

ELECTRICAL CHARACTERISTICS (25°C Ambient $V_F = 1.5$ V @ $I_F = 200$ mA for all units)

TYPE NO.	Nominal Zener Voltage @ I_{ZT} (V_Z) Volts	Test Current I_{ZT} mA	Max Zener Impedance		Max DC Zener Current I_{ZM} mA	$I_R = 10\mu A$ Max @ Reverse Voltage V_R	Typical Zener Voltage/temp. Coeff. %/°C
			Z_{ZT} @ I_{ZT} ohms	Z_{ZK} @ $I_{ZK} = 1.0mA$ ohms			
1N3821	3.3	76	10	400	276	1	-.075
1N3821A	3.3	76	10	400	276	1	-.075
1N3822	3.6	69	10	400	252	1	-.065
1N3822A	3.6	69	10	400	252	1	-.065
1N3823	3.9	64	9	400	238	1	-.055
1N3823A	3.9	64	9	400	238	1	-.055
1N3824	4.3	58	9	400	213	1	-.040
1N3824A	4.3	58	9	400	213	1	-.040
1N3825	4.7	53	8	500	194	1	-.020
1N3825A	4.7	53	8	500	194	1	-.020
1N3826	5.1	49	7	550	178	1	+.005
1N3826A	5.1	49	7	550	178	1	+.005
1N3827	5.6	45	5	600	162	2	+.020
1N3827A	5.6	45	5	600	162	2	+.020
1N3828	6.2	41	2	700	146	3	+.035
1N3828A	6.2	41	2	700	146	3	+.035
1N3829	6.8	37	1.5	500	133	3	+.040
1N3829A	6.8	37	1.5	500	133	3	+.040
1N3830	7.5	34	1.5	250	121	3	+.045
1N3830A	7.5	34	1.5	250	121	3	+.045

Courtesy of Motorola Semiconductor Products Inc.

TUNNEL DIODE SPECIFICATIONS

1N3150

Outline Drawing No. 1

The 1N3150 is a germanium tunnel diode which makes use of the quantum mechanical tunneling phenomenon thereby attaining a unique negative conductance characteristic and very high frequency performance. This device is designed for low level switching and small signal applications with frequency capabilities up to 1.3 Kmc. It features closely controlled peak point current, good temperature stability and extreme resistance to nuclear radiation.

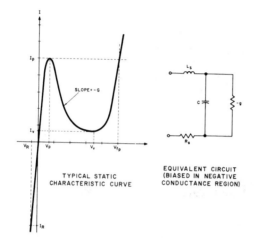

TYPICAL STATIC
CHARACTERISTIC CURVE

EQUIVALENT CIRCUIT
(BIASED IN NEGATIVE
CONDUCTANCE REGION)

SPECIFICATIONS

ABSOLUTE MAXIMUM RATINGS: (25°C)

Current

Forward (—55 to +100°C)		100	ma
Reverse (—55 to +100°C)		100	ma

Temperature

Storage	T_{STG}	—55 to +100	°C
Operating Junction	T_J	—55 to +100	°C
Lead Temperature ¹⁄₁₆″ ±¹⁄₃₂″ From Case for 10 seconds	T_L	260	°C

ELECTRICAL CHARACTERISTICS: (25°C) (½″ Leads)

		Min.	Typ.	Max.	
Peak Point Current	I_p	20	22	24	ma
Valley Point Current	I_v		2.9	4.80	ma
Peak Point Voltage	V_p		60		mv
Valley Point Voltage	V_v		350		mv
Reverse Voltage ($I_R = 22$ ma)	V_r			30	mv
Forward Peak Point Current Voltage	V_{fp}	450	500	600	mv
Peak Point Current to Valley Point Current Ratio	I_p/I_v		8		
Negative Conductance	$-G$		100×10^{-3}		mho
Total Capacity	C		60	150	pf
Series Inductance	L_s*		6		nh
Series Resistance	R_s		.15	1.0	ohm

*Inductance will vary 1-12 nh (10^{-9} henries) depending on lead length.

Courtesy of General Electric Company

PHOTOCELLS

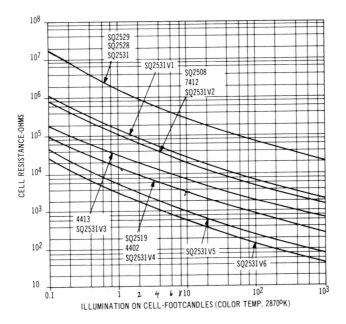

DC Cell Resistance of 1/4" — Diameter Broad-Area Photoconductive
Cells as a Function of Cell Illumination

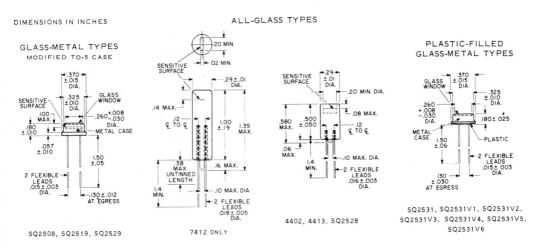

DIMENSIONS IN INCHES   ALL-GLASS TYPES

GLASS-METAL TYPES
MODIFIED TO-5 CASE

SQ2508, SQ2519, SQ2529

7412 ONLY

4402, 4413, SQ2528

PLASTIC-FILLED
GLASS-METAL TYPES

SQ2531, SQ2531V1, SQ2531V2,
SQ2531V3, SQ2531V4, SQ2531V5,
SQ2531V6

Courtesy of Radio Corporation of America Laboratories

PHOTOCELLS

1/4"-Diameter Broad-Area Cadmium-Sulfide Photoconductive Cells

RCA TYPES				MAXIMUM RATINGS			CHARACTERISTICS AT 25° C				
Glass-Metal Types[a]	All-Glass Types[a]	Plastic-Filled Glass-Metal Types[b]	Spectral Response	Voltage Between Terminals DC or Peak AC volts	Power Dissi-pation[c] watt	Photo-current ma	Voltage Between Terminals dc volts	Illumi-nation[d] foot-candles	Photocurrent[e] ma Min.	Max.	Max. Decay Current[f] μa
SQ2529	SQ2528	SQ2531	S-15	300	0.05	5	12	1	0.004	0.012	0.1
–	–	SQ2531V1	S-15	200	0.05	5	12	1	0.04	0.12	1
SQ2508	7412	SQ2531V2	S-15	200	0.05	5	12	1	0.065	0.275	1
–	4413	SQ2531V3	S-15	110	0.05	5	12	10	1.4	2.75	12
SQ2519	4402	SQ2531V4	S-15	300	0.05	5	12	10	1.69[g]	–	12
–	–	SQ2531V5	S-15	110	0.05	7	12	1	1	3	15
–	–	SQ2531V6	S-15	110	0.05	7	12	1	1.6	4.8	15

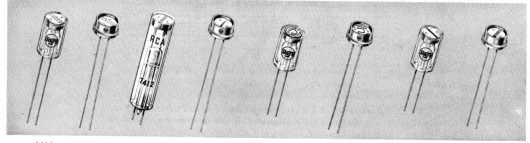

4413	SQ2531V3	7412	SQ2508	4402	SQ2519	SQ2528	SQ2529
			SQ2531V1		SQ2531V4		SQ2531
			SQ2531V2		SQ2531V5		
					SQ2531V6		

a   The maximum ambient operating temperature range for these cells is −75° C to +60° C.

b   The maximum ambient operating temperature range for these cells is −40° C to +60° C.

c   In continuous service with sensitive surface of cell fully illuminated. The dissipation rating applies up to the maximum ambient operating temperature.

d   For conditions where the light source is a tungsten-filament lamp operated at a color temperature of 2870° K.

e   This characteristic is determined after the cell has been exposed for a period of 16 to 24 hours to 500 footcandle illumination (white fluorescent light).

f   Measured 10 seconds after removal of incident-illumination level.

g   This characteristic is determined after the cell has been exposed for a period of 16 to 24 hours to 50 to 100 footcandle illumination (white fluorescent light).

Courtesy of Radio Corporation of America Laboratories

TYPES 2N404, 2N404A
P-N-P ALLOY-JUNCTION GERMANIUM TRANSISTORS

High-Frequency Transistors for Computer and Switching Applications

Close parameter control and the JEDEC TO-5 welded package ensure device reliability and stable characteristics

environmental tests

To ensure maximum reliability, stability, and long life, all units are aged at 100°C for 100 hours minimum prior to electrical characterization. All transistors are thoroughly tested for complete adherence to specified design characteristics. In addition, continuous qualification tests are made comprising temperature-humidity cycling, shock, and vacuum leak testing under rigid in-process control procedures.

mechanical data

Metal case with glass-to-metal hermetic seal between case and leads. Unit weight is approximately 1 gram. These units meet JEDEC TO-5 registration.

All leads insulated from the case.

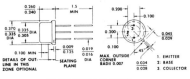

ALL DIMENSIONS IN INCHES

*absolute maximum ratings at 25°C free–air temperature (unless otherwise noted)

	2N404	2N404A
Collector-Base Voltage	25 v	40 v
Collector-Emitter Voltage (see note 1)	24 v	35 v
Emitter-Base Voltage	12 v	25 v
Collector Current	100 ma	150 ma
Emitter Current	100 ma	150 ma
Total Device Dissipation (see note 2)	150 mw	150 mw
Operating Collector Junction Temperature	85°C	100°C
Storage Temperature Range	−65°C to +100°C	−65°C to +100°C

NOTES: 1. Punch-through voltage.
      2. For 2N404 derate linearly to 85°C free-air temperature at the rate of 2.5 mw/°C;
        For 2N404A derate linearly to 100°C free-air temperature at the rate of 2.0 mw/°C.
*Indicates JEDEC registered data.
    The maximum power dissipation at 25°C case temperature is 300 mw.

Courtesy of Texas Instruments Incorporated

TYPES 2N404, 2N404A
P-N-P ALLOY-JUNCTION GERMANIUM TRANSISTORS

electrical characteristics at 25°C free-air temperature (unless otherwise noted)

parameter		test conditions	2N404			2N404A			unit
			min	typ	max	min	typ	max	
I_{CBO}	Collector cutoff current	$V_{CB} = -12$ v, $I_E = 0$	—	−1	−5*	—	−1	−5*	μa
		$V_{CB} = -12$ v, $I_E = 0$ $T_A = 80°C$	—	−40	−90*	—	−40	−90*	μa
I_{EBO}	Emitter cutoff current	$V_{EB} = -2.5$ v, $I_C = 0$	—	−1	−2.5*	—	−1	−2.5*	μa
BV_{CBO}	Collector-base breakdown voltage	$I_C = -20\mu a$, $I_E = 0$	−25*	—	—	−40*	—	—	v
BV_{EBO}	Emitter-base breakdown voltage	$I_E = -20\mu a$, $I_C = 0$	−12*	—	—	−25*	—	—	v
h_{FE}	DC forward current transfer ratio	$V_{CE} = -0.15$ v, $I_C = -12$ ma	30	100	—	30	100	—	—
		$V_{CE} = -0.20$ v, $I_C = -24$ ma	24	110	—	24	110	—	—
V_{BE}	Base-emitter voltage	$I_B = -0.4$ ma, $I_C = -12$ ma	—	−0.26	−0.35*	—	−0.26	−0.35*	v
		$I_B = -1$ ma, $I_C = -24$ ma	—	−0.30	−0.40*	—	−0.30	−0.40*	v
$V_{CE(sat)}$	Collector-emitter saturation voltage	$I_B = -0.4$ ma, $I_C = -12$ ma	—	−0.08	−0.15*	—	−0.08	−0.15*	v
		$I_B = -1$ ma, $I_C = -24$ ma	—	−0.08	−0.20*	—	−0.08	−0.20*	v
V_{pt}	Punch-through voltage†	$V_{EBfl} = -1$ v	−24*	—	—	—	—	—	v
V_{EBfl}	Emitter-base floating potential	$V_{CB} = -35$ v	—	—	—	—	−0.2	−1*	v
h_{fe}	AC common-emitter forward current transfer ratio	$V_{CE} = -6$ v, $I_C = -1$ ma $f = 1$ kc	—	135	—	—	135	—	—
h_{ie}	AC common-emitter input impedance	$V_{CE} = -6$ v, $I_C = -1$ ma $f = 1$ kc	—	4	—	—	4	—	Kohm
h_{oe}	AC common-emitter output admittance	$V_{CE} = -6$ v, $I_C = -1$ ma $f = 1$ kc	—	50	—	—	50	—	μmho
h_{re}	AC common-emitter reverse voltage transfer ratio	$V_{CE} = -6$ v, $I_C = -1$ ma $f = 1$ kc	—	7x10⁻⁴	—	—	7x10⁻⁴	—	—
C_{ob}	Common-base output capacitance	$V_{CB} = -6$ v, $I_E = 0$ $f = 1$ mc	—	9	20*	—	—	—	pf
		$V_{CB} = -6$ v, $I_E = 1$ ma $f = 2$ mc	—	—	—	—	9	20*	pf
f_{hfb}	Common-base alpha cutoff frequency	$V_{CB} = -6$ v, $I_E = 1$ ma	4*	12	—	4*	12	—	mc

†V_{pt} is determined by measuring the emitter-base floating potential V_{EBfl} using a voltmeter with 11 megohms minimum input impedance. The collector-base voltage, V_{CB} is increased until $V_{EBfl} = -1$ v; this value of V_{CB} ($V_{pt} + 1$). Care must be taken not to exceed maximum collector-base voltage specified under maximum ratings.

switching characteristics at 25°C free-air temperature

parameter		test conditions	2N404			2N404A			unit
			min	typ	max	min	typ	max	
t_d	Delay time	See Circuit 1	—	0.14	—	—	0.15	—	μsec
t_r	Rise time	See Circuit 1	—	0.20	—	—	0.27	—	μsec
t_s	Storage time	See Circuit 1	—	0.38	—	—	0.38	—	μsec
t_f	Fall time	See Circuit 1	—	0.19	—	—	0.24	—	μsec
Q_{sb}	Stored base charge	See Circuit 2	—	800	1400*	—	800	1400*	pcb

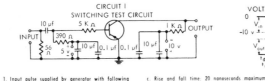

CIRCUIT I
SWITCHING TEST CIRCUIT

VOLTAGE WAVEFORMS

NOTES: 1. Input pulse supplied by generator with following characteristics:
   a. Output impedance: 50 ohms
   b. Repetition rate: 1 KC

c. Rise and fall time: 20 nanoseconds maximum
2. Waveforms monitored on scope with following characteristics:
   a. Input resistance — 10 megohms minimum

b. Input capacitance — 15 pf maximum
c. Risetime — 15 nanoseconds maximum
3. All resistors ±1% tolerance.

Courtesy of Texas Instruments Incorporated

TYPES 2N404, 2N404A
P-N-P ALLOY-JUNCTION GERMANIUM TRANSISTORS

TYPICAL CHARACTERISTICS

COMMON-EMITTER COLLECTOR CHARACTERISTICS ... AS MEASURED ON TEKTRONIX 575 CURVE TRACER

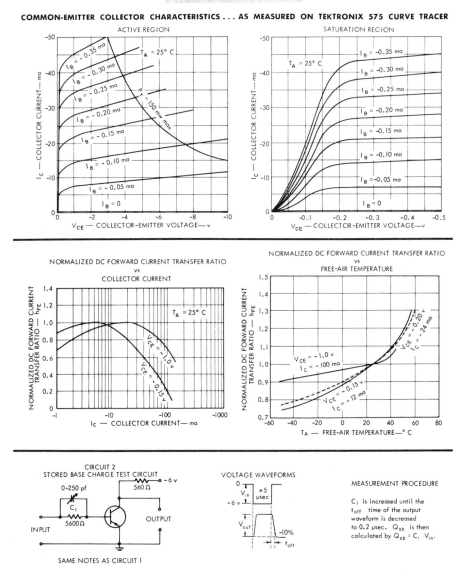

CIRCUIT 2
STORED BASE CHARGE TEST CIRCUIT

VOLTAGE WAVEFORMS

MEASUREMENT PROCEDURE

C_1 is increased until the t_{off} time of the output waveform is decreased to 0.2 μsec. Q_{sb} is then calculated by $Q_{sb} = C_1 V_{in}$.

SAME NOTES AS CIRCUIT 1

Courtesy of Texas Instruments Incorporated

TYPES 2N404, 2N404A
P-N-P ALLOY-JUNCTION GERMANIUM TRANSISTORS

TYPICAL CHARACTERISTICS

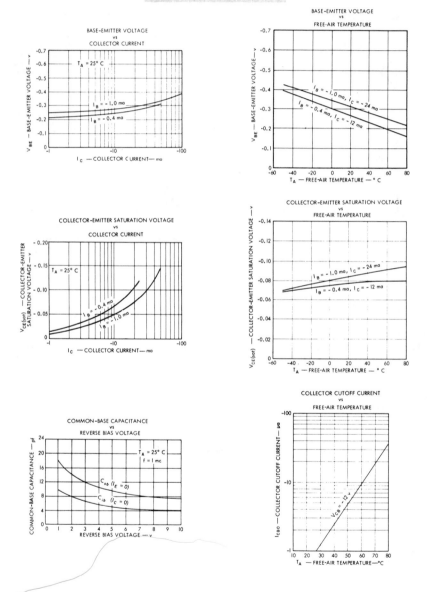

Courtesy of Texas Instruments Incorporated

TYPES 2N250A AND 2N251A
P-N-P ALLOY-JUNCTION GERMANIUM POWER TRANSISTORS

INTERMEDIATE-POWER TRANSISTORS
FOR
MILITARY AND COMMERCIAL APPLICATIONS

environmental tests

To ensure maximum integrity, stability and long life, all finished devices are heat aged at + 110°C for 100 hours and temperature cycled from − 55°C to + 100°C for four complete cycles over an 8-hour period prior to thorough testing for rigid adherence to specified characteristics.

mechanical data

The use of silver alloy to assemble the mounting base and the use of resistance welding to seal the can, provides a hermetically sealed enclosure. During the assembly process the absence of flux, combined with extreme cleanliness, prevents sealed-in contamination.

The mounting base provides an excellent heat path from the collector junction to a heat sink which must be in intimate contact to permit operation at maximum rated dissipation. The approximate weight of the unit is 18 grams.

*The transistors are in a JEDEC TO-3 case.

* THE COLLECTOR IS IN ELECTRICAL CONTACT WITH THE CASE

0.525 RAD MAX

0.450 MAX
0.350 †
0.250 MIN

0.875 MAX DIA

1.050 MAX

0.188 RAD MAX BOTH ENDS

0.135 MAX

BASE SEAT

0.312 MIN
EMITTER

0.043/0.038 DIA 2 LEADS

1.573 MAX

1.197/1.177

0.675/0.655

0.440/0.420

0.161/0.151 DIA 2 HOLES

COLLECTOR

BASE

CASE TEMPERATURE MEASUREMENT POINT

† THE TI SEATED HEIGHT IS 0.350 INCHES MAXIMUM.

DIMENSIONS ARE IN INCHES

absolute maximum ratings at 25°C case temperature (unless otherwise noted)

	2N250A	2N251A
Collector-Base Voltage	40 v	60 v
Collector-Emitter Voltage (see Note 1)	35 v	55 v
Emitter-Base Voltage	← 20 v →	
Collector Current	← 7 a →	
Base Current	← 2 a →	
Total Device Dissipation at (or below) 25°C Case Temperature (see Note 2) . .	← 90 w →	
Operating Collector Junction Temperature	← + 100°C →	
Storage Temperature Range	← − 55 to + 100°C →	

*Indicates JEDEC registered data.

NOTES: 1. This value applies when base-emitter voltage, $V_{BE} = + 0.2$ v.
  2. Derate linearly to + 100°C case temperature at the rate of 1.2 w/C°.

TYPES 2N250A AND 2N251A
P-N-P ALLOY-JUNCTION GERMANIUM POWER TRANSISTORS

electrical characteristics at 25°C case temperature (unless otherwise noted)

PARAMETER		TEST CONDITIONS	TYPE	MIN.	MAX.	UNIT
BV$_{CBO}$	Collector-Base Breakdown Voltage	I$_C$ = $-$2 ma, I$_E$ = 0	2N250A 2N251A	$-$40 $-$60		v
BV$_{CEO}$	Collector-Emitter Breakdown Voltage	I$_C$ = $-$500 ma, I$_B$ = 0 (see note 3)	2N250A 2N251A	$-$25* $-$35*		v
BV$_{CEX}$	Collector-Emitter Breakdown Voltage	I$_C$ = $-$2 ma, V$_{BE}$ = $+$0.2 v	2N250A 2N251A	$-$35 $-$55		v
BV$_{EBO}$	Emitter-Base Breakdown Voltage	I$_E$ = $-$2 ma, I$_C$ = 0	All	$-$20*		v
I$_{CBO}$	Collector Cutoff Current	V$_{CB}$ = $-$10 v, I$_E$ = 0	All		$-$500	μa
I$_{CBO}$	Collector Cutoff Current	V$_{CB}$ = $-$30 v, I$_E$ = 0 V$_{CB}$ = $-$60 v, I$_E$ = 0	2N250A 2N251A		$-$1.0* $-$2.0*	ma
I$_{CBO}$	Collector Cutoff Current	V$_{CB}$ = $-$20 v, I$_E$ = 0 T$_C$ = 70°C V$_{CB}$ = $-$30 v, I$_E$ = 0 T$_C$ = 70°C	2N250A 2N251A		$-$5* $-$5*	ma
h$_{FE}$	Static Forward Current Transfer Ratio	V$_{CE}$ = $-$1.5 v, I$_C$ = $-$500 ma	All	35*		—
h$_{FE}$	Static Forward Current Transfer Ratio	V$_{CE}$ = $-$1.5 v, I$_C$ = $-$3 a	All	25*	100*	—
V$_{BE}$	Base-Emitter Voltage	I$_B$ = $-$150 ma, I$_C$ = $-$3 a	All		$-$1.0*	v
V$_{CE(sat)}$	Collector-Emitter Saturation Voltage	I$_B$ = $-$150 ma, I$_C$ = $-$3 a	All		$-$0.7*	v
|h$_{fe}$|	Small-Signal Common-Emitter Forward Current Transfer Ratio	V$_{CE}$ = $-$2 v, I$_C$ = $-$1 a, f = 80 kc	All	2*		—

NOTE: 3. If the transistor is tested without a heat sink, perform this test with a 100 msec current pulse and a duty cycle less than 2%.

*Indicates JEDEC registered data.

Courtesy of Texas Instruments Incorporated

TYPES 2N250A AND 2N251A
P-N-P ALLOY-JUNCTION GERMANIUM POWER TRANSISTORS

TYPICAL CHARACTERISTICS

COMMON-EMITTER COLLECTOR CHARACTERISTICS

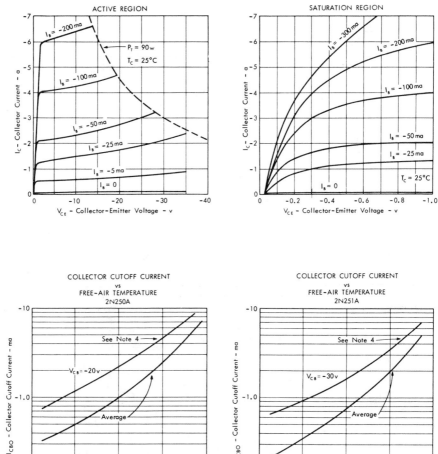

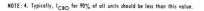

NOTE: 4. Typically, I_{CBO} for 90% of all units should be less than this value.

TYPES 2N250A AND 2N251A
P-N-P ALLOY-JUNCTION GERMANIUM POWER TRANSISTORS

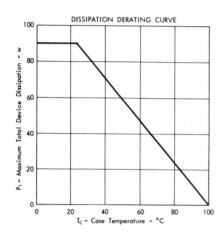

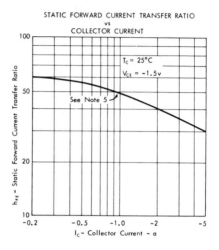

NOTE: 5. Typically, h_{FE} for 90% of all units should be greater than this value.

TYPICAL APPLICATION DATA

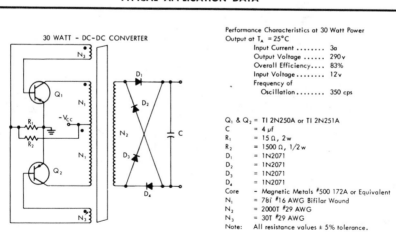

30 WATT – DC–DC CONVERTER

Performance Characteristics at 30 Watt Power
Output at T_A = 25°C

    Input Current 3a
    Output Voltage . . . . . . 290 v
    Overall Efficiency. . . . 83%
    Input Voltage 12v
    Frequency of
      Oscillation . . . . 350 cps

Q_1 & Q_2 = TI 2N250A or TI 2N251A
C   = 4 µf
R_1 = 15 Ω, 2w
R_2 = 1500 Ω, 1/2 w
D_1 = 1N2071
D_2 = 1N2071
D_3 = 1N2071
D_4 = 1N2071
Core   – Magnetic Metals #500 172A or Equivalent
N_1 = 78ï #16 AWG Bifilar Wound
N_2 = 2000T #29 AWG
N_3 = 30T #29 AWG
Note: All resistance values ± 5% tolerance.

Courtesy of Texas Instruments Incorporated

Silicon
Unilateral Switch

(SUS)

The General Electric D13D1 is a diode thyristor with electrical characteristics that closely approximate those of an "ideal" four layer diode. The device uses a silicon monolithic integrated structure to achieve an 8 volt switching voltage, an on voltage of 1.75 volts at 200ma and temperature coefficient of switching voltage of less than 0.05%/°C. A gate lead is provided to give access to the circuit between the top of the zener and the base of the PNP.

Silicon Unilateral Switches are specifically designed and characterized for use in monostable and bistable applications where stability of the switching voltage is required over wide temperature variations. They are ideally suited for telephone switching, SCR triggering and for a variety of logic and memory applications.

EQUIVALENT CIRCUIT

absolute maximum ratings:

25°C (unless otherwise specified)

Storage Temperature Range	−65 to +200	°C
Junction Temperature Range	−55 to +150	°C
Power Dissipation*	350	mw
Peak Reverse Voltage	−30	volts
DC Forward Current *	200	ma
Peak Recurrent Forward Current (1% duty cycle, 10 μsec pulse width, $T_A = 100°C$)	1.0	amp
Peak Non-Recurrent Forward Current (10 μsec pulse width, $T_A = 25°C$)	5.0	amps

*Derate linearly to zero at 150°C.

CIRCUIT SYMBOL

electrical characteristics:

25°C (unless otherwise specified)

STATIC	MIN.	TYP.	MAX.	UNITS
Forward Switching Voltage, V_S	6	8	10	V
Forward Switching Current, I_S			500	μa
Holding Current, I_H			1.5	ma
Reverse Current				
($V_R = −30V$ @ $T_A = 25°C$)			.1	μa
($V_R = −30V$ @ $T_A = 100°C$)			10.0	μa
Forward Current (off state)				
($V_F = 5V$ @ $T_A = 25°C$)			1.0	μa
($V_F = 5V$ @ $T_A = 100°C$)			20.0	μa
Forward Voltage Drop (on state)				
($I_F = 200$ ma)			1.75	V
Temperature Coefficient of Switching Voltage ($T_A = −55°C$ to $+100°C$)			±.05	%/°C
DYNAMIC				
Turn-on Time, t_{on} (See Circuit 1)			1.0	μsec
Turn-off Time, t_{off} (See Circuit 2)			25.0	μsec
Peak Pulse Voltage (See Circuit 3)	3.5			V
Capacitance (0V., f = 1 MHz)		2.5		pF

Courtesy of General Electric Company

C30, C32

**Light Industrial and Consumer
Medium Current SCR
25 Amperes RMS Max.
Outline Drawing No. 4**

The C32 Silicon Controlled Rectifier is a three-junction semiconductor device for use in power switching and control applications requiring a blocking voltage of 400 volts or less and average load currents (full-wave rectified) up to 16 amperes. The C32 is provided in the popular "Press Fit" cup housing to insure ease of installation in large volume applications. Low cost makes this device suitable for high volume consumer and Light Industrial applications.

The C30 is the same as the C32 except that it is mounted on a $\frac{7}{16}$" hex and $\frac{1}{4}$"–28 stud as an added convenience to those manufacturers with production facilities more adaptable to "nut and bolt" type assembly.

- Flexibility of Mounting (Available in cup construction to solder, glue, or press fit, and as a stud device)
- One-piece Terminals
- High Surge Current Capabilities
- Low Power Required for Triggering

Type	Minimum Forward Breakover Voltage, $V_{(BR)FO}$*	Repetitive Peak Reverse Voltage V_{ROM} (rep)*	Nonrepetitive Peak Reverse Voltage (<5.0 Millisec) V_{ROM} (non-rep)*
C30U, C32U	25 V	25 V	35 V
C30F, C32F	50 V	50 V	75 V
C30A, C32A	100 V	100 V	150 V
C30B, C32B	200 V	200 V	300 V
C30C, C32C	300 V	300 V	400 V
C30D, C32D	400 V	400 V	500 V

MAXIMUM ALLOWABLE RATINGS

Repetitive Peak Forward Blocking Volatge, PFV	500 volts
RMS Forward Current, On-State	25.0 amperes (all conduction angles)
Average Forward Current, On-State	13 amperes at 75°C case (half wave rectified sine wave)
	19 amperes at 75°C case (full wave rectified sine wave)
Peak One Cycle Surge Forward Current I_{FM} (surge)	225 amperes
Peak Gate Power Dissipation, P_{GM}	5.0 watts
Average Gate Power Dissipation, $P_{G(AV)}$	0.5 watts
Peak Reverse Gate Voltage, V_{GRM}	5.0 volts
Max. Storage Temperature, T_{stg}	100°C
Max. Operating Junction Temperature	100°C
Stud Torque (C30 Only)	25 inch-pounds

CHARACTERISTICS

Test	Symbol	Min.	Typ.	Max.	Units	Test Conditions
Peak Reverse and Forward Blocking Current*	I_{ROM} and I_{FOM}					$T_J = 100°C$
C30U, C32U		—	1.0	10.0	ma	$V_{ROM} = V_{FOM} = $ 25 volts peak
C30F, C32F		—	1.0	10.0	ma	= 50 volts peak
C30A, C32A		—	1.0	7.0	ma	= 100 volts peak
C30B, C32B		—	1.0	3.5	ma	= 200 volts peak
C30C, C32C		—	1.0	2.3	ma	= 300 volts peak
C30D, C32D		—	1.0	1.7	ma	= 400 volts peak
Gate Trigger Current	I_{GT}	—	4.0	25.0	mAdc	$T_J = 25°C$, $V_{FX} = 6Vdc$, $R_L = 60$ ohms
Gate Trigger Voltage	V_{GT}	—	0.8	1.5	Vdc	$T_J = 25°C$, $V_{FX} = 6Vdc$, $R_L = 60$ ohms
		0.2	0.5	—	Vdc	$T_J = 100$ C, $V_{FXM} = $ rated, $R_L = 1000$ ohms
Peak on Voltage	V_{FM}	—	1.30	1.5	V	$T_J = 25°C$, $I_{FM} = 50$ A peak, single half sine wave pulse, 2.0 millisec. wide
Holding Current	I_{HO}	—	10.0	50.0	mAdc	$T_J = 25$ C, anode supply = 24 Vdc

*Values apply for zero or negative gate voltage only. Maximum case to ambient thermal resistance for which maximum V_{ROM} (rep) ratings apply equals 18°C per watt.

2N2646 & 2N2647

Unijunction Transistors—Silicon Types
Outline Drawing No. 10

The General Electric 2N2646 and 2N2647 Silicon Unijunction Transistors have an entirely new structure resulting in lower saturation voltage, peak-point current and valley current as well as a much higher base-one peak pulse voltage. In addition, these devices are much faster switches. The 2N2646 is intended for general purpose industrial applications where circuit economy is of primary importance, and is ideal for use in triggering circuits for Silicon Controlled Rectifiers and other applications where a guaranteed minimum pulse amplitude is required. The 2N2647 is intended for applications where a low emitter leakage current and a low peak point emitter current (trigger current) are required (i.e. long timing applications), and also for triggering high power SCR's.

ABSOLUTE MAXIMUM RATINGS: (25°C)

Power Dissipation (Note 1)............300 mw
RMS Emitter Current....................50 ma
Peak Emitter Current (Note 2)........2 amperes
Emitter Reverse Voltage...............30 volts
Interbase Voltage......................35 volts
Operating Temperature Range −65°C to +125°C
Storage Temperature Range.. −65°C to +150°C

ELECTRICAL CHARACTERISTICS: (25°C)

PARAMETER		2N2646			2N2647			
		Min.	Typ.	Max.	Min.	Typ.	Max.	
Intrinsic Standoff Ratio ($V_{BB} = 10V$)	η	0.56	0.65	0.75	0.68	0.75	0.82	
Interbase Resistance ($V_{BB} = 3V$, $I_E = 0$)	R_{BBO}	4.7	7	9.1	4.7	7	9.1	KΩ
Emitter Saturation Voltage ($V_{BB} = 10V$, $I_E = 50$ ma)	$V_{E(SAT)}$		2			2		volts
Modulated Interbase Current ($V_{BB} = 10V$, $I_E = 50$ ma)	$I_{B2(MOD)}$		12			12		ma
Emitter Reverse Current ($V_{B2E} = 30V$, $I_{B1} = 0$)	I_{EO}		0.05	12		0.01	0.2	μa
Peak Point Emitter Current ($V_{BB} = 25V$)	I_P		0.4	0.5		0.4	2	μa
Valley Point Current ($V_{BB} = 20V$, $R_{B2} = 100\Omega$)	I_V	4	6		8	11	18	ma
Base-One Peak Pulse Voltage (Note 3)	V_{OB1}	3.0	6.5		6.0	7.5		volts
SCR Firing Conditions (See Figure 26, back page)								

NOTES:

1. Derate 3.0 MW/°C increase in ambient temperature. The total power dissipation (available power to Emitter and Base-Two) must be limited by the external circuitry.
2. Capacitor discharge—10 μfd or less, 30 volts or less.
3. The Base-One Peak Pulse Voltage is measured in the circuit below. This specification on the 2N2646 and 2N2647 is used to ensure a minimum pulse amplitude for applications in SCR triggering circuits and other types of pulse circuits.
4. The intrinsic standoff ratio, η, is essentially constant with temperature and interbase voltage. η is defined by the equation:
   $$V_P = \eta\ V_{BB} + V_D$$
   Where V_P = Peak Point Emitter Voltage
   V_{BB} = Interbase Voltage
   V_D = Junction Diode Drop (Approx. .5V)

FIGURE 1

FIGURE 2
Unijunction Transistor Symbol with Nomenclature used for voltage and currents.

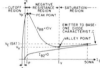

FIGURE 3
Static Emitter Characteristics curves showing important parameters and measurement points (exaggerated to show details).

G-E SCR's, RECTIFIERS, AND UNIJUNCTION TRANSISTORS WORK WELL TOGETHER!

G-E Controlled Rectifier (SCR) Type	Compatible Rectifier					Compatible Unijunction Triggering Transistor
	G-E Rectifier Type	Max On-Current $I_{F\ AV.}$ at Stud Temperature	Peak 1 Cycle Surge	Max. Rectifier Transient $V_{RM\ (non-rep)}$	Package	
C5, C7, 2N1595-1599	1N536 1N547	.75 A at 50°C Amb.	15 A	800 V	Double Ended Lead	2N2646
	1N2610 1N2615	.75 A at 50°C Amb.	30 A	775 V		
C8, C9	1N1341A 1N1348B	7 A at 140°C	150 A	800 V	7/16" Hex	2N2646
C10, C11, C12	CAR A27	8.5 A at 150°C	240 A	∞	7/16" Hex	
C20, C22, C30	A40 or A41 A44 or A45	15 A at 150°C	300 A	600 V	9/16" Hex	2N2646
C35, C38, C40	1N1199A 1N1206A	12 A at 150°C	240 A	800 V	7/16" Hex	2N2646
	1N2154 1N2160	25 A at 145°C	400 A	800 V	11/16" Hex	2N2646
	CAR A38	22 A at 140°C	500 A	∞	11/16" Hex	
C36,C37	1N1341A 1N1348A	7 A at 140°C	150 A	800 V	7/16" Hex	2N2646
	1N1199A 1N1206A	12 A at 150°C	240 A	800 V	7/16" Hex	2N2646
C45, C46, C50, C52, C55 C56, C60, C61, C150	1N3289 1N3293 (A70)	70°A at 150°C	1600 A	1300 V	1 1/16" Hex	2N2647
	CAR A76	70 A at 150°C	1600 A	∞		
C80, C85	1N3736 3742 (A90)	200 A at 150°C	4500 A	1300 V	1-1/4" Hex	2N2647
	CAR A92	200 A at 150°C	4500 A	∞		
6RW71	1N3736 3742 (A90)	200 A at 150°C	4500 A	1300 V	1 1/4" Hex	2N2647
	CAR A92	200 A at 150°C	4500 A	∞		
	6RW62	390 A at 150°C	7000 A	1000 V	1-5/8" Hex	2N2647

Stack assemblies available for all rectifier types listed.

2N4220
thru
2N4222

2N4220A
thru
2N4222A

SILICON N-CHANNEL
JUNCTION FIELD-EFFECT TRANSISTORS

Depletion Mode (Type A) devices designed for general-purpose amplifier and switching applications.

- Low Transfer Capacitance — C_{rss} = 2.0 pF (Max)

- Low Input Capacitance — C_{iss} = 6.0 pF (Max)

- Low Gate Leakage Current — I_{GSS} = 100 pA (Max)

- Low Noise Figure — NF = 2.5 dB (Max) @ 100 Hz ("A" Versions)

SILICON N-CHANNEL
JUNCTION FIELD-EFFECT
TRANSISTORS

TYPE A

FEBRUARY 1968 — DS 5187 R1
(Replaces DS 5187)

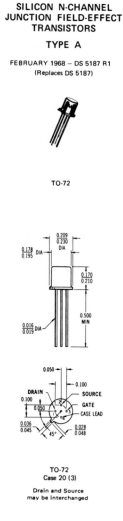

TO-72

TO-72
Case 20 (3)

Drain and Source
may be interchanged

MAXIMUM RATINGS (T_A = 25°C)

Characteristic	Symbol	Rating	Unit
Drain-Source Voltage	V_{DS}	30	Vdc
Drain-Gate Voltage	V_{DG}	30	Vdc
Gate-Source Voltage	V_{GS}	30	Vdc
Drain Current	I_D	15	mAdc
Total Device Dissipation	P_D	300	mW
Derate Above 25°C		2.0	mW/°C
Operating Junction Temperature	T_J	175	°C
Storage Temperature Range	T_{stg}	-65 to +200	°C

Courtesy of Motorola Semiconductor Products Inc.

2N4220 thru 2N4222
2N4220A thru 2N4222A

ELECTRICAL CHARACTERISTICS ($T_A = 25°C$ unless otherwise noted)

Characteristic		Symbol	Min	Typ	Max	Unit
OFF CHARACTERISTICS						
Gate-Source Breakdown Voltage ($I_G = -10\ \mu Adc,\ V_{DS} = 0$)		$V_{(BR)GSS}$	-30	-	-	Vdc
Gate Reverse Current		I_{GSS}				nAdc
($V_{GS} = -15\ Vdc,\ V_{DS} = 0$)			-	-	-0.1	
($V_{GS} = -15\ Vdc,\ V_{DS} = 0,\ T_A = 150°C$)			.	-	-100	
Gate-Source Voltage		V_{GS}				Vdc
($I_D = 50\ \mu Adc,\ V_{DS} = 15\ Vdc$)	2N4220, 2N4220A		-0.5	-	-2.5	
($I_D = 200\ \mu Adc,\ V_{DS} = 15\ Vdc$)	2N4221, 2N4221A		-1.0	-	-5.0	
($I_D = 500\ \mu Adc,\ V_{DS} = 15\ Vdc$)	2N4222, 2N4222A		-2.0	-	-6.0	
Gate-Source Cutoff Voltage ($I_D = 0.1\ nAdc,\ V_{DS} = 15\ Vdc$)		$V_{GS(off)}$				Vdc
	2N4220, 2N4220A		-	-	-4.0	
	2N4221, 2N4221A		-	-	-6.0	
	2N4222, 2N4222A		-	-	-8.0	
ON CHARACTERISTICS						
Zero-Gate-Voltage Drain Current* ($V_{DS} = 15\ Vdc,\ V_{GS} = 0$)		I_{DSS}*				mAdc
	2N4220, 2N4220A		0.5	-	3.0	
	2N4221, 2N4221A		2.0	-	6.0	
	2N4222, 2N4222A		5.0	-	15	
DYNAMIC CHARACTERISTICS						
Forward Transfer Admittance* ($V_{DS} = 15\ Vdc,\ V_{GS} = 0,\ f = 1.0\ kHz$)		$|y_{fs}|$*				μmhos
	2N4220, 2N4220A		1000	2500	4000	
	2N4221, 2N4221A		2000	3500	5000	
	2N4222, 2N4222A		2500	4500	6000	
Output Admittance* ($V_{DS} = 15\ Vdc,\ V_{GS} = 0,\ f = 1.0\ kHz$)		$|y_{os}|$*				μmhos
	2N4220, 2N4220A		-	-	10	
	2N4221, 2N4221A		-	-	20	
	2N4222, 2N4222A		-	-	40	
Drain-Source Resistance ($V_{DS} = 0,\ V_{GS} = 0$)		$r_{ds(on)}$				Ohms
	2N4220, 2N4220A		-	500	-	
	2N4221, 2N4221A		-	400	-	
	2N4222, 2N4222A		-	300	-	
Input Capacitance ($V_{DS} = 15\ Vdc,\ V_{GS} = 0,\ f = 1.0\ MHz$)		C_{iss}	-	4.5	6.0	pF
Reverse Transfer Capacitance ($V_{DS} = 15\ Vdc,\ V_{GS} = 0,\ f = 1.0\ MHz$)		C_{rss}	-	1.2	2.0	pF
Common-Source Output Capacitance ($V_{DS} = 15\ Vdc,\ V_{GS} = 0,\ f = 30\ MHz$)		C_{osp}	-	1.5	-	pF
Noise Figure ($V_{DS} = 15\ Vdc,\ V_{GS} = 0,\ R_S = 1.0\ Megohm,\ f = 100\ Hz$)		NF				dB
	2N4220A		-	-	2.5	
	2N4221A		-	-	2.5	
	2N4222A		-	-	2.5	

*Pulse Test: Pulse Width = 630 ms, Duty Cycle = 10%

FIGURE 1 – EQUIVALENT LOW FREQUENCY CIRCUIT

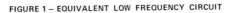
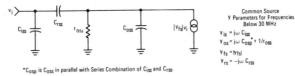

Common Source
Y Parameters for Frequencies
Below 30 MHz

$y_{is} = j\omega\ C_{iss}$
$y_{os} = j\omega\ C_{osp}* + 1/r_{oss}$
$y_{fs} = |y_{fs}|$
$y_{rs} = -j\omega\ C_{rss}$

*C_{osp} is C_{oss} in parallel with Series Combination of C_{iss} and C_{rss}.

Courtesy of Motorola Semiconductor Products Inc.

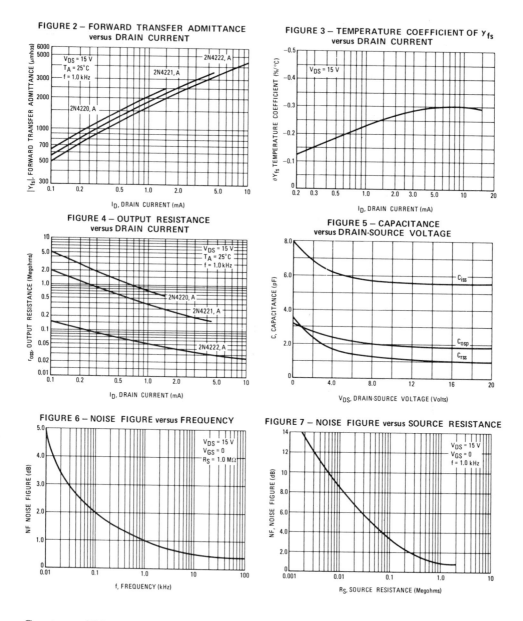

FIGURE 2 – FORWARD TRANSFER ADMITTANCE versus DRAIN CURRENT

FIGURE 3 – TEMPERATURE COEFFICIENT OF Y_{fs} versus DRAIN CURRENT

FIGURE 4 – OUTPUT RESISTANCE versus DRAIN CURRENT

FIGURE 5 – CAPACITANCE versus DRAIN-SOURCE VOLTAGE

FIGURE 6 – NOISE FIGURE versus FREQUENCY

FIGURE 7 – NOISE FIGURE versus SOURCE RESISTANCE

2N4220 thru 2N4222
2N4220A thru 2N4222A

Courtesy of Motorola Semiconductor Products Inc.

Transistor a-c Equivalent Circuit Formulas

A.   T-equivalent formulas

Common Base

$$r_{ib} = r_e - r_b - \frac{r_b(\alpha r_c + r_b)}{(R_L)' + r_c + r_b}$$

$$r_{ob} = r_c + r_b - \frac{r_b(\alpha r_c + r_b)}{R_s + r_b + r_e}$$

$$G_v = \frac{(R_L)'(\alpha r_c + r_b)}{[(R_L)' + r_c + r_b](R_s + r_e + r_b) - r_b(\alpha r_c + r_b)}$$

$$G_i = \frac{R_c(\alpha r_c + r_b)}{(R_L + R_C)[(R_L)' + r_c + r_b]}$$

Common Emitter

$$r_{ie} = r_e + r_b + \frac{r_c(\alpha r_c - r_e)}{(R_L)' + r_c(1 - \alpha) + r_e}$$

$$r_{oe} = r_c(1 - \alpha) + r_e + \frac{r_c(\alpha r_c - r_e)}{R_s + r_e + r_b}$$

$$G_v = \frac{-(R_L)'(\alpha r_c - r_e)}{(R_s + r_b + r_e)[(R_L)' + r_c(1 - \alpha) + r_e] + r_c(\alpha r_c - r_e)}$$

$$G_i = \frac{(\alpha r_c - r_e)R_C}{[(R_L)' + r_e + r_c(1 - \alpha)](R_C + R_L)}$$

Common Collector

$$r_{ic} = \frac{r_b + r_c(\beta + 1)[(R_L)' + r_e)]}{r_c + (\beta + 1)[(R_L)' + r_e)]}$$

$$r_{oe} = r_e + \frac{r_c(1 - \alpha)(r_b + R_s)}{r_b + r_c + R_s}$$

$$G_v = \frac{(R_L)'(\beta + 1)}{R_s + r_b + [(R_L)' + r_e](\beta + 1)}$$

$$G_i = \frac{r_c R_L}{[r_c(1 - \alpha) + (R_L)' + r_e](R_L + R_E)}$$

B.   Hybrid Equivalent Formulas

(In the following equations the subscript x denotes b, e, or c for the Com. B, E or C configurations respectively).

$$r_{ix} = \frac{(R_L)'\Delta h + h_{ix}}{h_{ox}(R_L)' + 1}$$

where

$$\Delta h = h_{ix}h_{ox} - h_{fx}h_{rx}$$

$$r_{ox} = \frac{R_S + h_{ix}}{R_S h_{ox} + \Delta h}$$

$$G_v = \frac{h_{fx}(R_L)'}{(R_L)'(h_{ox}R_S + \Delta h) + h_{ix} + R_S}$$

$$G_i^* = \frac{h_{fx}R_L}{(R_L + R_C)[h_{ox}(R_L)' + 1]}$$

* Replace R_C with R_E for Com. C.

Vacuum Tube Devices

Since the advent of the transistor and semiconductor technology, the role of vacuum tubes in the fields of communications, radar and automatic control has been rapidly diminishing. Although they no longer enjoy the widespread use which characterized the first half of the century, vacuum tubes have maintained superiority in various areas including microwave and very high power applications. For this reason, and because of the many similarities between vacuum tubes and certain semiconductor devices, a brief discussion of vacuum tube principles is presented below. For a more comprehensive treatment the references cited at the end of this appendix should be consulted.

1

The first practical vacuum tube device was developed as a result of work done by Thomas Edison and J. A. Fleming at the turn of the century. The *vacuum tube diode* is comprised of a heated *cathode* surrounded by a metal *anode* (or *plate*) enclosed in an evacuated tube, usually glass or metal. Figure IV.1 shows a typical vacuum diode construction. In normal operation the cathode is heated to a temperature high enough to cause electrons

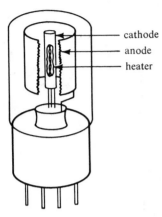

FIG. IV.1.   VACUUM DIODE CONSTRUCTION

to be emitted from its surface, and a positive potential is applied to the plate to attract these electrons. These electrons moving from the cathode to the plate constitute a current. This current will only flow when the plate is positive with respect to the cathode. When the plate is negative relative to the cathode, the emitted electrons are repelled by the plate and no current flows.

Because it must be an efficient emitter of electrons, the cathode of a vacuum tube must be constructed of special material. Although free electrons in any conductor will escape from the solid if given enough heat energy, some materials are more suitable because of a greater emission efficiency or because of a greater resistance to high temperatures. The most modern cathode material is

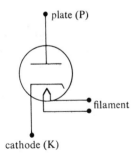

FIG. IV.2.   CIRCUIT SYMBOL FOR VACUUM DIODE

oxide-coated metal. The cathode consists of a metal sleeve coated with a mixture of barium and strontium oxides and is the most efficient emitter of electrons used to date. As shown in Figure IV.1, the oxide-coated cathode is usually indirectly heated by a separate heater or filament. The heater is usually heated by an a-c current. The conventional circuit symbol for the vacuum tube diode is shown in Figure IV.2. Normally, the heater is omitted in the circuit symbol since it is not electrically connected with the diode.

2

The electrical characteristics of a typical vacuum diode are shown in Figure IV.3 for two different cathode temperatures $T1$ and $T2$ (with $T1 > T2$). The cathode temperature is controlled by varying the filament power. The variation of plate current I_P with plate to cathode voltage E_P is similar for both temperature cases, with the curve for the higher temperature existing at higher plate currents. This seems reasonable since a higher cathode temperature will cause the emission of a larger number of free electrons and thus a greater current flow from cathode to plate.

Several significant features are evident in the curves of Figure IV.3. First, the plate current initially increases rapidly as the plate voltage is increased positively from zero. As E_P is increased further, the rate of increase in I_P becomes smaller and smaller

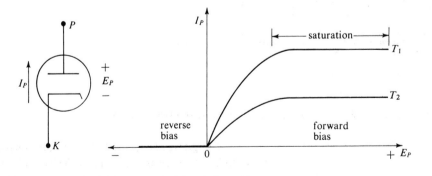

FIG. IV.3.   TYPICAL VACUUM DIODE PLATE CHAR-
ACTERISTICS

until a region of saturation exists in which I_P remains virtually constant. This saturation region exists when all the electrons which the cathode can emit at a given temperature are collected by the plate and any further increase in plate potential cannot draw any more electron current. Secondly, regardless of the cathode temperature, no plate current flows when E_P is negative. Thus, the vacuum diode has the property of *rectification*. That is, it can conduct current in one direction only. This property is illustrated in Figure IV.4. Here, a voltage consisting of alternately positive

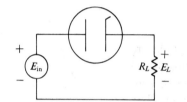

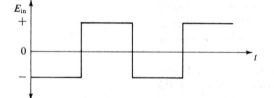

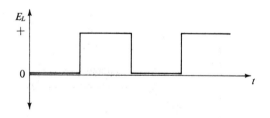

FIG. IV.4.   VACUUM DIODE RECTIFICATION

and negative pulses is applied to a circuit consisting of a vacuum diode and a load resistor. The diode is said to *rectify* the input voltage since it allows current to flow only when the input makes the plate positive relative to the cathode, in this case when E_{in} is positive. When current flows a voltage is developed across R_L. When E_{in} is negative the current is zero and E_L is zero.

It should be pointed out that in practical vacuum diodes the reverse current (plate negative relative to the cathode) is not exactly zero due to leakage currents. Typically the diode's resistance is around 10 megohms in the reverse direction. This compares to a typical value of 100 ohms in the forward direction, making it a very good rectifier.

3

One of the most important steps in modern electronics was the invention of the *triode*. In 1907 deForest added a third electrode to the vacuum tube diode to form a triode. This third electrode, called a *control grid*, opened up a whole new era in the field of radio communications. In the triode, the cathode and plate retain their functions as an emitter of electrons and a collector of electrons respectively. The control grid is usually a fine wire helix located between them, nearer to the cathode, as shown in Figure IV.5.

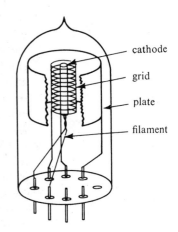

FIG. IV.5.   CONSTRUCTION OF A TRIODE

The purpose of the control grid is to regulate the movement of electrons between the cathode and plate. The plate is still held at a positive potential as in the diode. However, unlike the diode, the flow of electrons from cathode to plate (plate current) depends not only on the plate-to-cathode voltage but also on the potential of the grid relative to the cathode. By varying the grid-to-cathode potential, the plate current may be increased or decreased even if

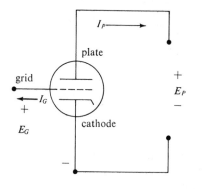

FIG. IV.6.   TRIODE CIRCUIT SYMBOL

the plate voltage is held constant. This control grid action can be better explained by referring to Figure IV.6 where the triode circuit symbol is shown with the electrode voltages properly labelled.

Let us assume that E_P is positive since a negative E_P will produce zero plate current as in the diode. If the control grid were not present the triode would behave essentially like the vacuum diode and a particular value of plate current would flow; call this value I_{PO}. With the grid present, as in the triode, we are at liberty to bias it at any potential relative to the cathode. With this potential, E_G, set to zero volts (that is, with $E_G = 0$), the grid will have little effect on the plate current and its value will remain I_{PO}. If the grid-to-cathode voltage is made negative ($E_G < 0$) a significant *decrease* in plate current will occur. This decrease is a result of the repelling effect which the negative grid has on the cathode-emitted electrons. As the grid is made more negative, the number of electrons which will travel from cathode to plate is decreased. In fact, a sufficiently negative value of E_G will cut off all of the plate current. In other words, even with a large plate-to-cathode positive voltage the plate current can be decreased to zero by making the grid voltage sufficiently negative. It is important to note that when E_G is negative, none of the traversing electrons collide with the grid. Instead, they are repelled by the negative potential and make their way to the plate by passing through the spacings in the grid mesh. Thus, $I_G = 0$ when $E_G \leq 0$.

When the grid voltage is made positive, the opposite effect takes place; an increase in plate current occurs and grid current begins to flow as a result of the positive grid's attraction for the emitted electrons. That is, when $E_G > 0$ we have $I_P > I_{PO}$ and $I_G > 0$. The vacuum triode is usually not operated with a positive grid because the grid current can become excessive. There are applications, however, where the grid is allowed to go positive periodically without damaging the tube.

The above results can be summarized as in Figure IV.7 where some typical current and voltage values are also given. Notice

FIG. IV.7.   SUMMARY OF GRID CONTROL

Grid voltage E_G	Plate voltage E_P	Plate current I_P	Grid current I_G
No grid present	+200v	10 ma	——
0v	+200v	10 ma	0 ma
−2v	+200v	4 ma	0 ma
−8v	+200v	0 ma	0 ma
+2v	+200v	16 ma	2 ma

that with $E_G = -8v$ the plate current is decreased to zero. This condition is called *cutoff*. Notice also that a decrease in grid potential from 0 to −2v causes a 60 per cent decrease in plate current (10 ma to 4 ma). This is a good indication of the grid's control over the plate current.

4

Although the data in Figure IV.7 illustrates the behavior of a triode tube it is usually necessary to use a more complete method of characterizing a given triode's operating characteristics. In particular, a set of curves called the *plate characteristics* are often utilized in analysis and design. Figure IV.8 contains the plate characteristics of the 6J5 triode. The plate characteristics consist of a family of curves each of which plots the variation of plate current with plate voltage for a given value of grid voltage. Let us now examine the 6J5 characteristics.

The curve labelled $E_G = 0$ is essentially the same curve which would be obtained if the grid were not present. In this case plate current will flow as soon as the plate voltage is increased from zero. For example, with $E_P = 25v$, a plate current of 1.7 ma

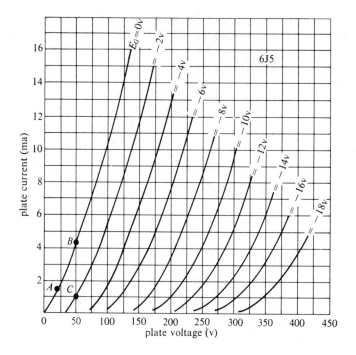

plate current (ma)

plate voltage (v)

6J5

$E_G = 0v$ $-2v$ $-4v$ $-6v$ $-8v$ $-10v$ $-12v$ $-14v$ $-16v$ $-18v$

FIG. IV.8.　　　TRIODE PLATE CHARACTERISTICS

flows (point *A*). Increasing the plate voltage to 50v increases the current to 4.3 ma (point *B*). With $E_G = -2v$ the curve shifts to the right indicating that for the same value of E_P a smaller I_P will flow than with $E_G = 0$. For example, at $E_P = 25v$ no plate current flows and, in fact, none will flow until E_P is increased to about 35 volts. At $E_P = 50v$ the plate current increases to only 1 ma (point *C*; compare this with point *B*). Similar behavior takes place as E_G is made even more negative. Notice, also, that the separation of successive curves remains fairly uniform. This is an important feature of the triode that allows it to be used as a linear amplifier.

5

The majority of applications of the triode vacuum tube utilize its ability to *amplify* an input signal voltage. A typical 6J5 triode amplifier is shown in Figure IV.9. It consists of two bias supplies E_{CC} and E_{BB}, a load resistor R_L, the 6J5 triode and, of course, the input signal e_s. The grid supply E_{CC} establishes the d-c grid-to-cathode potential E_G; that is, $E_G = -E_{CC}$. The plate supply E_{BB}

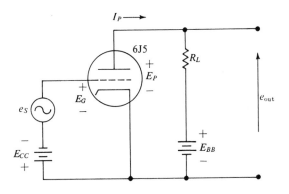

FIG. IV.9. TRIODE AMPLIFIER CIRCUIT

provides the d-c plate-to-cathode potential which allows plate current to flow. The load R_L is used to develop the output signal voltage across. The amplification process can be easily understood if we consider it in two separate steps. The first step is the establishment of the d-c operating point (frequently called the Q-point) which is determined with no signal applied ($e_s = 0$) by the values of E_{CC}, E_{BB} and R_L. Under the no-signal condition a certain d-c plate current I_{PO}, plate voltage E_{PO} and grid voltage E_{GO} are thus established. This condition will persist indefinitely until a signal is introduced at the grid. The input signal e_s, which we will consider to be pure a-c, will serve to alter the grid-cathode voltage by alternately adding to and subtracting from the d-c value $E_{GO} = -E_{CC}$. The resultant total grid-cathode voltage consists of an a-c signal riding on a d-c level [see Figure 10 (A)]. Since we have found that a change in grid voltage will produce a change in plate current, we can expect that the signal portion of the grid voltage will induce a signal portion of plate current. The resultant plate current waveform consists of the a-c plate current riding on a d-c level (I_{PO}) and is shown in Figure 10(B). Notice that the plate current signal is *in phase* with the grid signal. This occurs since the portion of the grid signal which is going positive reduces the total grid-cathode negative potential thus allowing an increase in plate current and vice-versa.

Because of this a-c component of plate current we can expect that the total plate voltage will also have a signal component produced across R_L. The resultant plate voltage waveform is shown in Figure 10(C). Notice that the a-c portion of plate voltage is 180° *out of phase* with the input signal. This phase shift occurs

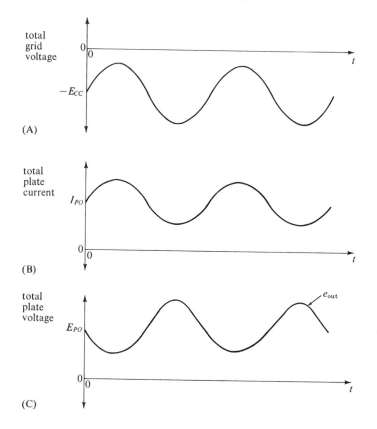

total grid voltage

(A)

total plate current

(B)

total plate voltage

(C)

FIG. IV.10.   TRIODE AMPLIFIER WAVEFORMS

because as the grid signal voltage goes positive, the plate current will increase thus increasing the voltage across R_L. Since the sum of the voltage drops across the tube (E_P) and R_L must be equal to the voltage supply E_{BB}, this results in a decrease in plate voltage as the grid signal increases and vice-versa, producing the 180° phase shift.

The output of the amplifier in Figure IV.9 is usually taken between plate and ground. In a well-designed amplifier the output signal e_{out} will have a magnitude several times greater than the input signal e_s. The ratio of these two signals is the voltage gain A_v. That is

$$A_v \equiv e_{out}/e_s$$

Typically, A_v is between 10 and 100 for this amplifier circuit. The value of A_v for a given amplifier depends on a very important property of a triode—the grid's ability to control the plate current.

As we saw previously, a small variation in grid voltage can cause a relatively large change in plate current since the grid is very close to the cathode. A measure of this property is the triode parameter called *transconductance* and is given the symbol g_m. Mathematically g_m is the ratio of the plate current change to the grid voltage change which produced it while holding plate voltage constant. That is

$$g_m \equiv \frac{\Delta I_P}{\Delta E_G}\bigg|_{E_P}$$

The units of transconductance are mhos, the reciprocal of ohms. Typical values of g_m for a triode are in the range of 1 to 10 millimhos (10^{-3} mhos). The higher the value of g_m, of course, the higher the triode's amplifying capability.

Another important triode parameter is *plate resistance*, r_p. The triode plate resistance is a measure of the plate voltage's control over the plate current. Mathematically it is given as the ratio of a change in plate voltage to the resultant change in plate current for a given value of grid voltage. That is

$$r_p \equiv \frac{\Delta E_P}{\Delta I_P}\bigg|_{E_G}$$

Typical values of r_p range from 2K to 20K. Because the control grid is much closer to the cathode than the plate, the plate voltage's control is much less than the grid's. For this reason the value of r_p is usually much greater than the *reciprocal* of g_m. We can express this as

$$r_p \gg \frac{1}{g_m}$$

or equivalently

$$r_p \times g_m \gg 1$$

The product of r_p and g_m is given the special symbol, μ (mu) and is called the *amplification factor*. That is

$$\mu \equiv r_p \times g_m$$

The value of μ typically ranges from 10 to 200. It is essentially a measure of the relative control ability of the grid as compared to the plate; it is also a good indication of the voltage gain available in a given amplifier. For the amplifier in Figure IV.9, for example, the approximate value of voltage gain can be obtained from the expression

$$A_v \approx \frac{\mu R_L}{r_p + R_L}$$

This expression shows that a higher voltage gain can be obtained by using a higher μ triode or by increasing R_L.

6

A very important characteristic of a triode amplifier is its very high input impedance. As mentioned previously, with a negative grid voltage only a minute grid current flows. This means that the current drain from the signal source will be very small. A typical input impedance is 1 megohm and is determined mainly by an external grid-to-ground resistance needed for stability.

Despite its very high input impedance, the triode does not approach the ideal voltage amplifier mainly due to its high *output impedance* which is essentially equal to r_p. However for values of $R_L \gg r_p$ the triode is close to being a perfect voltage amplifier with $A_v \approx \mu$, independent of R_L.

7

The inherent capacitances that exist between the three electrodes form one of the principal drawbacks of the triode amplifier. Typically, in the 5 to 20 picofarad range, these *inter-electrode capacitances* do not affect the amplifier operation at low and medium frequencies, but at high frequencies (above 50 KHZ) their effect on input impedance and gain is noticeable.

In an effort to reduce the inter-electrode capacitances, and thereby improve the high frequency capabilities of the triode, the *tetrode* and then the *pentode* were developed. In the tetrode a *screen grid* was introduced to the basic triode construction between the control grid and plate. It did accomplish the reduction in capacitances but other undesirable effects brought about the development of the pentode. A typical example of pentode construction is shown in Figure IV.11 along with the pentode circuit symbol. A third grid, the *suppressor grid*, is present between the screen grid and plate. The effects of the pentode construction on the electrical behavior of the tube are the lower inter-electrode capacitances (fractions of pf), higher values of μ (100 to 1000) and higher values of r_p (100K to 1 megohm) than the triode. A simple pentode amplifier circuit is shown in Figure IV.12. Note that the screen grid is biased positively in relation to the cathode in order to help accelerate electrons toward the plate. The suppressor grid

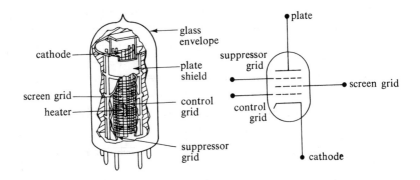

FIG. IV.11.   PENTODE CONSTRUCTION AND ELEC-
TRONIC SYMBOL

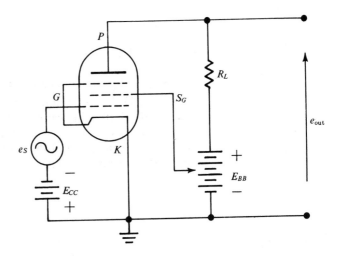

FIG. IV.12.   PENTODE AMPLIFIER

is normally connected to the cathode. The approximate voltage
gain of this pentode amplifier is

$$A_v \approx \frac{u}{r_p} \times R_L = g_m \times R_L$$

and is typically higher than for a triode.

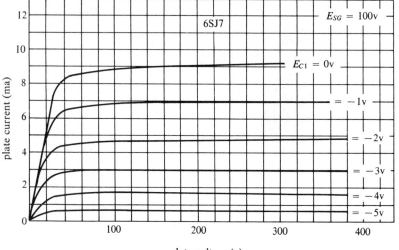

FIG. IV.13.   PENTODE PLATE FAMILY

A typical pentode plate family of characteristic curves is shown in Figure IV.13. In comparison to the triode curves, the pentode curves are flatter, indicating that the plate voltage has a smaller effect on plate current, which results in a higher r_p and μ. This is because of the effect of the screen and suppressor grids shielding the cathode from the plate.

References

Brazee, J. G., *Semiconductor and Tube Electronics.* New York: Holt, Rinehart and Winston Inc., 1968.

Romanowitz, H. A. and R. E. Puckett, *Introduction to Electronics.* New York: John Wiley & Sons, Inc., 1968.

Appendix V

Device Symbols

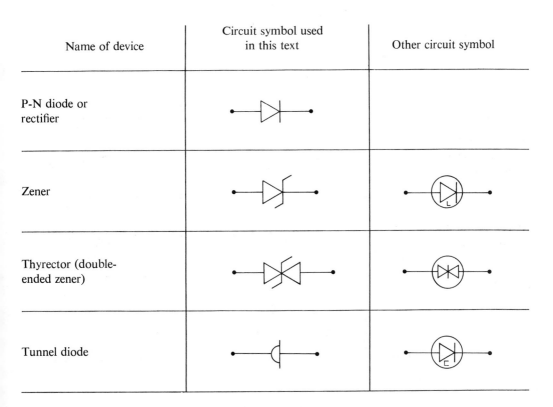

Name of device	Circuit symbol used in this text	Other circuit symbol
P-N diode or rectifier		
Zener		
Thyrector (double-ended zener)		
Tunnel diode		

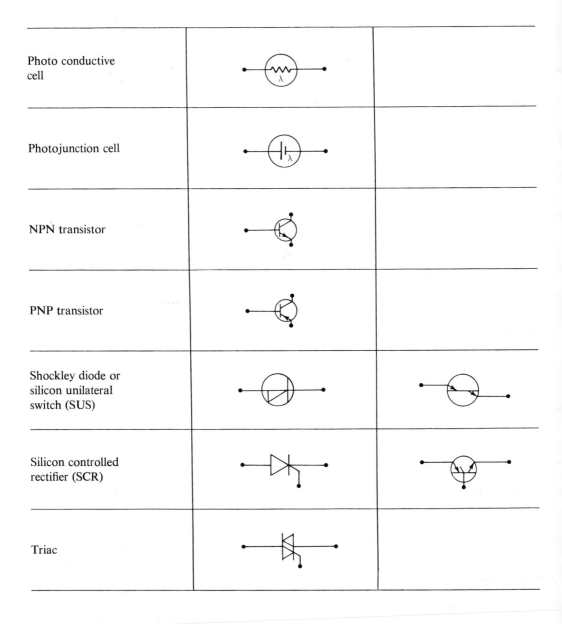

Photo conductive cell		
Photojunction cell		
NPN transistor		
PNP transistor		
Shockley diode or silicon unilateral switch (SUS)		
Silicon controlled rectifier (SCR)		
Triac		

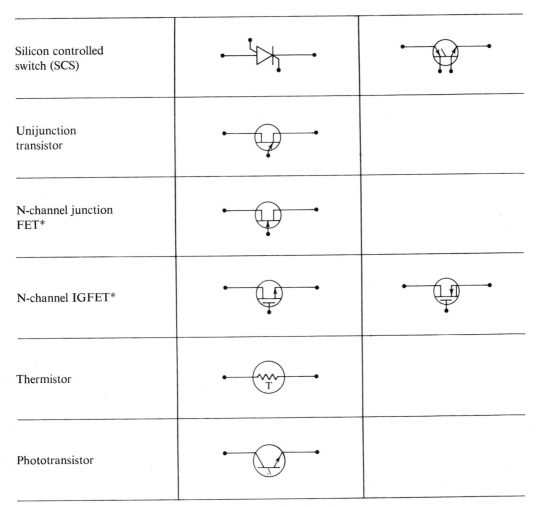

Silicon controlled switch (SCS)		
Unijunction transistor		
N-channel junction FET*		
N-channel IGFET*		
Thermistor		
Phototransistor		

* P-channel FETs have same symbols with arrow in opposite direction.

Answers To Selected Problems

CHAPTER 3: **3.1.** $V_{ac} = -6v$; $V_{bc} = +12v$; $V_{ab} = -18v$. **3.5.** $I_a = 15$ma; 5ma; 0ma.

CHAPTER 5: **5.21.** (a) 150v; (b) 500ma. **5.24.** 2μa @ 36°C. **5.25.** 8ma and .7v (V_{F0}). **5.26.** 5.3ma; .7v(V_{F0}). **5.27.** $\approx$ 0v; 50v. **5.29.** 9ma; 11ma. **5.32.** PRV > 10v. **5.33.** (a) $-2v$; (b) 2v; (c) 4v; (d) 6.7v; (e) 6.7v; (f)——; (g) I_F(max); V_{RDC}. **5.35.** 65mw. **5.37.** 1w. **5.41.** (a) .2°C/mw; (b) 500ma; (c) 48Ω; (d) P_D(max) = 425mw. **5.42.** I_R(max) = 4ma → R(min) = 5K.

CHAPTER 6: **6.5.** (a) 3ma; (b) 20v. **6.7.** Yes. **6.9.** (a) 5.6v; (b) 5.684v. **6.10.** (a) 4.3v; (b) 4.171v. **6.11.** (a) 833mw. **6.13.** 10.7v; 0v. **6.15.** $\approx$50Ω.

CHAPTER 7: **7.8.** (a) $V_F \approx 0$; $I_F = 6$ma; (b) $V_F \approx .5v$; $I_F = 23.5$ma. **7.10.** (a) $R_1 = R_2$ chosen between 273Ω and 546Ω; (b) $R_1 = R_2$ chosen $\leq$ 273Ω but > 120Ω; (c) $R_1 = R_2 = R_3$ chosen as in step (a).

CHAPTER 8: **8.4.** 1.5ma. **8.7.** $\approx$100 f.c. **8.8.** $\approx$10 f.c. **8.12.** 5.25K **8.15.** R $\leq$ 300Ω. **8.18.** (a) $I_{PH} = .75$ma; $V_{PH} = .375v$; (b) $P_L = .28$mw; (c) $I_{PH} = 1$ma; $V_{PH} = .25v$; $P_L = .25$mw.

CHAPTER 9: **9.11.** (a) $I_E = 20$ma. **9.13.** For $I_E = 10$ma, $I_C = 9.91$ma and $I_B = .09$ma. **9.22.** $I_C \approx I_E = .5$ma. **9.23.** (a) 5.3ma. **9.24.** (a) $I_C = I_E = 10$ma, $V_{CB} = 20v$; (b) 333Ω. **9.25.** (a) $I_E = .23$ma, $I_C = .215$ma, $V_{CB} = 8.91v$; (b)——; (c) $I_E = 2.3$ma, $I_C = 2$ma, $V_{CB} \approx 0$. **9.26.** 1.8v. **9.27.** $I_C = 10$ma, $I_B = 5$ma. **9.33.** .106ma. **9.37.** $R_C = 70\Omega$. **9.38.** $I_B = 34.8\mu$a; $I_E = 5.25$ma; $V_E = 5.25v$. **9.40.** $I_E = 5.3$ma; $V_E = 5.3v$. **9.41.** (a) 40v; (b) 20Ω; (c) 37.4Ω. **9.43.** (a) 25°C $- I_C = 2.3$ma, $V_{CE} = 9.7v$; (b) 75°C $- I_C = 5.34$ma, $V_{CE} = 6.66v$.

CHAPTER 10: **10.1.** Reproduction only. **10.2.** (a) 1; (b) 12. **10.4.** $A_i = A_p$ = 10. **10.6.** (a) $G_v = 1000$; (b) $G_v = 909$, ($R_L = 1$K), $G_v = 500$, ($R_L = 100\Omega$); (c) $G_v = 909$; (d) $G_i = 90,900$, $G_p = 8.34 \times 10^7$; (e) $G_i = 500,000$, $G_p = 2.5 \times 10^8$.

CHAPTER 11: **11.5.** 40Ω; .99. **11.6.** .4ma; .38ma. **11.20.** (a) 10ma, 9.9ma, 12.3v; (b) 1ma p-p; (c) .985ma p-p, 3.25v p-p; (d) 325; (e) 320. **11.25.** 10Ω; 3.3K. **11.26.** 203. **11.29.** 5. **11.30.** (b) 325. **11.34.** 10μa; 600μa; 610μa. **11.36.** (c) A_v = 233; $A_p = 16,310$. **11.38.** $G_v = 117.5$; $G_i = 32.4$; $G_p = 3800$. **11.40.** (b) $G_v = 117.5$. **11.43.** $V_B \approx 6.67v$; $I_C = I_E \approx 6$ma; $V_{CE} \approx 8v$. **11.47.** $Z_B = 606.2$K @ $R_L = 10$K. **11.48.** $Z_{ic} = 31.4$K @ $R_L = 10$K. **11.49.** .94 @ $R_L = 10$K. **11.50.** 56.7Ω @ $R_S = 2$K. **11.57.** $r_e = 6\Omega$; $r_b = 150\Omega$. **11.59.** $r_{ib} = 15.5\Omega$ @ 2ma. **11.61.** $r_{ie} = 1565\Omega$ @ 2ma. **11.65.** 90; 1K; 20K. **11.69.** 200kHz; 16.7 MHz.

CHAPTER 12: **12.2.** 0v and $-12v$. **12.12.** 150. **12.14.** $-5.2v$. **12.15.** $P_1 = 144$mw; $P_{in} = 1.35$mw; gain = 107. **12.18.** $I_B = .907$ma; $I_C = 54.4$ma; $I_I = 20$ma; $I_D = 34.4$ma; $V_{CE} = 1v$.

CHAPTER 13: **13.13.** (a) 60w; (b) .7ma; (c) 25. **13.14.** (a) 1.04μsec; (b) 100; (c) 22; (d) 8pf. **13.15.** 337.5.

CHAPTER 14. **14.10.** R(min) = 7.3K; R(max) = 8K; F(min) = 1136Hz; F(max) = 1250Hz. **14.12.** R $\leq$ 12.7K; $C = \dfrac{20 \times 10^{-3}}{R}$ farads. **14.19.** (a) 100v; (b) 100v; (c) 4ma; (d) .8v; (e) 10ma; (f) 100°C; (g) 5v; (h) 25A. **14.21.** (a) No; (b) Yes; (c) Yes. **14.22.** .015msec. **14.26.** 2.17v. **14.28.** 10K.

CHAPTER 15: **15.4.** (a) 16.7v; (b) 42Hz. **15.6.** f(min) = .625Hz; f(max) = 79Hz. **15.7.** R < 5.75K; $C = \dfrac{8.3 \times 10^{-3}}{R}$ farads. **15.8.** Yes; 75Ω.

CHAPTER 16: **16.6.** 3v; 5v; 0v. **16.8.** (a) 30v; (b) 15ma; (c) 300 mw; (d) .1na, 100na; (e) .5 to 3ma; (f) 2500μmhos; (g) 500Ω. **16.10.** $A_v \approx 2.8$.

Index

Absolute zero, 42–43
Acceptor impurity, 51–53:
  energy level of, 52
Active region operation, 161, 169
Alpha, d-c (α_{DC}), 166
Ampere, definition, 18
Amplifiers, (general) 213–224:
  amplification and reproduction, 213–224
  current amplifier, 216
  impedance matching with, 223–224
  input and output impedance, 218
  power amplifier, 217
  relationships, 218–223
  voltage amplifier, 215
  (*see also* Transistor amplifiers)
Atom, 1–14:
  Bohr, 1–2
  combinations of, 8–11
  excitation of, 6, 7
Atomic bonding, 8–11
Atomic number, 3
Atomic weight, 3
Avalanche breakdown, 67–68, 103

Base region, 160
Bias (*see* Forward bias, Reverse bias)

Bohr atom, 1–2
Bonding, atomic, 8–11

Channel, 408
Collector-base junction, 160
Collector-clamping, 328–330
Collector leakage current, 163
Collector region, 160
Common-base amplifiers:
  basic circuit, 234–235
  clipping of output in, 254–255
  current gain, 229, 235, 236
  cut-off frequency, 302
  general representation, 246–250
  graphical analysis of, 251–256
  input impedance, 230, 244–245
  output impedance, 245–246
  power gain, 243–244
  summary, 256
  voltage gain, 237–243, 248
Common-base configuration, 170–183:
  characteristic curves, 172–175
  circuit analysis, 175–183
  d-c current gain, 172
Common-collector amplifiers:
  basic circuit, 278

Common-collector amplifiers: (*Cont.*)
  current gain, 285
  input impedance, 281
  output impedance, 284
  power gain, 285–286
  summary, 287
  voltage gain, 282
Common-collector configuration, 195–197
Common-emitter amplifiers:
  basic circuit, 257
  current gain, 231, 257–258
  cut-off frequency, 303
  general representation, 265–268
  graphical analysis, 268–272
  input impedance, 232, 259, 263–264
  output impedance, 264–265
  power gain, 262–263
  Q-point stability, 272–277
  summary, 277
  voltage gain, 258–262
Common-emitter configuration, 183–195:
  characteristic curves, 187–190
  circuit analysis, 190–195
  d-c current gain, 185
Concentration gradient, 21
Conductivity, definition, 19
Conductor, description, 13:
  energy band diagram of, 14
Coulomb, definition, 18
Covalent bonding, 8–11:
  in semiconductors, 41–42
Current gain, definition, 216
Cut-off region operation, 170

Depletion region, 63
Device analysis, 25–35
Diffusion current, 21
Donor impurity, 48–51:
  energy level, 49
Dopent diffusion, 339
Doping, definition, 48
Drain, 408
Drift current, 21

Electric current, 17–19
Electron energies, 3–5
Electron–hole pair, 44
Electron orbits, 3–5

Electrons, 1–2
Electron-volt, 3
Emitter-base junction, 160
Emitter region, 160
Energy bands, 11–14
Extrinsic semiconductor, 48–56:
  effect of temperature on, 54

Field-effect transistors, insulated gate type
    (IGFET):
  basic operation, 418–422
  characteristics, 421
  depletion operation, 421
  enhancement operation, 420
  general comments, 423
  structure, 418–419
Field-effect transistors, junction type (JFET):
  basic amplifier, 416–418
  basic operation, 408–413
  characteristic curves, 410
  ratings and parameters, 413
  structure, 408
  transfer characteristic, 412
Foot-candle, definition, 142
Forward-bias:
  of P-N junction, 68–70
Four-layer diodes:
  bilateral, 359
  characteristics and operation, 356–360
  circuit applications, 361–368
  forward switching voltage, 356
  holding current, 357
  rate effect in, 361
  ratings, 360
  relaxation oscillator, 362–366
  switching current, 357

Gain (*See* Amplifiers)

Hall effect, 433
Heat sinks, 343
Hole current, description, 45–47
Hole, definition, 44

IGFET (*See* Field-effect transistors)
Insulator, description, 13:
  energy band diagram of, 14

Integrated circuits, monolithic:
  components, 440
  formation process, 441–443
  isolation techniques, 439
  structure, 438
Integrated circuits, other types:
  compatible, 445
  MOSFET, 446
  multi-chip, 446
  thin film, 443–445
Intrinsic semiconductors, 42–47:
  effect of heat on, 43–45
Inverter, transistor, 325–327
Ionic bonding, 8–11
Ionization, definition, 7
Ions, definitions, 7, 8
I-V characteristic, definition, 27

JFET (*See* Field-effect transistors)
Junction (*See* P-N junction)

Lasers, 430
Latching, 352
Latching current, 375, 379
Light, 142
Load-line 75–78, 111, 131, 175–177, 190
Load-line, a-c, 252, 269
Load-line, d-c, 251, 268

Microelectronics, 437
Mobility, 47
MOS, 419
MOS capacitor, 419
MOSFET, 420

N-channel, 408
Negative resistance:
  of tunnel diode, 127
  of unijunction transistor, 395
Neutrons, 1–2
NPN transistor, 160
N-Type impurity, 48–51
N-Type semiconductor, 48–51, 54

Pauli's exclusion principle, 3
P-channel, 410

Photoconductive cells, 142–149:
  applications, 147–149
  description, 142–143
  materials, 142–143
  ratings and specifications, 146–147
  resistance-illumination curve, 144
  response time, 145–146
Photoelectric devices, 141–154
Photon, 142
Photoresistors (*See* Photoconductive cells)
Phototransistors, 429
Photovoltaic cells, 149–154:
  applications of, 153–154
  as circuit elements, 153
  efficiency, 151
  I-V characteristics, 150
  junction photo-voltaic type, 149–150
Pinch-off, 409–410
P-N diode, 71–94:
  a-c resistance of, 82–83
  applications, 87–91
  effects of temperature on, 74–76
  power dissipation, 91–93
  ratings, 72–73
P-N diode circuit analysis, 76–86:
  approximate method, 82–86
  load-line method, 76–82
P-N junction, description, 59–65:
  capacitance, 94
  forward bias operation, 68–70
  I-V characteristic of, 70
  leakage current, 66
  reverse bias operation, 65
  reverse breakdown, 67
PNPN devices, 351–387:
  basic operation, 353–356
  general description, 351–352
  structure, 352–353
  triggering, 355
  (*See also* Four-layer diodes and Silicon controlled rectifiers)
PNP transistor, 160
Potential barrier, 63
Power gain, 217
Power transistors, 343–344
Protons, 1–2
P-type impurity, 51–53
P-type semiconductor, 51–54

Q-point, definition, 234
Quiescent, 234

Rate effect, 361
Recombination, 46
Rectification, 87–91
Rectifier, P-N, 87
Regulation:
  percentage of, 115
  of voltage, 113–118
Resistance, 20
Resistivity, definition, 19
Reverse bias, 65
Reverse breakdown, 67–68:
  (*See also* Zener breakdown)

Saturated region operation, 170
Semiconductor, description, 13:
  covalent bonding in, 41–42
  energy band diagram of, 14
  extrinsic, 48–56
  Intrinsic, 42–47
Shockley diode (See Four-layer diode)
Silicon controlled rectifiers:
  basic operation, 368–370
  characteristics, 369
  construction, 368
  gate triggering, 373–376
  light-activated, 387
  ratings, 371–372
  turn-off, 376–377, 380
  used as a-c switch, 380–386
  used as d-c switch, 377–380
Silicon controlled switch, 386
Silicon dioxide, 342–343, 439
Solar cell, 151
Source, 408
Space-charge potential, 63
Space-charge region, definition, 63
Strain gages, 434
SUS and SBS (*See* Four-layer diode)

Thermal generation, definition, 44:
  energy band description of, 45
Thermal resistance, 91
Thermistors, 431
Transient operation (of Transistor switch), 321–323

Transistor, junction:
  basic operation, 161–170
  configurations (*See* Common-base, Common emitter and Common-collector)
  structure, NPN, 160
  structure, PNP, 160
  temperature effects on, 199–201
  (*See also* Unijunction transistor, Field-effect transistor)
Transistor, power, 343–344
Transistor amplifiers, 227–305:
  basic operation, 227–234
  effects of frequency on, 300–305
  (*See also* Common-base, common-emitter and common-collector amplifiers)
Transistor data sheets, 344–347
Transistor equivalent circuits:
  hybrid equivalent, 294–300
  T-equivalent, 287–294
Transistor switch, 317–330:
  applications of, 325–330
  non-saturated, 321
  power dissipation in, 323–325
  saturated, 321
  steady-state operation, 319–321
  total switching time, 323
  transient operation, 321–323
  turn-off time of, 322
  turn-on time of, 321
Transistor technology, 335–347
Transistor types:
  alloy, 337-338
  epitaxial mesa, 341
  mesa, 340–341
  microalloy, 338–339
  microalloy diffused, 339–340
  silicon epitaxial planar, 343
Transition time, 317
Triac, 387
Trigger angle, 382
Triggering (*See* SCR, PNPN devices)
Tunnel diode, 125–136:
  as a circuit element, 130–133
  description of operation, 125–126
  I-V curve, 127
  memory, 139–140
  negative resistance of, 127
  specifications, 128–130

Tunnel diode 125–136: (*Cont.*)
  switching circuits, 133–136
  symbols, 128

Unijunction transistors:
  basic operation, 393–396
  circuit operation, 397–403
  parameters and ratings, 396–397
  relaxation oscillator, 397–403
  structure, 394
  used as SCR trigger, 403–405

Vacuum tube devices, 475–487:
  diode, 475–479
  pentode, 486–487
  tetrode, 486
  triode, 479–486

Valence, 5
Valence electrons, definition, 5
Varactor diodes, 435
Voltage gain, 215

Zener breakdown, 103–105
Zener diodes, 103–120:
  as a circuit element, 111–113
  impedance, 108
  I-V characteristic, 105–107
  knee current, 107
  nominal voltage, 107
  as a reference element, 118–120
  specifications and ratings, 106–111
  symbol, 106
  as a voltage regulator, 113–118
  voltage temperature coefficient, 108–110